Models of Music Therapy Interventions in School Settings: From Institution to Inclusion

EDITOR

BRIAN L. WILSON
Western Michigan University
Kalamazoo, Michigan

EDITORIAL CONSULTANT

DAVID S. SMITH
Western Michigan University
Kalamazoo, Michigan

TECHNICAL ASSISTANCE

WORDSETTERS
Kalamazoo, Michigan

Models of Music Therapy Interventions in School Settings: From Institution to Inclusion

Edited by

Brian L. Wilson
School of Music
Western Michigan University

American Music Therapy Association, Inc.

Published 1996
Second Printing 1998

The American Music Therapy Association, Inc.
8455 Colesville Road, Suite 1000
Silver Spring, MD 20910

Printed in The United States of America

LIST OF CONTRIBUTORS

MARY S. ADAMEK
University of Iowa
Iowa City, Iowa

KATHLEEN A. COLEMAN
Private Practice
Grapevine, Texas

ALICE-ANN DARROW
University of Kansas
Lawrence, Kansas

JACQUELYN A. DIMMICK
W. P. Day Early Childhood Center
Cleveland, Ohio

LAURIE A. FARNAN
Central Wisconsin Center for the Developmentally Disabled
Madison, Wisconsin

AMELIA GREENWALD FURMAN
Minneapolis Public Schools
Minneapolis, Minnesota

CHARLES E. FURMAN
University of Minnesota
Minneapolis, Minnesota

SUSAN C. GARDSTROM
Michigan State University
Lansing, Michigan

NED D. GLADFELTER
The Pilot School
Wilmington, Delaware

ELLEN R. GRIGGS-DRANE
Western Michigan University
Kalamazoo, Michigan

CAROL CULTON HEINE
Wartburg College
Waverly, Iowa

JANE E. HUGHES
Leon County Schools
Tallahassee, Florida

MARCIA EARL HUMPAL
W. P. Day Early Childhood Center
Cleveland, Ohio

FAITH L. JOHNSON
Milwaukee Public Schools
Milwaukee, Wisconsin

BRENDA J. ROBBINS
Leon County Schools
Tallahassee, Florida

HEATHER A. SCHUNK
University of Kansas
Lawrence, Kansas

ANGELA M. SNELL
Monroe County Intermediate School District
Monroe, Michigan

BRIAN L. WILSON
Western Michigan University
Kalamazoo, Michigan

CONTENTS

Section One:
Theoretical Issues

IN THE BEGINNING: A REVIEW OF EARLY SPECIAL EDUCATION SERVICES AND LEGISLATIVE/REGULATORY ACTIVITY AFFECTING THE TEACHING AND PLACEMENT OF SPECIAL LEARNERS

Mary S. Adamek

THE availability of public education in the United States for disabled students continues to evolve and move in new directions. Before the 1880s, students who were disabled were not even considered to be eligible for public education. When public education became available for these students, a separate, segregated model was implemented. Currently, the education system in the United States is moving towards an integrated educational system where the needs of the individual student are key in developing approaches to educate the child.

Early Years of Education

One of the first people to introduce the idea of educating persons with disabilities was an American physician named Benjamin Rush. Rush discussed this concept in the late 1700s, yet the first educational program for persons with disabilities was not established until 1817. This program, founded by Thomas Gallaudet, was at the American Asylum for the Education and Instruction of the Deaf and Dumb in Connecticut (Stainback, Stainback, & Bunch, 1989). Other programs for deaf, blind, and mentally disabled students soon followed in various cities around the United States.

As early as the 1880s, compulsory school attendance for disabled students was being discussed among educators as additional special programs continued to develop to service these students. By the early 1900s, schooling had become the social norm for the majority of nondisabled children in the United States. Classes in most schools were designed to meet the needs of the average students, while those students who were below average were serviced in special programs by special teachers in asylums or government supported institutions. While some disabled students participated in public special education programs, many students with disabilities were not receiving any educational services at this time.

Around 1910, the education of some disabled students was moved from the institutions to the public school setting, in the form of separate, segregated classrooms. The formation of segregated classes was initially met with great enthusiasm. Educators believed that separate classes would be favorable for special students, especially when otherwise faced with the option of educating disabled students in the regular classroom. They believed that separate classes could offer the disabled students the benefits of a low teacher to student ratio, more individualized instruction, more academic success in a less competitive environment, and remedial instruction so that some children could return to the regular classroom (Winzer, 1993).

Between 1910 and 1930, the number of segregated classrooms in public schools increased dramatically. Allied professional and support services increased with the expansion of state and federal funding for special education services. This commitment on the part of the federal government was reinforced by the 1930 White House Conference on Child Health and Protection, a milestone in the field of special education. It was at this conference that special education received national recognition as a justifiable component of the educational system (Winzer, 1993).

The 1930s witnessed a decline in special education services for disabled students. Many factors contributed to this decline, including the fact that the entire country was struggling with the Great Depression. Other factors, including poorly trained teachers, ineffective curricula, and a low rate of success for disabled students, led to discouragement and pessimism about the future of special education (Winzer, 1993). Although it was the intent of educators at that time to provide equal access to education for the disabled students, the reality was less effective than originally planned. Separate classes frequently served to eliminate a broad range of students described as atypical, defective, backward, recalcitrant, and mentally retarded. These students were subject to exclusion and sweeping segregation from the regular classroom.

By the 1940s, the special education classroom had eroded to deplorable conditions and became as limiting and custodial as the earlier institutional settings. Children with vastly different disabilities were placed together in classes, teachers were poorly trained, and little effort was made to actually teach. The students were isolated and stigmatized by their placement in the segregated special education environment. Although the number of special classes and day programs for disabled students had increased since the early 1900s, the educational programs in residential institutions and asylums continued to educate the majority of these students through the mid 1900s (Stainback, Stainback, & Bunch, 1989).

Special education experienced another round of renewal in the 1940s and 1950s. As parent groups became more involved in special education, legislation expanded and interest in the needs of the disabled individual increased among many education professionals. In addition, educators revised curricula to eliminate some of the repetitious drill from earlier programs in order to include greater emphasis on social participation and job skills. For the first time in history, the public began to realize the need for equal opportunities for individuals with developmental disabilities. It was during this time that the ideals of due process, equal protection under the law, and protection from cruel and unusual punishment were established as basic constitutional rights for these citizens.

Awareness of equal rights for mentally retarded students extended into the public school classroom. Efforts were focused on improving and expanding public school services for mentally retarded students, and moving away from institutionalization and isolation. "The net result of all these changes was huge expansions in numbers: between 1948 and 1968 the number of children in public school special education classes in the United States went from 357,000 to 2,252,000, or from 1.2 to 4.5 percent of the total enrollment in kindergarten to grade twelve" (Winzer, 1993, p. 376).

This expansion of special education continued during the 1960s due to increased federal and state support. The number of institutions for training special educators also increased from fewer than 40 in 1958 to more than 400 in 1976. In 1963, President Kennedy signed a law that expanded legislation to provide special education services for most children with severe disabilities. This legislation expanded the definition as to which students should receive special education services. The new definition included not only children who were mentally retarded, but also those who were emotionally impaired; had speech, hearing, or visual impairments; or who had other health impairments.

Institutionalization of the most severely disabled children continued into the 1960s. Many who were classified as either severely mentally retarded or juvenile delinquents were housed in facilities that were underfunded and inhumane. Public outcry concerning the conditions under which many institutionalized individuals with developmental disabilities lived helped lay the groundwork for change. By the 1970s a movement to deinstitutionalize and integrate individuals who were mentally retarded into the community was in place throughout the country.

In the school setting, this effort toward normalization included an educational process that eventually became known as mainstreaming. The beliefs underlying this movement were that all children had individual differences, and these differences must be respected by members of the school community. Educational services had to be developed to meet the needs of each individual student. As normalization practices continued to expand, educators came to the understanding that all children had a right to a free, appropriate education. It was during this time that the educational system began to shift from servicing disabled students in segregated special education classes to educating disabled students in the regular education classroom setting supported by special education professionals (Winzer, 1993).

Since the beginning of the twentieth century, the special education movement in the United States had made substantial progress in providing educational services to disabled students, yet by the 1970s there were still many problems to overcome. Funding for special programs was sometimes inadequate and difficult to obtain, identification and placement of disabled students was often inconsistent and inappropriate, and parental involvement was discouraged. In addition, special educators and regular educators were in competition for the limited funding that was available. These difficulties led to increased separation of the special education and regular education programs, with little cooperation between the two.

By 1975, there were approximately 8,000,000 disabled children in the United States. Approximately 3,000,000 of these children were not receiving appropriate education in the public schools, and another 1,000,000 were totally excluded from public school education. At that time in our history more than half of the disabled children in the United States were receiving inappropriate public school education, or none at all (Rothstein, 1990).

Early Years of Music in Special Education

Music has been an important part of the training and education of students classified as deaf, blind, and "mentally defective" dating back to the early 1800s. Jean-Marc-Gaspard Itard (1775–1838) was one of the first people to utilize music in the diagnosis of hearing and speech impairment and to develop auditory discrimination skills. A student of Itard, Edouard Seguin (1812–1880) continued the work of his teacher and developed a methodology for using music to teach auditory and speech skills to mentally defective students (Solomon, 1980). Lowell Mason taught vocal music and piano at the Perkins School for the Blind in South Boston from 1832 until

1836. In the school's 1835 annual report, it was stated that music was an important part of the curriculum (Heller, 1987).

Two pioneers in the use of music for the deaf were William Wolcott Turner and David Ely Bartlett. These men published their accounts of teaching music to a hearing impaired student in an 1848 article that was printed in the *American Annals for the Deaf and Dumb*. This work began a trend that would later lead to current practices of teaching music to deaf and hard of hearing students (Darrow & Heller, 1985). In the late 1800s, some schools for deaf and blind students utilized music as part of the curriculum, including singing, clapping, playing drums and other rhythm instruments, and playing simple instruments such as whistles and bells (Solomon, 1980).

For many years, music has been a part of the programming in institutions for children who are mentally retarded. Sheerenberger (1953) described how singing and rhythm activities were developed to meet the current needs of the children in an institutional setting. Music activities were also used to prepare the children for interactions with the community.

The use of music in early special education settings was primarily with children who were deaf, hard of hearing, blind, or mentally retarded. Early educators found music to be a reinforcing, valuable tool to enhance the accomplishments of the students and to facilitate learning. These practices are the foundation on which educators and therapists continue to expand the use of music in special education.

Solomon (1980) noted four themes that emerged from a study of the use of music in early special education settings. First, music was seen as an important part of early attempts to train and educate disabled children. Second, singing was used to involve children who did not speak, to promote proper breathing, and to improve articulation. Third, music activities were used as diagnostic tools before the development of audiology equipment. And, fourth, music has been used in the education of deaf students since the early 19th century.

As educational opportunities increased for disabled students, so did the literature regarding the use of music in special education settings. In her content analysis of music research involving students with disabilities, Jellison (1988) cited research literature from 1975–1986 that documented the effectiveness of music as therapy for students in special education settings.

Litigation and Legislative History Prior to PL 94–142

The racial desegregation decision in the 1954 *Brown v. Board of Education* was the first landmark in special education case law. This decision did not concern the rights of disabled students, yet it laid the groundwork for the future of integrated educational settings. In *Brown v. Board of Education*, Chief Justice Warren ruled that educating black children separately from white children did not provide an equal educational experience, due to the stigma of being educated separately and the lack of interaction with children of other backgrounds (Rothstein, 1990). Not only did this decision bring an end to exclusionary educational policies toward racial minorities, it also paved the way for the elimination of exclusionary policies for students with disabilities. This case led to the determination by some educators that educating children in a segregated environment was adverse. Advocates for the rights of the disabled applied the principles of the *Brown* decision to eliminate policies that were discriminatory to disabled individuals.

The right to a free and appropriate education for all children labeled as mentally retarded was established in the groundbreaking case *Pennsylvania Association of Retarded Citizens (PARC) v. Commonwealth* in 1971. In this class action lawsuit, the federal district court in Philadelphia overturned a Pennsylvania law that allowed the public schools the freedom to exclude children who were mentally retarded. Based on evidence documenting how these children could benefit from education, the *PARC* decision stipulated that mentally retarded children could not be excluded from schools, due process must be followed before a change of placement could occur, and integration was favored over segregated, restrictive placements (Weiner, 1985).

In 1972, one year after the *PARC* decision, the federal district court of Washington, D.C., went further to solidify the educational rights of children with disabilities. Following the principle that education was important in order for all individuals to live as independently as possible, the *Mills v. Board of Education* decision "mandated that due process include procedures relating to the labeling, placement, and exclusionary stages of decision making" (Rothstein, 1990, p. 3). Also included in these procedures was a right to a hearing, a right to appeal, and a right to access information. The *Mills* decision also dictated that the Washington, D.C. school district must educate students with special needs, even if school district money was limited. The court said that these students should not suffer due to financial shortcomings any more than students who are not disabled (Weiner, 1985). While *PARC* established the right to a free and appropriate education for children who were mentally retarded, *Mills v. Board of Education* expanded the *PARC* decision to also include children with disabilities other than mental retardation. The *Mills* decision later provided the basic framework for PL 94–142.

A third milestone that paved the way for the rights of individuals with disabilities, and eventually Public Law 94–142, was the Rehabilitation Act, Section 504 which was passed in 1973. This Act, along with later amendments, guaranteed the rights of persons with disabilities in educational and employment settings, if those settings received support from the federal government (Stainback, Stainback, & Bunch, 1989).

Public Law 94–142

After the *PARC* and *Mills* decision, the Rehabilitation Act, Section 504, and pressure from parents, courts, and legislators, Public Law 94–142 was passed in 1975 and became effective in 1977. This law, also called Education for All Handicapped Children Act of 1975, stipulated that no child can be denied free and appropriate education, and that education must take place in the least restrictive environment. The right to an education was extended to all children with handicaps, not just those children with mental retardation. In addition, the law proposed that this education was to take place in the least possible segregated environment.

PL 94–142 is basically a grant statute that assures the rights of the individual. Based on this law, a state can obtain federal funding to support the education of disabled children aged 3 through 21 if that state develops a plan to provide a free and appropriate public education to all handicapped children in the state. This programming must emphasize special education and related services designed and implemented to meet the unique needs of the individual student. While there are many specific parameters and details of PL 94–142, the following are the basic underlying principles included in the law:

- Education must be provided for all disabled children.

- Programming must take place in the least restrictive environment.
- Education is to be appropriate and individualized to the needs of the child.
- It must be provided free of charge.
- Parents have the right to be involved in the development of their child's education program.
- Procedural protections must be in place to ensure that the requirements are met. (Rothstein, 1990)

Each state and school district must have a plan to ensure that all of the requirements of the law are being met. Other important areas of the law address parent involvement and consultation, due process, nondiscriminatory evaluation, confidentiality, and inservice training for teachers and other professional personnel.

Although the mandate to comply with the requirements of PL 94–142 applies only to states that seek federal funding to support special education, all states accept that funding and must therefore comply with the law. Public education institutions are also subject to the requirements of the 1973 Rehabilitation Act, which prohibits discrimination based on handicap and provides equal protection and due process stipulations.

Major Components of PL 94–142

Individual Education Plan (IEP)

The law states that the education of the disabled child must be appropriate and individualized to the needs of the child. This is implemented through the Individual Education Plan (IEP) that is developed jointly by education and health care professionals, parents, and child advocates who are involved with the student. All students who are placed in special education must have an IEP (Gearheart, Weishahn, & Gearheart, 1992; National Council on Disability, 1989).

Procedures for writing the IEP vary from school district to school district, but PL 94–142 mandates that each IEP contain the following elements: assessment information about the individual's present level of functioning, long-term and short-term goals and objectives for the student, plans for initiation and duration of service, plans for specific educational services to be provided and to what extent the student will be involved in regular education, and criteria for evaluation of the student's progress. Most school districts develop their own standard format for writing the IEP. In addition to the required information, many districts include information concerning who is responsible for delivering services, specific methods and materials that will be used, and other information relevant to the education of the child.

All professionals who are involved with the student are expected to participate in some level on the written plan and/or at the annual evaluation meeting. Regulations mandate that the people present at the writing of the IEP include: a school system representative who is familiar with due process involved in special education, the child's teacher, parents and/or guardians, and the student, when appropriate. (Coleman, 1992). Other professionals who are involved in evaluation or ongoing service to the child may also be included in the IEP meeting, at the discretion of the parents or school personnel. This might include the school psychologist, speech and language pathologist, other special education teachers, music therapist, occupational therapist, physical therapist, and legal experts such as attorneys or parent advocates (Lerner, 1988).

Least Restrictive Environment (LRE) and Mainstreaming

One of the fundamental principles of PL 94–142 is the idea of educating disabled students with nondisabled students to the greatest extent possible. The regulations in PL 94–142 concerning education in the "least restrictive environment" are interpreted differently by various local school districts. Educating a student in the least restrictive environment is often referred to as "mainstreaming," although this term was not actually mentioned in the statutory or regulatory language of the law (Rothstein, 1990). It is the responsibility of the state educational agency to ensure that each public agency establishes and implements appropriate procedures to meet the requirements. The law states:

1. That to the maximum extent appropriate, handicapped children, including children in public or private institutions or other care facilities are educated with children who are not handicapped, and
2. That special classes, separate schooling or other removal of handicapped children from the regular educational environment occurs only when the nature or severity of the handicap is such that education in regular classes with the use of supplementary aids and services cannot be achieved satisfactorily. [(20 U.S.C. 1412(5)(B); 1414(a)(C)(iv)]

The rationale for placing students in the least restrictive environment where education takes place along with nondisabled peers is based on several premises. One premise is that educating disabled students in segregated settings is inherently stigmatizing to the student. Also, there is a concern that there will be lower expectations for a disabled child in a separate class, and thus the child will not achieve what might be possible. Another important premise for integration is the value of interaction between disabled and nondisabled students working together.

The mandates concerning the least restrictive environment allow for a continuum of placement alternatives, but with the goal of providing individualized programming in the most appropriate setting. For the disabled student, this could mean placement ranging from the entire day spent in a regular education classroom (least restrictive), to residential treatment (most restrictive), and any number of options in between. The concept of least restrictive environment suggests movement from a more restrictive setting to a less restrictive, more integrated setting, whenever possible (Reynolds & Fletcher-Janzen, 1990). The philosophy is to provide services to the child in the least restricted environment that is appropriate for the individual child's needs, without causing undue disruption to the other children in the class (Rothstein, 1990). The vague parameters for this regulation have led to varying interpretations of the law by individual school districts.

Amendments to PL 94–142

Although the basic premise of PL 94–142 has remained the same, amendments have been added to the law in an effort to broaden and improve educational services for students with disabilities. When it was passed in 1975, PL 94–142 was referred to as the Education for All Handicapped Children Act (EAHCA). After a series of amendments to the original act in the early 1980s, PL 94–142 came to be known as the Education of the Handicapped Act (EHA). Then in 1986, PL 99–457 amended the EHA to provide services for children with disabilities between the ages of 3 and 5, and it established new incentives for early intervention programs for children aged birth through 2. In 1990, PL 101–476 amended the EHA and it was renamed the Individuals with Disabilities Education Act (IDEA). IDEA retained the basic principles of PL 94–142, but made several changes in terminology. The term "disabilities" was substituted for the term "handicapped" in the new document. The new document also specifically requires service for children with listed disabilities, including mental retardation, autism, hearing impairment or deafness, visual impairment or blindness, serious emotional disturbances, specific learning disabilities, orthopedic impairments, speech or language impairment, and other health impairments. IDEA also listed specific services that should be made available to children when appropriate. Some of the services on this list include counseling services, medical services, audiology, occupational therapy, physical therapy, recreation, and speech pathology. While other services were listed, it was not intended to be an all inclusive list. Rather, the list was meant to be representative of a broad range of services and reflective of the intent of the law (Gearheart, Weishahn, & Gearheart, 1992).

Music Under PL 94–142

While neither music therapy or music education is specifically mentioned in the law, Congress urged the use of arts therapies in the implementation of services of PL 94–142 (Alley, 1979). The Senate Report on PL 94–142 included the following statements about the arts:

> The use of the arts as a teaching tool for the handicapped has long been recognized as a viable, effective way not only of teaching special skills, but also of reaching youngsters who had otherwise been unteachable. The Committee envisions that programs under this bill could well include an arts component and, indeed, urges that local educational agencies include the arts in programs for the handicapped funded under this act. Such a program could cover both appreciation of the arts by the handicapped youngsters, and the utilization of the arts as a teaching tool per se. (Senate Report No. 94–168, 1975, p. 13)

In the implementation section, under Services-Program Options, the law itself states that:

> each public agency shall take steps to insure that its handicapped children have available to them the variety of educational programs and services available to nonhandicapped children in the area served by the agency, including art, music, . . . [20 U.S.C. 1412(2)(A); 1414(a)(1)(C)]

Music therapy services can enhance the education of a disabled child in the areas of academics, physical rehabilitation, self-help skills, emotional well being, and social skills. These services can be provided in a variety of integrated to segregated settings to meet the individual needs of the students. Even though the law does not specifically mention music therapy services or mandate music for students with disabilities, the intent of the legislation was to ensure that students with disabilities receive the same educational experiences provided to nondisabled students. It is important to be aware of the language of the law as cited above to support the case for music therapy and music education for students in special education programs. The Senate Report on PL 94–142 and the implementation section, under Services-Program Options, should be cited by individuals who are interested in developing music therapy programs in public schools where programs do not yet exist. The intent of the law is clear. Music therapists must promote the addition and expansion of music therapy services in the public schools in order to enhance the education of disabled students and to ensure that the individual student's rights are being preserved.

Conclusions

Music is valued in the American society. Participation in music is frequently a group activity, which provides for reinforcement, self-esteem, and aesthetic experiences. All of these things promote the positive value of music. Music is also a highly normalizing activity in which people of all abilities can participate. Music is a means to bring together groups of people, and can be used to integrate special education and regular education students in schools (Alley, 1979). Music can facilitate academic learning, socialization, communication, and behavioral skills (Jellison, 1988).

Almost 20 years ago, Alley (1977) stated that in order for music therapy to be considered and accepted as an educational discipline, music therapists must provide services that are: "1) unique enough to be viewed as complementary to, but not overlapping with, standard educational disciplines; 2) specific to educational objectives communicated in educational jargon; 3) accountable for pupil progress; and 4) competitive for available funding resources" (p. 50). These important factors must still be considered today when implementing music therapy services in educational settings.

References

Alley, J. M. (1977). Education for the severely handicapped: The role of music therapy. *Journal of Music Therapy, 14,* 50–59.

Alley, J. M. (1979). Music in the IEP: Therapy/education. *Journal of Music Therapy, 16,* 102–110.

Coleman, M. C. (1992). *Behavior disorders: Theory and practice, second edition.* Boston, MA: Allyn and Bacon.

Darrow, A. A., & Heller, G. N. (1985). Early advocates of music education for the hearing impaired: William Wolcott Turner and David Ely Bartlett. *Journal of Research in Music Education, 33,* 269–279.

Gearheart, B., Weishahn, M., & Gearheart, C. (1992). *The exceptional student in the regular classroom.* New York: Macmillan.

Heller, G. N. (1987). Ideas, initiatives, and implementations: Music therapy in America, 1789–1848. *Journal of Music Therapy, 24,* 35–46.

Jellison, J. (1988). A content analysis of music research with handicapped children (1975–1986): Applications in special education. In C. E. Furman (Ed.), *Effectiveness of music therapy procedures: Documentation of research and clinical practice.* Silver Spring, MD: National Association for Music Therapy.

Lerner, J. W. (1988). *Learning disabilities: Theories, diagnosis, and teaching strategies.* Boston, MA: Houghton Mifflin Company.

National Council on Disability. (1989). *The education of students with disabilities: Where do we stand? A report to the President and the Congress of the United States.* Washington, DC: National Council on Disability.

Reynolds, C., & Fletcher-Janzen, E. (Eds). (1990). *Concise encyclopedia of special education.* New York: John Wiley & Sons, Inc.

Rothstein, L. F. (1990). *Special education law.* White Plains, NY: Longman.

Senate Report No. 94–168, p. 13, 1975.

Sheerenberger, R. (1953). Description of a music program at a residential school for the mentally handicapped. *American Journal of Mental Deficiency, 57,* 573–579.

Solomon, A. L. (1980). Music in special education before 1930: Hearing and speech development. *Journal of Research in Music Education, 28,* 236–242.

Stainback, W., Stainback, S., & Bunch, G. (1989). Introduction and historical background. In S. Stainback, W. Stainback, & M. Forest (Eds.), *Educating all students in the mainstream of regular education* (pp. 3–14). Baltimore, MD: Paul H. Brookes.

Weiner, R. (1985). *P.L. 94–142: Impact on the schools.* Arlington, VA: Capitol Publications.

Winzer, M. (1993). *The history of special education: From isolation to integration.* Washington, DC: Gallaudet University Press.

CHANGING TIMES: THE EVOLUTION OF SPECIAL EDUCATION

Brian L. Wilson

THE structure of special education and the educational opportunities provided for individuals with disabilities have changed dramatically since the passage of PL 94–142 (now known as the IDEA). Between 1977, the year in which the law first took effect, and 1992, there was a 23% increase in the number of students receiving services (U.S. Department of Education, as cited in Fuchs & Fuchs, 1994). Although the growth of special education could be defended as a natural consequence of an improved system to identify special learners and provide the special educational opportunities that are needed for those students, many find such increases to be convincing evidence of a system that is out of control.

Not long after the implementation of PL 94–142, a growing number of educators, politicians, and parents began to question whether the intent of the law to educate as many children as possible in the least restrictive environment was being adequately addressed. It was their contention that even more children should receive all of their education in general education settings. Critics argued that the special education system was becoming self-serving, frequently guilty of overidentifying or misdiagnosing the number of students requiring special services, and lacking in credible evidence of the efficacy of maintaining "separate but equal" educational opportunities (Gartner & Lipsky, 1987; Hallahan, Kauffman, Lloyd, & McKinney, 1988; Stainback & Stainback, 1984). Further fanning the flames for reform were statistics showing that increasing numbers of students with disabilities continued to be taught in segregated, rather than integrated, settings even though the intent of the "least restrictive environment" (LRE) clause was to do just the opposite. Eventually many students, especially those with milder disabilities, were integrated in the mainstream (at least for part of their education), yet many others with more severe disabilities remained in segregated classrooms or residential/day schools with little contact with regular education students.

The Regular Education Initiative

In the early 1980s the pressure to provide more integrated educational experiences and to limit the number of specialized education offerings continued to gain momentum. More commonly known as the *Regular Education Initiative (REI)*, the idea of a "merger" between special education and regular education gained national attention during a professional conference in 1985. Madeline C. Will, then Assistant Secretary for the U.S. Office of Special Education and Rehabilitative Services, told the special educators gathered at this meeting that the "so-called 'pull-out' approach to the educational difficulties of students with learning problems has failed in many instances to meet the educational needs of these students and has created, however unwittingly, barriers to their successful education" (Will, 1986, p. 412). Based on her belief that the structure was not working as effectively as it should have been, Will issued a charge to special educators that an extensive self-examination of the entire special education delivery system was warranted. Relying heavily on the Adaptive Learning Environments Model (ALEM) developed by Margaret Wang and her colleagues (Wang, 1980; Wang & Birch, 1984), Will called for a partnership to be developed between general and special education.

> The Adaptive Learning Environments Model (ALEM)
>
> The ALEM was developed in an effort to replace "pull-out" programs in regular schools, especially resource rooms and compensatory education programs. The overall goal was to provide successful school environments that maximize learning and mastery of academic subjects while the student concurrently gains confidence and develops coping strategies for the classroom (Wang, 1980). Among the primary components of the ALEM are the following:
>
> 1. Instruction is provided in general education settings on a full-time basis.
> 2. Support and services from specialists are delivered within the general education setting.
> 3. Academic skills are developed through the use of highly structured prescriptive learning based on built-in diagnostic procedures.
> 4. Students plan and manage their own learning in an open-ended, exploratory atmosphere that fosters social and personal development.
> 5. Educational plans are designed for each student to accommodate unique strengths and needs.
> 6. Flexibility is encouraged when arranging the learning environment.
>
> Since its introduction, the ALEM has received a mixed review from the special education profession. While there is some evidence that placing students with disabilities into ALEM classrooms can positively influence their academic performance and social skills (Fuchs & Fuchs, 1988), the research reported by Wang and her associates has been criticized for serious methodological weakness, overemphasis on the *physical placement* of students rather than the content and success of the learning, and for not being subjected to the rigors of scientific research (Hallahan, Keller, McKinney, Lloyd, & Bryan, 1988). Consequently, attempts to enact large-scale full-time mainstreaming programs based on the efficacy of the ALEM have often been viewed as inappropriate given the limitations of the existing research base (Fuchs & Fuchs, 1988; Hallahan, Keller, et al., 1988; Keogh, 1990).

Grounded in the belief that a "dual system" of education was ineffective, Will (1986) further proposed the dismantling of the traditional dual system of education management in favor of the unification of special education with general education. This platform was strongly endorsed by the REI movement which supported a de-emphasis of educational segregation by promoting the development of one unified system of education to meet the unique needs of all children. The REI debate that followed challenged educators to reevaluate their current practices regarding the identification, instruction, and placement of all at-risk children and not just those with traditional disabilities. By doing so, proponents envisioned that a large percentage of children who were educationally disadvantaged would be able to receive support services through the use of large-scale, full-time mainstreaming efforts instead of the more traditional case-by-case approach (Davis, 1990).

Opponents to the REI countered that any attempt to dismantle the dual education system before a new system was in place was premature and irresponsible. Without the means to assess and identify those with learning problems, they feared that the rights of the students with disabilities would be in jeopardy. Others questioned the logic of assuming that the general education system, which was under increasing pressure to improve standardized test scores, could best accommodate the same students that previously failed in it. They argued that some students do require special educational environments with teachers and others who have highly specialized skills and favorable attitudes toward individuals with disabilities (Braaten, Kauffman, Braaten, Polsgrove, & Nelson, 1988; Byrnes, 1990).

Full Inclusion

While the REI resulted in many children who had previously been in self-contained classrooms and separate schools being taught with regular education students, those with more severe disabilities were frequently left behind. Advocates for this group of learners asserted that all students should have access to the mainstream regardless of the severity of the student's disability. This desire to include all students in the regular classroom has become more commonly known as the *inclusive schools movement* or *full inclusion*. Although there is no singular, universally accepted definition, it is generally agreed that inclusion means providing appropriate educational experiences for any child, regardless of disability, in the same classroom, or at least the same school, that the student would attend if he or she did not have a disability (Lombardi, 1994). Whereas the REI suggests that regular classroom teachers be more accommodating and responsive to those students with disabilities who are already included for all or part of their day, full inclusion insists that all education services be provided in the regular classroom with support services brought into the room only as absolutely necessary. In effect the proponents of inclusion believe that the services should come to the student rather than bringing the student to the services.

While there are several important philosophical distinctions between the REI and full inclusion movement, the major difference has been the issue of placement. Those supporting full inclusion argue that all students with disabilities can have a more meaningful educational experience when taught with their nondisabled peers in the regular classroom during the entire school day. Advocates for the REI contend that consideration of the LRE must be secondary to, and balanced against, the primary objective of providing an appropriate education (Kauffman & Lloyd, 1995). Put another way, supporters of the REI believe that placement is *an* issue, while full inclusionists believe that placement is *the* issue.

A second major disparity between these two ideologies centers around the anticipated outcomes of the educational experience. Whereas the REI has maintained the importance of the acquisition of a knowledge base and skill development (Fuchs & Fuchs, 1994), full inclusionists tend to measure success in terms of social acceptance of special learners by both teachers and classmates. Snell (1991) concluded that the three most salient benefits resulting from integration of regular and special needs students were "the development of social skills across all school age groups, the improvements in the attitudes that nondisabled peers have for their peers with disabilities, and the development of positive relationship and friendships between peers" (pp. 137–138).

A third philosophical difference centers around whether maintaining a separate system for providing educational services for students with disabilities is even needed. Rather than attempting to reform special education, full inclusionists want to eliminate it. Although such action could signal the end of labeling practices, special education programs, and special classes, it is not intended to eliminate necessary support services; specialists and consultants would follow the special learner into the regular classroom. Ultimately, this could lead to greater numbers of students receiving services including those deemed to be "at-risk" (Pearpoint & Forest, 1992).

Opponents of full inclusion see all of this as little more than the "dumping" of students into regular classrooms. They contend that inclusion is basically a misguided effort to achieve a "normalized" environment for a group of students whose limited level of functioning has typically precluded them from being considered for placement in the regular classroom. Critics also question whether the presence of a number of specialists in the regular classroom will not disrupt ongoing classroom activities and further stigmatize the special needs student (Kauffman, 1989).

Obstacles to the Integration of Special Learners Into Regular Classrooms

Several of the major tenets of both the REI and the full inclusion movement (e.g., working toward improved interaction between professionals, better coordination of services for students, looking for the most effective and economical methods of serving students with disabilities, identifying special learners only when necessary, and supporting research that will lead to the best possible instruction for all students) have received nearly universal endorsements among professionals. However, other components associated with these changes in the delivery system have been substantially more controversial and have been vigorously debated in the literature:

1. **Will the push for integration in general education settings and against labeling result in fewer students with disabilities receiving needed services?**

Whether students receive services will depend to some extent on if they are even identified as needing those services. In the past, special education has been accused of exaggerating the number of students needing special services (Algozzine, Ysseldyke, & Christenson, 1983; Biklen & Zollers, 1986). Shepard (1987) has suggested that 90% of special education students are very mildly disabled, if at all, and indistinguishable from low achievers. Reynolds, Wang, & Walberg (1987) consider three fourths of special education students to be "judgementally handicapped" (p. 391).

In their review of the extant literature, Hallahan and Kauffman (1994) admit that labeling a person as disabled may lead others to view that individual differently. While most would find capricious labeling and increased stigmatization of children to be unpalatable, the problems associated with labeling may have been overstated. Labels can "help explain behavior that is out of the ordinary and lead to a better understanding and sensitivity toward the labeled person" (Hallahan & Kauffman, 1994, p. 502). Without labels, children may be erroneously accused of being "lazy" or "trouble-makers," when in reality their learning disabilities are the reason for their lack of achievement or disruptive behaviors. Braaten et al. (1988) argue that special learners, especially those with emotional and behavioral disorders, are often labeled by peers and teachers as deviant or different long before they are referred to special education. Furthermore, they contend that removing the label does not remove the problem. Many educators and parents are also concerned that financial support for needed services may be in jeopardy if learning problems are not identified in some manner. If there is not a system to determine learning problems it is not clear how appropriate educational programs can be designed, implemented, and funded.

2. **Is there sufficient empirical evidence to support the belief that the integration of regular and special education students promotes the social and academic skills of all?**

Opponents of the inclusive schools movement frequently question whether the claims that students with disabilities will achieve greater mastery of academic concepts and improve their social skills are based more on wishful thinking than research validation. In general, the efficacy studies that have been conducted over the past half century indicate that special learners placed in integrated classrooms have performed as well as, or better than, their counterparts in self-contained settings.

In their analysis of 261 studies comparing students with severe and profound disabilities in integrated placements with their peers in segregated placements, Halvorsen and Sailor (1990) concluded that students in integrated placements demonstrated greater socialization skills (e.g., fewer inappropriate behaviors, more independence, and increased communication skills) than those in more segregated settings. Other studies have reported similar outcomes, especially in relation to the development of appropriate social skills and successful interactions with nondisabled peers. Corbin (as cited in Lombardi, 1994) found that parents of special needs students who had been fully included in five different elementary schools reported greater improvement in both their children's academic and social learning when compared to their previous segregated settings. The teachers also reported that the regular education students maintained their academic performance, were understanding and accepting of the students with disabilities, and became role models for those students. In a study (Lombardi, Nuzzo, Kennedy, & Foshay, 1994) involving high-school age students there was a lower dropout rate, fewer classroom disturbances, and acceptable academic gains when students with disabilities were placed in regular classrooms. Peck, Donaldson, and Pezzoli (1990) interviewed 21 nondisabled high school students who had social experiences with peers with severe disabilities and found that those experiences resulted in improved self-concept, social-cognitive growth, reduced fear of human differences, and increased tolerance of other people. In addition, a longitudinal study of early elementary students reported increased reading achievement, decreased special-education referrals, reduced retention rates, and improved attendance when students were involved in "Success for All," a district-wide early intervention program serving large numbers of disadvantaged students (Madden, Slavin, Karweit, Dolan, & Wasik, 1993).

Critics charge that these studies are seriously flawed since mainstreamed participants rarely were determined by random assignment and tended to be stronger academically and/or socially at the beginning of the study (Fuchs & Fuchs, 1995; Hallahan & Kauffman, 1994). Rogers (1994) further cautions that published studies extolling the benefits of inclusion generally reflect model programs "with adequate instructional support and with caring teachers who value each of their students sufficiently to assure that every child is challenged" (p. 4). Advocates for full inclusion acknowledge that learners with severe intellectual limitations rarely obtain the same degree of academic success as students with mild or moderate impairments. To rectify this situation, they are calling for fundamental changes in the very foundation of general education by deemphasizing (or eliminating) a standard curriculum and knowledge base in favor of a more process-oriented approach to education (Stainback, Stainback, & Moravec, 1992). Using this approach, children would be encouraged to learn "as much as they can" in any given subject area without being held accountable to typical testing and evaluation procedures.

Although the existing special education structure has been sharply criticized for failing to help students achieve academically or socially (Gartner & Lipsky, 1987), it seems unwarranted to conclude that special education programming over the past 20 years has been ineffective. In their meta-analysis, Carlberg and Kavale (1980) found that special class placement produced substantially better outcomes than regular class placement for students classified as learning disabled and behaviorally disordered/emotionally disturbed. However, regular classroom placement produced slightly better results than special class placement when all types of students were considered together and when students with a low IQ were considered alone. Sindelar and Deno (1978) reported no discernable difference in academic improvement of children with mild mental retardation between resource and mainstream classes but did find that resource rooms were more effective than regular classrooms in improving the academic achievement of students with learning disabilities or emotional and behavioral problems. Similarly, Madden and Slavin (1983) found that students with more serious learning problems benefited the most from placement in special classes.

3. Is it realistic to expect that general education teachers can and will accommodate the special needs of students with disabilities?

While those advocating for the inclusion of greater numbers of special learners in the regular classroom may have assumed that their agenda would be embraced by general educators, this has not necessarily been the case. The REI/full inclusion debate has largely involved faculty in higher education, specifically faculty in special education, while K–12 educators/administrators and other consumers have been less involved in the discussion about the proposed changes (Meese, 1994).

The following assumptions appear to be the foundation upon which a merger between general and special education is being built (Kauffman, 1989):

1. Students are more alike than different and can benefit from the application of education equally to all students. Distinguishing students as disabled/nondisabled has no educational purpose since atypical educational methods are not required to meet their needs.
2. Good teachers are good teachers, regardless of the student. They should be able to teach all students with only minor changes in teaching strategies and without the need for special training. Special education has become a convenient way for general educators to avoid their responsibility to teach all students.

3. All children can receive a quality education without the need to identify some students as different and without special programs, budgets, training programs, teachers, or classes. Special targeting of funds for specific students is inefficient, confusing, and often abused for financial gain. The few students who may need some special services do not need to be formally identified to ensure that they receive appropriate services.
4. Education outside the regular classroom is not required for anyone. All students can be instructed and managed effectively in regular classrooms. Moreover, the separation of students from their ordinary chronological-age peers is an immoral, segregationist act that has no legitimate place in our free and egalitarian society.
5. Physically separate education is inherently discriminatory and unequal. The most important equity issue is the site, not the quality of instruction. (p. 258)

Research regarding regular classroom teachers' perceptions of more inclusive classrooms indicates that many continue to support traditional programming (self-contained classrooms, pull-out programs) as the most effective way to address the needs of special education students (Coates, 1989; Davis & Maheady, 1991; Houck & Rogers, 1994; Semmel, Abernathy, Butera, & Lesar, 1991). Even when teachers do support more integration of special learners into the regular classroom, they frequently report a lack of knowledge about the needs of these students and little understanding of the methods and materials that should be used in their education. This is a dichotomy similar to the one experienced with the implementation of PL 94–142. At that time, regular education teachers, while often philosophically supportive of the principles contained in the new law, remained generally resistant to the integration of disabled students in general classroom settings. Their resistance was not only attributed to such factors as the teachers' reported limited knowledge base, lack of experience of working with students with disabilities, and lack of technical support from specialists, but also to the reformers' failure to recognize that change of this magnitude affects the entire culture of the educational system.

In addition, the type and severity of a student's disability appears to be a factor correlated with both general and music educators' feelings about mainstreaming and willingness to include special learners in their classrooms. For example, regular educators in Illinois reported that they were more willing and able to integrate students with physical, speech and hearing impairments than they were those with moderate to severe developmental delays (Phillips, Allred, Brulle, & Shank, 1990). Music educators tend to be more positive toward the integration of students with less severe disabilities (e.g., learning disabilities, orthopedic problems) than they are towards those with more severe disabilities (multiple impairments, mental retardation, and emotional & behavioral disorders) into music classes (Gfeller, Darrow, & Hedden, 1990; Sideridis & Chandler, 1995; Wilson & McCrary, 1996).

Full Inclusion or a Service Continuum?

Certainly the notion of placing all students in regular classrooms is emotionally charged and politically expedient. State governments, looking for ways to reduce spending, question whether the continued existence of a dual educational system (regular education and special education) has already outlived its usefulness. Many parents of students with disabilities are demanding that their children have as much contact as possible with their nondisabled peers in hopes of enhancing the probability that their children will learn more socially appropriate behaviors. On the other hand, parents of nondisabled students may wonder whether the presence of special learners in the regular classroom will consume an inordinate amount of the teacher's attention resulting in a diluted curriculum.

Several crucial issues will need to be addressed in order that the rights of all children are maintained and protected before the doors of the regular education classroom are opened to everyone. First, how will children with disabilities be guaranteed appropriate services if mechanisms are not in place to assess and identify those who have significant learning problems? Should general educators be expected to manage these problems with only very limited assistance? How will the negative attitudes and the lack of preparation of many general education teachers be sufficiently addressed so that the regular education classroom is a place for success and not failure? Are effective strategies for teaching exceptional children readily available? Finally, will special education students be placed in regular classrooms inappropriately, too soon, or too many at once? Will providing support services in the classroom actually further stigmatize the student with special needs? Will attempts to limit federal mandates, reduce administrative structure, and encourage local control of education (with concomitant reductions in federal funding) only serve to return the country to conditions that existed prior to the passage of PL 94–142?

Sorting through the rhetoric as to how and when special learners should be integrated into the mainstream can be a daunting task. Various groups advocating for students with disabilities have engaged in passionate disagreements as to which philosophical approach is best for their constituency. A review of the position statements of 15 national associations on this topic indicated that the majority opinion favors maintaining a full continuum of services (i.e., a range of placement and service options) rather than offering only the single option of full inclusion (Verstegen & Martin, 1996). In other words, most advocates for the special learner continue to support the inclusion of exceptional children as stipulated in the least restrictive environment clause of the IDEA.. While all interested parties in this national debate would probably agree that access to the mainstream is the ultimate goal for all students, it does seem overly simplistic to assume that any single educational setting or teaching approach will be able to meet the needs of those students, regardless of their abilities or disabilities. Every student is unique and requires an education based on the strengths and limitations that each student possesses.

Implications for Music Therapy/Music Education

Changes in the placement of, and educational services available for, students with disabilities has also had a direct effect on the music classroom. Music educators assigned to educationally segregated or integrated music classes have voiced concerns similar to those of their general education colleagues as how to best meet the needs of the children they have been asked to teach. Music educators report that they often feel inadequate about working with special learners, possibly due to very limited experience with exceptional students, a lack of administrative support, limited involvement in decisions regarding the placement of special education children in music classes, and little knowledge of appropriate methods for teaching integrated classrooms (Darrow, 1990; Gfeller, Darrow, & Hedden, 1990; Gilbert & Asmus, 1981).

Despite the fact that music teachers continue to report having little or no formal training to adequately prepare them for teaching in inclusive situations (Frisque, Niebur, & Humphreys,

1994), there is evidence that their attitude towards teaching all children in the mainstream may be changing. In her survey of Texas music educators, Jellison (1992) found that a large majority (over 90%) felt positive about teaching students with disabilities whether in the regular classroom or in more traditional settings. It is important to note, however, that (a) most of the respondents taught children with only moderate disabilities, and (b) the majority thought that a music therapist rather than a music educator should be responsible for music instruction for students with disabilities. When preservice elementary education majors, preservice music education majors, and inservice music teachers were asked to indicate their perceptions regarding the integration of students with mental retardation in a regular music classroom, Jellison and Duke (1994) found that the inservice teachers were more likely to consider the integrated classroom as being a potentially less successful placement for all students than did their preservice counterparts. However, the authors also found that all respondents were likely to view the inclusion of any child, whether disabled or not, more positively if the student exhibited appropriate social behaviors.

As in other general education settings, the criteria for evaluating the success of mainstreaming in music education may be based on the acquisition of functional knowledge, the development of social/interpersonal relationships, or both. Although the Music Educators National Conference discourages the placement of special learners in music classes for reasons other than music ability, administrators may place students with disabilities in music classes in order to satisfy mainstreaming mandates, because it is assumed that few prerequisite academic or behavioral skills are required, or simply because the child is known to "like music." A recent survey of music educators in Arizona revealed that the majority of respondents believed that most special needs students in general music, band, chorus, or string programs were placed there primarily because of student interest and for socialization purposes (Frisque et al., 1994).

The regular music classroom is not the only placement option available, nor is it always the most appropriate environment for the special learner. Music instruction can also be provided in the self-contained classroom or in separate facilities. Some special learners may be referred to a music therapist employed within the school system to help them master the musical and/or behavioral skills necessary to be successfully integrated into the music classroom. Such services can be provided individually, with disabled peers, or within the mainstreamed classroom. Students placed in music education classes may also be concurrently receiving music therapy services. Kostka (1993) and Jellison and Gainer (1995) have published case studies which imply that the acquisition of positive social and behavioral skills learned in music therapy appear to transfer to the music education setting.

Conclusions

Nearly 30 years have passed since Lloyd Dunn challenged the justification of special education for students who were mildly retarded (Dunn, 1968). He warns that "by removing students with disabilities from regular classes we contribute to the delinquency of regular education. We reduce the need for regular teachers to deal with individual differences. It is morally and educationally wrong." (p. 20) Without question, there have been significant changes in the way that children with special needs are being taught. The 1992–93 school year marked the first time the proportion of students with disabilities attending mostly regular classes outnumbered those in separate classes or more restrictive settings (Lipsky & Gartner, 1996). Yet the push to include even more students in the mainstream continues. The LRE clause, one of the centerpieces of PL 94–142 with its range of placements and services, is now being challenged in the courts. Increasingly, rulings are less likely to come down on the side of school officials on the LRE issue when the recommendations are for more restrictive placements (Osborne & Dimattia, 1994). Today a school district's decision to place a student in a segregated setting will probably be upheld only if school officials can demonstrate that sincere attempts at inclusion have failed or strong evidence to support the belief that an inclusive setting will not be the best choice for the student can be presented (Osborne & Dimattia, 1995).

To be responsive to these changes, music educators must continue to develop teaching strategies and curriculum models that ensure the success of all the students assigned to their classes. The following recommendations are suggested as music educators, often working in tandem with music therapists and other specialists, strive to provide the highest quality education for all students:

1. Keep the needs of the child paramount when decisions regarding placement must be made. Students who are recommended for inclusion should be provided with meaningful learning experiences and not placed in music classrooms simply to comply with political agendas.

2. Request support (from administrators and colleagues) in the form of relevant information (via workshops, inservice training, etc.) when asked to implement models of inclusion. Of all the support specialists, music therapists are perhaps in the best position to provide successful, music-based intervention strategies.

3. Ask for information resulting from IEP decisions. Since music educators rarely attend IEP meetings, they usually have little information about the students being placed in their classes and little influence over their decisions. Too often, music educators are "out of the loop" when placement decisions are made.

4. Realize that, like other general educators, music educators may feel overburdened and unfairly criticized for their perceived lack of response to sweeping changes in special education mandates. Become more assertive in asking for support (e.g., aide, consultants) when asked to implemented mainstreaming programs.

5. Reform music education and teacher certification programs so that coursework addressing the unique role of music with special learners and hands-on experience with students who have disabilities is a requirement and not just an elective.

Whether the integration of the majority of special needs students into regular classes is a good idea or not is no longer the issue. Inclusion is a now a reality in classrooms all over the country. Nevertheless, it should not be viewed as a panacea to cure all of the past ills of special education. Given the volume of evidence in the extant literature, it seems presumptuous and cavalier to assume that general educators have the ability to make needed instructional adaptations in their classroom for students with disabilities, and that those same students will automatically make a satisfactory adjustment to the regular class, without some type of support. Responsible inclusion requires careful planning and adequate support before any student with disabilities is placed in a regular class. Both regular educators and special education personnel must be properly prepared for their changing roles.

References

Algozzine, B., Ysseldyke, J. E., & Christenson, S. (1983). An analysis of the incidence of special class placement: The masses are burgeoning. *Journal of Special Education, 17,* 141–147.

Biklen, D., & Zollers, N. (1986). The focus of advocacy in the LD field. *Journal of Learning Disabilities, 19,* 579–586.

Braaten, S., Kauffman, J. M., Braaten, B. A., Polsgrove, L., & Nelson, C. M. (1988). The Regular Education Initiative: Patent medicine for behavioral disorders. *Exceptional Children, 55,* 21–27.

Byrnes, M. (1990). The Regular Education Initiative debate: A view from the field. *Exceptional Children, 56,* 345–349

Carlberg, C., & Kavale, K. (1980). The efficacy of special v. regular class placement for exceptional children: A meta-analysis. *The Journal of Special Education, 14,* 295–309.

Coates, R. D. (1989). The Regular Education Initiative and opinions of regular classroom teachers. *Journal of Learning Disabilities, 22,* 532–536.

Darrow, A. A. (1990). Research on mainstreaming in music education. *Update, 9*(1), 35–37.

Davis, J. C., & Maheady, L. (1991). The Regular Education Initiative: What do three groups of education professionals think? *Teacher Education and Special Education, 14,* 211–220.

Davis, W. E. (1990). Broad perspectives on the Regular Education Initiative: Response to Byrnes. *Exceptional Children, 56,* 349–351.

Dunn, L. (1968). Special education for the mildly retarded: Is much of it justifiable? *Exceptional Children, 35,* 5–22.

Frisque, J., Niebur, L, & Humphreys, J. (1994). Music mainstreaming: Practices in Arizona. *Journal of Research in Music Education, 42,* 94–104.

Fuchs, D., & Fuchs, L. (1988). Evaluation of the Adaptive Learning Environments Model. *Exceptional Children, 55,* 115–127.

Fuchs, D., & Fuchs, L. (1994). Inclusive schools movement and the radicalization of special education reform. *Exceptional Children, 60,* 294–309.

Fuchs, D., & Fuchs, L. (1995). Special education can work. In J. M. Kauffman, J. W. Lloyd, D. P. Hallahan, & T. A. Astuto (Eds.), *Issues in educational placement: Students with emotional and behavioral disorders* (pp. 363–377). Hillsdale, NJ: Lawrence Erlbaum Associates.

Gartner, A., & Lipsky, D. K. (1987). Beyond special education: Toward a quality system for all students. *Harvard Educational Review, 57,* 376–395.

Gfeller, K., Darrow, A. A., & Hedden, S. K. (1990). Perceived effectiveness of mainstreaming in Iowa and Kansas schools. *Journal of Research in Music Education, 38,* 90–101.

Gilbert, J. P., & Asmus, E. P. (1981). Mainstreaming: Music educators' participation and professional needs. *Journal of Research in Music Education, 29,* 31–38.

Hallahan, D. P., & Kauffman, J. M. (1994). Toward a culture of disability in the aftermath of Deno and Dunn. *Journal of Special Education, 27,* 496–508.

Hallahan, D. P., Kauffman, J. M., Lloyd, J. W., & McKinney, J. D. (1988). Introduction to the series: Questions about the Regular Education Initiative. *Journal of Learning Disabilities, 21,* 3–11.

Hallahan, D. P., Keller, C. E., McKinney, J. D., Lloyd, J. W., & Bryan, T. (1988). Examining the research base of the Regular Education Initiative: Efficacy studies and the adaptive learning environments model. *Journal of Learning Disabilities, 21*, 29–35.

Halvorsen, A. T., & Sailor, W. (1990). Integration of students with severe and profound disabilities: A review of the research. In R. Gaylord-Ross (Ed.), *Issues and research in special education* (pp. 110–172). New York: Teachers College Press.

Houck, C. K., & Rogers, C. J., (1994). The special/general education integration initiative for students with specific learning disabilities: A "snapshot" of program change. *Journal of Learning Disabilities, 27*, 435–453.

Jellison, J. (1992). Music and students with disabilities: A preliminary study of Texas music educators' experiences, attitudes, and perceptions. *Texas Music Education Research*. Austin, TX: Texas Music Educators Association.

Jellison, J., & Duke, R. (1994). The mental retardation label: Music teachers' and prospective teachers' expectations for children's social and music behaviors. *Journal of Music Therapy, 31*(3), 166-185.

Jellison, J., & Gainer, E. (1995). Into the mainstream: A case-study of a child's participation in music education and music therapy. *Journal of Music Therapy, 32*, 228–247.

Kauffman, J. M. (1989). The Regular Education Initiative as Reagan-Bush education policy: A trickle-down theory of education of the hard-to-teach. *The Journal of Special Education, 23*, 256–278.

Kauffman, J. M., & Lloyd, J. W. (1995). A sense of place: The importance of placement issues in contemporary special education. In J. M. Kauffman, J. W. Lloyd, D. P. Hallahan, & T. A. Astuto (Eds.), *Issues in educational placement: Students with emotional and behavioral disorders* (pp. 3–20). Hillsdale, NJ: Lawrence Erlbaum Associates.

Keogh, B. K. (1990). Narrowing the gap between policy and practice. *Exceptional Children, 57*, 186–190.

Kostka, M. J. (1993). A comparison of selected behaviors of a student with autism in special education and regular music class. *Music Therapy Perspectives, 11*, 57–60.

Lipsky, D., & Gartner, A. (1996). Inclusive education and school restructuring. In W. Stainback & S. Stainback (Eds.), *Controversial issues confronting special education: Divergent perspectives, 2nd edition* (pp. 3–15).

Lombardi, T. (1994). Responsible inclusion of students with disabilities. *Phi Delta Kappan, 75*, 7–39.

Lombardi, T., Nuzzo, D., Kennedy, K., & Foshay, J. (1994). Perceptions of parents, teachers and students regarding an integrated education inclusion program. *High School Journal, 77*, 315–21.

Madden, N.A., & Slavin, R.E. (1983). Effects of cooperative learning on the social acceptance of mainstreamed academically handicapped students. *Journal of Special Education, 13*(1), 32–37.

Madden, N. A., Slavin, R. E., Karweit, N. L., Dolan, L. J., & Wasik, B. A. (1993). Success for all: Longitudinal effects of a restructuring program for inner-city elementary schools. *American Educational Research Journal, 30*, 123–148.

Meese, R. L. (1994). *Teaching learners with mild disabilities: Integrating research and practice.* Pacific Grove, CA: Brooks/Cole.

Osborne, A. G., & Dimattia, P. (1994). The IDEA's least restrictive environment mandate: Legal implications. *Exceptional Children, 61*, 6–14.

Osborne, A. G., & Dimattia, P. (1995). Counterpoint: IDEA's LRE mandate: Another look. *Exceptional Children, 61*, 582–584.

Peck, C. A., Donaldson, J., & Pezzoli, M. (1990). Some benefits nonhandicapped adolescents perceive for themselves from their social relationships with peers who have severe handicaps. *Journal of the Association for Persons with Severe Handicaps, 15*, 241–249.

Pearpoint, J., & Forest, M. (1992). Foreword. In S. Stainback & W. Stainback (Eds.), *Curriculum considerations in inclusive classrooms: Facilitating learning for all students* (pp. xv–xviii). Baltimore: Paul Brookes.

Phillips, W. L., Allred, K., Brulle, A. R., & Shank, K. S. (1990). The Regular Education Initiative: The will and skill of regular educators. *Teacher Education and Special Education, 13*(3–4), 182–186.

Reynolds, M. C., Wang, M. C., & Walberg, H. J. (1987). The necessary restructuring of special and regular education. *Exceptional Children, 53*, 391–398.

Robinson, C. E. (1994, November). *Choral music educators' beliefs about the causes of success and failure of mainstreamed students in music.* Paper presented at the National Association for Music Therapy Annual Conference, Orlando, FL.

Rogers, J. (1994). *Inclusion: Moving beyond our fears.* Bloomington, IN: Phi Delta Kappa.

Semmel, M. I., Abernathy, T. V., Butera, G., & Lesar, S. (1991). Teacher perceptions of the Regular Education Initiative. *Exceptional Children, 58*, 9–23.

Shepard, L. A. (1987). The new push for excellence: Widening the schism between regular and special education. *Exceptional Children, 53*, 327–329.

Sideridis, G., & Chandler, J. (1995). Attitudes and characteristics of general music teachers toward integrating children with developmental disabilities. *Update, 14*(1), 11–15.

Sindelar, P. T., & Deno, S. C. (1978). The effectiveness of resource programming. *Journal of Special Education, 12*(1), 17-28.

Snell, M. E. (1991). Schools are for all kids: The importance of integration for students with severe disabilities and their peers. In J. W. Lloyd, A. C. Repp, & N. N. Singh (Eds.), *The Regular Education Initiative: Alternative perspectives on concepts, issues, and models* (pp. 133–148). Sycamore, IL: Sycamore.

Stainback, W., & Stainback, S. (1984). A rationale for the merger of special and regular education. *Exceptional Children, 51*, 102–111.

Stainback, W., Stainback, S., & Moravec, J. (1992). Using curriculum to build inclusive classrooms. In S. Stainback & W. Stainback (Eds.), *Curriculum considerations in inclusive classrooms: Facilitating learning for all students* (pp. 65–84). Baltimore: Paul Brookes.

Verstegen, D., & Martin, P. (1996). *A summary of position statements on the inclusion of special education students in the general classroom and excerpts on funding from fifteen national associations.* (ERIC Document Reproduction Service No. ED 386880)

Wang, M. (1980). Adaptive instruction: Building on diversity. *Theory into practice, 19*, 122–127.

Wang, M., & Birch, J. (1984). Comparison of a full-time mainstreaming program and a resource room approach. *Exceptional Children, 51*, 33–40.

Will, M. (1986). Educating children with learning problems. A shared responsibility. *Exceptional Children, 52*, 411–415.

Wilson, B. L., & McCrary, J. (1996). The effect of instruction on music educators' attitudes toward students with disabilities. *Journal of Research in Music Education, 44*, 26–33.

RESEARCH ON MAINSTREAMING: IMPLICATIONS FOR MUSIC THERAPISTS

Alice-Ann Darrow

From the beginning of mainstreaming until today, the music classroom has served as a common placement for students with disabilities. Music educators were pioneers in the movement to integrate students with disabilities into the regular classroom (Atterbury, 1990; Graham & Beer, 1980). Too often, however, the placement of these students in the music classroom was due to administrators' misconception about the academic environment of the music classroom. They believed any student could be integrated into a class to sit and merely listen to music. Administrators were, and often still are (Goeke, 1994), unaware that music educators are responsible for implementing a structured curriculum that involves music reading, writing, creating, and listening as well as performance skills, such as singing and playing. In the early years of mainstreaming, music educators were given little or no training in adapting the music curriculum for students with disabilities. Although many preservice music educators now receive some preparation regarding the characteristics and general education of students with disabilities, in most cases, their preparation does not include actual teaching experiences with students who have various disabilities or information regarding systematic and viable instructional strategies that facilitate the success of all students in a mainstreamed environment (Gfeller, Darrow, & Hedden, 1990).

As a result of the inclusion movement and the common placement of students with disabilities into regular music programs, the role of the music therapist has been redefined in many schools. As a part of their newly defined role, the school music therapist is often called upon to team teach with or to serve as a consultant to music educators. Though some school music therapists still work with students who have severe disabilities in the self-contained classroom, most are required to work with students in multi-level groupings. Given the educational environment, the music therapist must be aware of and sensitive to instructional objectives that address not only therapeutic goals, but also the musical development of students with disabilities. Fortunately, many music therapy and music education goals overlap. Both types of goals can often be met through similar classroom activities. Music therapists, along with other specialists, have been able to provide valuable information regarding the modification of materials and methodology often needed to support individual students in the mainstreamed music classroom.

The rapid movement toward inclusion has required that music therapists increase their knowledge of mainstreaming practices. There is a great deal that music therapists can learn from the related research literature. Mainstreaming research, both in the general classroom and in the music classroom, will be reviewed with implications given for music therapists. The Resources section of this book also includes a bibliography of research related to students with specific communication, cognitive, sensory, physical, and social disabilities.

Mainstreaming Research in General Education

Mainstreaming is a difficult concept to study empirically. There are numerous problems that can complicate any comparative field investigation in education: finding equivalent teachers and students, eliminating teacher biases, maintaining equal school resources, changing services within the schools, and standardizing definitions between sites (Reynolds & Birch, 1988). There are several additional problems that make research in the specific area of mainstreaming difficult:

1. Lack of a valid source of measurement for effective mainstreaming;
2. The variety of disabilities often represented by single terms such as "disabled, handicapped, special, or exceptional";
3. The variety of mainstreamed class configurations (ranging from few students with one disability to many students with various disabilities);
4. Lack of consensus regarding appropriate instructional objectives for the mainstreamed classroom;
5. Varying degrees of support services for educators in the mainstreamed classroom; and
6. Lack of specific information regarding the degree to which teacher attitude and preparation influence the effectiveness of mainstreaming.

(Darrow, 1990, p. 35)

Despite these methodological problems, a number of researchers have attempted to examine mainstreaming practices and efficacy. The following research studies were selected for review because they (a) address problems of the mainstreamed classroom, (b) represent quality research, and (c) are applicable to both music therapy and music education. The research is organized by the four most commonly identified problems related to mainstreaming (Salend, 1994):

Varied Abilities in Mainstreamed Classes
Grading Mainstreamed Students
Teacher/Student Attitudes Toward Mainstreamed Students
Efficacy of the Mainstreamed Setting

Varied Abilities in the Mainstream Classroom

One of the common complaints made by teachers of many mainstreamed classrooms is that the abilities of their students' are too varied; consequently, group instruction is extremely difficult. Researchers have offered opposing opinions regarding the heterogeneous and homogeneous grouping of students for instructional purposes (Evertson, Sanford, & Emmer, 1981; Stallings, 1985). A review of the literature indicates that the differential use of both heterogeneous and homogeneous grouping can be beneficial for students as well as teachers (Slavin, 1987). A study by Swank, Taylor, Brady, Cooley, and Freiberg (1989) highlights the trade-offs in both kinds of classrooms. These researchers found that mainstreamed students exhibited fewer behavioral problems and spent more time on-task and with learning materials in heterogeneous classes; teachers, however, provided more direct and active instruction in homogeneous classes. One of the benefits of heterogeneous student grouping is the provision of peer models and the presence of peer pressure to conform. One of the benefits of homogeneous grouping of students, however, is that teachers can implement group lessons more easily.

Students in music programs are commonly placed in performing groups on the basis of their musical ability; hence, groups are titled beginning band, concert band, symphonic band, etc. Many mainstreamed students, because of physical or cognitive disabilities, are often difficult to place in ability-assigned groups. The research would suggest that there are advantages to placing students of varying abilities in the same group. The challenge is for the music teacher or music therapist to find ways of providing individualized or small group instruction. A good mainstreaming teacher will also find ways to maximize the benefits of peer modeling, peer pressure, peer tutors, and cross-age tutors. An excellent study by Madsen, Smith, and Feeman (1988) outlines the combined use of cross-age tutors and music to encourage academic success as well as to promote self-esteem. In this study, older special education students with behavioral problems served as tutors for young academically deficient kindergartners. The data from this study indicate several important and valuable strategies for music teachers and therapists working in the mainstreamed classroom:

1. Set the occasion for students to feel good about themselves. Students with behavioral problems are rarely in a position to receive recognition for good deeds and, hence, to feel good about themselves. Since these opportunities for recognition seldom occur by chance, they must be set up by the music teacher or therapist.

2. Make sure students with disabilities are given the opportunity to be tutors as well as to be tutored. Students with disabilities, like all other students, need to learn to assist others as well as to receive assistance. They also need to be recognized for their abilities rather than only for their disabilities.

3. Music serves as a valuable contingency for student participation, task completion, and as a teaching aid for academic work. Music's flexibility as well as its popular appeal make it a useful tool for the mainstreamed classroom.

Grading Mainstreamed Students

School music therapists are working in an educational environment that often requires them to assign grades to students for music learning and participation. Assigning grades in music is difficult for a number of reasons. The music therapist is usually working with many more students than the average classroom teacher; therefore, assessment and record keeping requires a considerable amount of time. Music therapists must also decide if they are evaluating students on the basis of musical skill, academic progress, effort, conduct, attendance, or any other number of related factors. If grades are determined by a combination of the aforementioned factors, they must assign each factor a percentage of the final grade. Most music therapists have been trained to administer ongoing assessments of their students' progress; assigning grades, however, is a separate issue. Music therapists often feel uncomfortable assigning grades solely on the basis of musical or academic progress.

Music therapists, like all teachers, are often concerned about whether they should alter their established grading practices for students with disabilities. Grading issues received little attention until students with disabilities were integrated into the general classroom (Lindsey, Burns, & Guthrie, 1984). A number of recent studies have addressed some of the aspects of grading

(Donahue & Zigmond, 1990; Valdes, Williamson, & Wagner, 1990; Zigmond, Levin, & Laurie, 1985). These descriptive studies indicate that most mainstreamed students received lower grades and are not graded on the same criteria as their peers. Researchers have found that music educators also have different educational objectives and grading practices for students with disabilities from those they have for students without disabilities (Frisque, Niebur, & Humphreys, 1994; Gfeller, Darrow, & Hedden, 1990). No experimental studies could be found that examined the effects of differential grading on student achievement. Though such studies would be useful, the inherent ethical issues involved make such research difficult to carry out.

There is a considerable body of research that deals with the nondiscriminatory assessment of students with disabilities, primarily for the purpose of determining service delivery (Bailey & Harbin, 1980; Fuchs & Fuchs, 1986; Marston & Magnusson, 1985; McLoughlin & Lewis, 1990). This research is related to intelligence testing, achievement testing, and disability diagnosis (Lewis & Doorlag, 1991). From this body of research and other sources related to best practices (Gearheart, Weishahn, & Gearheart, 1992; Smith, Polloway, Patton, & Dowdy, 1995), the following suggestions for grading students with disabilities are offered:

1. Consider brief narrative reports on students' progress rather than the assignment of letter grades.
2. Utilize cooperative assignment grades (e.g., grades for group compositions).
3. Investigate alternative procedures for evaluating assignments (e.g., singing a piece rather than playing it, or identifying the piece by name and composer).
4. Emphasize effort or the acquisition of new skills as the basis for grades.
5. Consider a point system for which students are offered or can self-select alternative options for earning points that determine their final grade.
6. Allow for alternative assignments related to music objectives (e.g., looking up information on the Internet about Mozart as an alternative to playing his music).

A recent music study by Johnson and Darrow (in press) found that students are also aware of some of the logistical problems associated with mainstreaming, such as assigning grades. Subjects in their study were positive about the inclusion of students with disabilities in their band programs; however, when subjects were presented statements such as, "students with disabilities should have to audition like other students who want to be in band," or "students with disabilities should be graded like other students," their views regarding mainstreaming became less clear. Students, like many teachers, may be in agreement regarding the philosophy underlying mainstreaming, but they are often bewildered when the philosophy is to be reflected in grade or chair (as in orchestra or band) assignments. The results of the Johnson and Darrow study suggest that inclusion may be like many other issues wherein people may agree on the idea but disagree, or are perhaps confused, regarding methods of implementation.

Teacher/Student Attitudes Toward Mainstreamed Students

Teachers' and students' attitudes affect their behaviors; therefore, their attitudes toward mainstreaming have important implications for the classroom interactions of students with disabilities. One of the arguments against mainstreaming is that teachers and students often have negative attitudes toward mainstreaming; consequently, students with disabilities are often isolated and stigmatized. Early studies indicated that, indeed, many teachers were opposed to mainstreaming (Baker & Gottlieb, 1980; Stevens & Braun, 1980) and that students without disabilities often had negative attitudes toward classmates with disabilities (Altman, 1981; Horne, 1985). Fortunately, more recent research indicates that these attitudes are changing (Larrivee & Horne, 1991; Williams, Fox, Thousand, & Fox, 1990).

Attitudes toward students with disabilities are often affected by information. Various studies have examined the effect of information on subjects' attitude toward students with disabilities (Fiedler & Simpson, 1987; Handlers & Austin, 1980; Simpson, 1980). The findings of these studies indicate that information dispels misconceptions, clarifies misunderstandings, and decreases fears; consequently, attitudes improve. Studies concerned with improving attitudes toward disabled students have also indicated the feasibility of facilitating acceptance through social interaction (Amsel & Fichen, 1988) and personal conversations (Evans, 1976).

Music therapists can serve as positive role models to teachers. Their behaviors must reflect the attitude that all students are accepted and valued. Music therapists' attitudes toward mainstreaming play an important role in determining the success or failure of mainstreaming. Teaching students to appreciate and accept individual differences can also facilitate the successful mainstreaming of students with disabilities (Simpson, 1980). Research has indicated that when negative attitudes exist, positive attitudes can be fostered through a variety of attitude change strategies (Conway & Gow, 1988; Donaldson, 1980). Attitude change strategies have four basic goals: (a) to provide information about disabilities, (b) to increase students' and teachers' comfort level with students who have disabilities, (c) to foster empathy, and (d) to facilitate accepting behavior toward people with disabilities (Barnes, Berrigan, & Biklen, 1978, p. 19).

Disability simulation is one type of strategy to teach positive attitudes toward students with a disability. Jones, Sowell, Jones, and Butler (1981) found that a training program that included simulations to sensitize students to the needs and experiences of others with disabilities led to an increase in positive attitudes toward persons with disabilities. Simulation experiences introduce others to the problems encountered by individuals with disabilities and give insight into the reactions of other individuals who do not have disabilities. Clore and Jeffrey (1972) noted that attitude changes via disability simulations were long lasting.

A second strategy is to introduce students to highly successful individuals who have disabilities. Lazar, Gensley, and Orpet (1971) found that they could promote positive attitudes toward individuals with disabilities by instituting an attitude change program that included a unit on individuals with disabilities who have made significant contributions to society. Two examples of well-known and respected musicians with disabilities are Itzak Perlman and Ray Charles. It is important for students to be aware that individuals with *disabilities* often have extraordinary *abilities*.

Inviting guest speakers, showing films, and reading books (Greenbaum, Varas, & Markel, 1980; Litton, Banbury, & Harris, 1980) are additional ways in which students can learn about individuals with disabilities. Leung (1980) found that a literature program consisting of 10 short stories and discussions concerning individuals with disabilities increased the number of positive and neutral interactions among mainstreamed students and their regular classroom teachers and peers, while the number of negative interactions decreased. Salend and Moe (1983) compared the effects of two interventions on student attitudes: students were exposed to books about disabilities (a) by listening to the teacher reading them, and (b) by listening to the books with the teacher highlighting the main points to be learned through discussion, simulations, and explanations. The second intervention, which combined books and activities, resulted in significant changes in student attitudes toward persons with a disability.

Providing students and teachers with information on disabilities often promotes understanding and reduces inappropriate questions. Information usually includes the characteristics and causes of disabilities, advocacy, and an awareness of negative attitudes and stereotypes directed toward individual disabilities (Simpson, 1980). Additional research has indicated that other successful strategies include reverse mainstreaming (McCann, Semmel, & Nevin, 1985), group discussions (Gottlieb, 1980), and continued communication between students and teachers without disabilities and those with disabilities (Salend & Knops, 1984).

Efficacy of the Mainstreamed Setting

An important body of research in the field of mainstreaming is related to the academic efficacy of the mainstreamed setting. A recent analysis of the mainstreaming literature indicates that much less attention has been given to the evaluation of student performance than to the assessment of teacher and student attitudes (Miller, Fullmer, & Walls, 1996). While teacher opinions regarding mainstreaming strongly influence practice (Smith, Polloway, Patton, & Dowdy, 1995), there is also research that has indicated a strong relationship between teachers' ratings of academic success and the social acceptance of students with disabilities as well as those students without disabilities (Roberts & Zubrick, 1993). As a result of their analysis of the mainstreaming literature, Miller, Fullmer, and Walls (1996) suggest greater attention be given to research that examines student academic achievement as well as specific instructional strategies.

Early efficacy studies were conducted by Dunn (1968) who reported data indicating damaging implications for segregated education. Based upon his data, Dunn concluded that students with mental retardation who were educated in special classes achieved no better academically than their peers educated in regular classrooms, and that in either setting, these students did not work up to their mental capacity. Furthermore, the higher their intellectual functioning, the less students liked special placements and the lower their self-esteem. Based upon Dunn's early studies and others reviewed by Smith, Price, and Marsh (1986), researchers began to examine the efficacy of mainstreamed settings for students with disabilities.

No research has conclusively provided justification for serving students solely through mainstreamed programs; however, much of the work that has been done indicates that students do as well or better in integrated settings than they do in self-contained classrooms or other segregated settings. Some researchers have found that mainstreamed students' academic performance is improved by placement in the regular classroom and that their social interactions in the regular classroom were no different from the social interactions of their peers without disabilities (Madden & Slavin, 1983; Ray, 1986). Stevens and Slavin (1991) analyzed studies that compared students with and without disabilities in achievement when cooperative learning was used in the classroom. They concluded that when cooperative learning instructional processes include individual accountability and group rewards, they are likely to have a positive effect on the achievement of students with and without disabilities. The data reported in this particular study indicate two important implications for music therapists and teachers working with students of varied abilities:

1. Students must be accountable for their own work, implying that work must also be individualized to meet the needs of varying academic abilities.

2. Group rewards, given for the academic accomplishments of students with disabilities, fosters an investment in classroom performance, and consequently, results in cooperation and shared learning.

In earlier studies (Calhoun & Elliot, 1977; Guerin & Szatlocky, 1974; Haring & Krug, 1975; Macy & Carter, 1978) as well as later studies (Leinhardt, 1980; Madden & Slavin, 1983; Miller, Fullmer, & Walls, 1996; Wang & Birch, 1984), researchers found that students placed in mainstreamed settings showed significantly greater gains in achievement than their counterparts educated in self-contained special education classes. Wang, Anderson, and Bram (1985) performed a meta-analysis of 50 studies comparing regular and special education placements and found that, across all types of disabilities, results indicated not only that the academic and social performance of students with special needs in mainstreamed settings were superior to those students educated in special classes, but also that the students who were mainstreamed on a full-time basis performed better than their peers who were mainstreamed on a part-time basis. In their research, Wang, Anderson, and Bram also examined program characteristics that are related to effective mainstreaming. They found that features commonly associated with successful mainstreaming programs were:

1. ongoing assessment of students' performance
2. adaptive instructional strategies and materials
3. individualized instruction
4. cooperative learning arrangements
5. student self-management strategies
6. use of consultation and instructional teaming.

These features of effective mainstreaming programs have important implications for music therapists working in schools. Music therapists can assist in the implementation of these identified characteristics by:

1. being knowledgeable about disability-related assessment issues and advising music educators accordingly;
2. assisting music educators in the actual assessment of students with disabilities;
3. advising music educators regarding appropriate instructional strategies, adaptive technology, instructional materials, and musical instruments;
4. providing individualized instruction for students with disabilities when needed;
5. supervising cooperative learning arrangements in the music classroom;
6. devising and helping to implement student self-management strategies; and most important,
7. serving as consultants to music educators and as members of instructional teams in the classroom.

There are researchers who have found no differences between students placed in segregated settings versus mainstreamed settings (Budoff & Gottlieb, 1976; Walker, 1974) or found that mainstreamed settings have not been effective placements for students with disabilities (Gottlieb, 1981; Gresham, 1982). Some research data indicate that students with specific disabilities, such as those with learning disabilities and behavior disorders, perform better in the self-contained classroom (Carlbert & Kavale, 1980). Other researchers have found data that indicate students with even mild mental retardation need support in the regular classroom and that they are often less popular than their peers (Bryan & Bryan, 1978; Myers, 1976; Siperstein, Bopp, & Bak, 1978). Some professionals in the field of special education contend, however, that many of the problems associated with mainstreaming in these early studies have now been resolved (Reynolds & Birch, 1988). Several researchers have found that inconsistent findings in efficacy studies are also a result of the schools' failure to implement mainstreaming appropriately (Stainback, Stainback, Courtnage, & Jaben, 1985). Zigler and Muenchow (1979) noted that school programs in the early years of PL 94–142 implemented the "least expensive" rather the "least restrictive" alternative for students with disabilities.

While the research on the efficacy of mainstreaming has reported varied results, there are substantial data to support the notion that students with disabilities can be successful in the music classroom. The key is for music therapists and music educators to work together to structure the classroom such that all students can be successful, musically and personally. The work of several researchers indicate that collaboration, sharing expertise, and sharing resources are necessary for the successful inclusion of students with disabilities (Bauwens, Hourcade, & Friend, 1989; Idol & West, 1991). Most importantly though, music therapists and music educators must share a common goal that all students are accepted as individuals and that all students deserve the opportunity to have music as a part of their education.

Mainstreaming Research in Music Education

Mainstreaming in music education has a long and varied history. Music educators were integrating students with disabilities into the music classroom long before the term *mainstreaming* came into use. Research might indicate, however, that our experience with mainstreaming has not necessarily served us well. Music educators have expressed, with considerable consistency over the years, serious concerns regarding the mainstreaming of students with disabilities into the music classroom.

Since the implementation of PL 94–142, thousands of students with disabilities have passed through music classrooms. It is time to address some of the problems with mainstreaming that still exist for music educators. The key to solving these problems may be through the collaborative research efforts of music therapists and music educators. Music therapists and music educators are likely candidates for collaboration. Idol and West (1991) explain that "educational collaboration is an interactive relationship first, then a technique or vehicle for change . . . a tool for problem solving" (p. 87).

Professionals in the field of music education and music therapy have different areas of expertise. Music educators are well versed in music curricular issues and the musical development of children. Music therapists are especially knowledgeable about functional music as well as instructional issues and adaptive strategies related to persons with disabilities. The educational preparation of music therapists includes much of the information that music educators need to successfully integrate students with disabilities into the mainstreamed classroom. Their professional preparation includes information related to various disabilities, adaptive instructional strategies, assistive technology, and adapted music materials. Music therapists can provide valuable assistance to music educators regarding the instruction of students with disabilities.

Another key to identifying and solving mainstreaming problems is through research. Collaborative research between music therapists and music educators is perhaps our greatest hope for bringing students with disabilities into the mainstream of music education. The following review of related research should provide useful information concerning some of the problems related to mainstreaming in music education. The review includes studies that were published over the past 20 years in the music therapy and music education research journals. For those who wish to read additional research regarding mainstreaming, a number of doctoral dissertations have been written about mainstreaming practices in specific school districts or states (Brown, 1981; Damer, 1979; Gavin, 1983; Hawkins, 1991; Nocera, 1981; Shepard, 1993; Smaller, 1989). Most of the related studies that have been published in the major research journals are descriptive in nature. The descriptive research includes studies that describe the status of mainstreaming in music education, mainstreaming practices with students who have specific disabilities, and the attitudes of music teachers and students toward mainstreaming.

Status of Mainstreaming in Music Education

In examining the status of music mainstreaming, researchers have frequently found that music educators feel they are not adequately prepared to teach in the mainstreamed classroom (Frisque et al., 1994; Gfeller et al., 1990; Gilbert & Asmus, 1981). The ability to adapt educational procedures to the learning characteristics of students with disabilities often requires specialized educational preparation. Music educators' lack of preparation is unfortunate since research has indicated that disability-related information is positively related to teachers' attitudes and willingness to integrate students with disabilities into the regular classroom (Stephens & Braun, 1980).

Three years after the implementation of PL 94–142 (The Education for All Handicapped Children Act), Gilbert and Asmus (1981) examined music educators' involvement with mainstreamed students, their knowledge of legislation concerning students with disabilities, and professional needs in developing and implementing music education programs for these students. A nationwide survey of general, instrumental, and vocal music educators revealed that 63% of the respondents were professionally involved with mainstreamed students, with significantly greater experience found at the elementary level. Despite this active involvement in mainstreaming, music educators expressed great concern regarding appropriate methods of teaching and evaluating these students. Music educators felt unprepared to meet the needs of special education students in the music classroom. Although many states now require a college special education course for all education majors, music educators still feel that they are not effectively educating students with disabilities (Frisque et al., 1994).

Additional concerns were revealed in a later study by Atterbury (1986). A random sample of elementary music educators in the Southern Division of the Music Educators National Conference (MENC) responded that decisions and placements in elementary music were not supported by appropriate administrative assistance. Only 1% of the respondents actively participated in the development of mainstreamed students' Individual Education Plans (IEPs). Furthermore, music educators said that they were often asked to accommodate too many mainstreamed students in the music classroom.

A later study of music educators in Kansas and Iowa (Gfeller et al., 1990) revealed little change in music educators' concerns regarding the mainstreamed classroom. More than 10 years after the passage of PL 94–142, music educators still reported an inadequate level of educational preparation and administrative support. Of greatest concern were the percentages of music educators who indicated mainstreamed students hindered the progress of other students (61%) and that special education students' music education needs would be better met in special classes (50%). A study by Frisque et al., (1994) published nearly five years later, reported findings nearly identical to those of Gfeller et al. (1990) regarding the status of mainstreaming. These findings, along with those of Atterbury (1986), would indicate that little has changed over the years since the implementation of PL 94–142.

A review of the research reveals a particularly critical issue faced by music educators in the mainstreamed music classroom. Researchers have found that music educators' wariness in mainstreaming students with disabilities has often been due to the perceived lack of support from administration regarding the placement of students with disabilities and the lack of planning time to prepare for the mainstreamed classroom (Gfeller et al., 1990). Smith (1989) found that music educators who experienced instructional support also enjoyed positive mainstreaming experiences, while those who had little support had negative mainstreaming experiences.

Mainstreaming Students With Specific Disabilities

One of the problems in mainstreaming survey studies has been the use of the global term *handicapped*. Researchers have found that music educators often feel that students with certain disabilities present significantly more problems than others (Frisque et al., 1994). The two groups of students with disabilities that have been identified as the most difficult to mainstream are those who have behavior problems or hearing losses (Frisque et al., 1994; Gfeller et al., 1990). Based on these findings, Darrow and Gfeller (1991) examined the status of public school music instruction for deaf and hard-of-hearing students and the factors that contributed to the successful mainstreaming of these students in the regular music classroom. Results of their study revealed the following: (a) more than half of all deaf and hard-of-hearing students attend regular music classes; (b) of those students not mainstreamed, more than half receive no music education in the self-contained classroom or otherwise; (c) many music educators lack the specific educational preparation necessary for teaching deaf and hard-of-hearing students; (d) important instructional or administrative support is often not available; (e) several factors, such as lack of communication with other professionals, are obstructions to the successful mainstreaming of deaf and hard-of-hearing students; and (f) few music educators have the same objectives for deaf and hard-of-hearing students as they do for students with normal hearing. Respondents also reported that rhythm-based methodologies such as Orff were the most successful with their deaf and hard-of-hearing students.

In another disability-specific study, Thompson (1986) examined the activities of three general music classes into which students with mental retardation had been mainstreamed. It was found that the predominant activity in these music classes was listening to teachers talk. Singing was the second most frequent activity, followed by listening to recorded music. Additional observations revealed that students with mental retardation were significantly less successful than their peers, although no significant differences were found between the two groups in off-task behaviors.

Jellison and Gainer (1995) examined the behavior of one specific child with mild mental retardation throughout an entire school year in both music education and music therapy settings. The purpose of their study was to describe the child's participation over time, and to provide data to assist in the decision-making process regarding her educational program. Frequency and type of task performance were measured as well as overall time on-task. Results showed that rates for individual correct responses were higher in music therapy than in music education and that her on-task behavior was twice as high in the music therapy setting than in the music education setting. These findings, though seemingly discouraging in regard to mainstreaming, are carefully discussed in regard to the many factors that affect the classroom behaviors of children with mental retardation.

For children who exhibit atypical social behaviors, the music education classroom can serve as a place to learn, not only music skills, but also the socially correct behaviors of their typical peers. In another case study, Kostka (1993) compared selected behaviors (arm flapping, body swaying, and appropriate participation) of a student with autism in special education and regular music classes. Results indicated that all three behaviors were less frequent in regular music classes. When comparisons were made according to activity (singing, playing, moving, listening), he was most attentive during music listening. Results indicate that, for this child, mainstreaming had a positive effect on his appropriate social behaviors. These data corroborate the findings of other studies in general education (Swank et al., 1989). Additional studies delineating the disability of mainstreamed students would be useful in defining specific problems in mainstreaming practices.

Attitudes Toward Mainstreaming

The degree to which music educators are successful in the mainstreamed classroom depends greatly upon their attitudes toward mainstreaming. Several researchers have examined the attitudes of future music educators and those already teaching in mainstreamed situations. Their data reveal the negative influence of inappropriate mainstreaming practices on the attitudes of teachers and students.

Stuart and Gilbert (1977) reported that college music education majors were less willing to work with mainstream students than were music therapy majors or students majoring in both music education and music therapy. These findings were based on undergraduates' responses to videotaped sequences of disabled individuals. With the mainstreamed music classroom clearly in sight, this study identified an urgent need to improve music education majors' attitudes toward working with mainstreamed students.

Later studies examined the attitudes of music educators and those of students in mainstreamed situations. White (1981/1982) was interested in possible differences in teacher attitudes toward the integration of mainstreamed students based on various factors, including years of teaching, educational level, previous experience with mainstreamed students, training in the areas of exceptionality, and area of teaching responsibility. None of these variables was found to contribute in any significant way to the positive or negative attitudes expressed by the respondents, a finding that corroborated an earlier study by Shehan (1977) and a later study by Gfeller et al. (1990). Although the majority of music teachers reported accepting or positive attitudes toward students with physical and cognitive disabilities, many respondents indicated that there should still be special schools for such students.

Elliott and Sins (1981/1982) were concerned with the attitudes of music students toward their mainstreamed peers. Middle school students were surveyed regarding their opinions and attitudes toward the presence of mainstreamed peers in the music classroom. The survey was administered to 27 music classes in four Southern and Midwestern states. Students' attitudes were viewed as an indication of their acceptance of mainstreamed students. No differentiation was made among disability conditions. Examples of questions designed to assess respondents' attitudes regarding mainstreamed students were:

- "Do you think having handicapped students in music class is a good idea?"
- "Do you think you could learn more in music class if handicapped students were not present?"

Examples of questions designed to assess respondents' opinions (by asking them to state what they believed were their peers' opinions) concerning mainstreamed students were:

- "Do your classmates think having handicapped students in music class is a good idea?"
- "Do your classmates sometimes say that they wish that handicapped students would not be in class?"

Results indicated that: (a) only 58.5% of the students answered positively concerning their own attitudes toward integration of mainstreamed students into the music classroom; (b) females tended to be more positive regarding their own attitudes and when projecting the opinions of their classmates; and (c) students in segregated classes were more positive than those in integrated classes, indicating that hypothetical experiences with mainstreamed classmates were viewed more positively than real experiences with mainstreamed peers. An interesting finding was that ninth graders made the largest percentage of positive responses and the sixth graders made the largest number of negative responses, indicating that over time, mainstreaming experiences may have a positive influence on the attitudes of students in the regular classroom.

Darrow and Johnson (1994) found similar results in their study of junior and senior high school music students' attitudes toward individuals with a disability. Junior high school students generally expressed a lower level of sensitivity toward people with disabilities than did the senior high school students. Females also demonstrated a greater acceptance of people with a disability than males in every disability subscale. Further results revealed a rank ordering of disabilities from the most to the least acceptable. The three most accepted disabilities for both gender groups and age groups were visible scars, heart condition, and deafness. The three least acceptable conditions were paralysis, AIDS, and blindness. Possible explanations for these data are that AIDS results in death, and both blindness and paralysis have serious implications for personal mobility, which is highly valued, particularly by young people.

Probably the most important aspect of attitudinal studies is the instrument with which attitude is assessed. In an early study, Stuart and Gilbert (1977) designed a videotape scale to measure attitude toward typical students and their musical behavior. Jellison (1985) developed an Acceptance Within Music Scale (AMS), a questionnaire designed to measure children's attitudes toward mainstreamed peers specific to music activities and to parallel existing items on a general Acceptance Scale (AS) with demonstrated validity for the measurement of children's attitudes toward mainstreamed peers. Both the AMS and the AS were administered to 136 public school children enrolled in Grades 3–6. Of the four dimensions assessed by the AMS, three were found to correspond very well with the Acceptance Scale. With an appropriate measurement device in place, the question arises as to possible interventions to improve the attitudes of teachers and students as well as their social interactions with mainstreamed students.

Experimental Research in Music Mainstreaming

The descriptive studies reviewed above have identified a number of problematic issues related to the mainstreamed music classroom. Very few experimental interventions have been implemented to examine the possibility of remediating these problems. The 1984 study by Jellison, Brooks, and Huck deserves recognition because it is quite possibly the first to address methods of improving attitudes and increasing positive interactions between students with and without disabilities in the music classroom. Jellison et al. examined the effect of three teaching conditions (large group, small cooperative group, and small cooperative group with a music listening contingency for cooperation) on the frequency of positive social interactions between students with and without disabilities in Grades 3–6. Pretest and posttest measures were also taken of students' general acceptance as well as acceptance of mainstreamed peers in the music classroom. Results indicated that the percentages of positive interactions were the highest for all grades under the small-group music contingency condition and the lowest under the large-group condition. Grades with the highest rates of positive interactions indicated a significant positive change for acceptance in music as well as general acceptance. This study provides valuable experimental data for music educators teaching in mainstreamed classrooms.

Humpal (1991) was also interested in the social interactions of young children with disabilities. The purpose of her study was to examine the effect of an integrated early childhood music program on the social interactions of children with disabilities and their typical peers. A field test was conducted with 15 students (age 4) from a typical preschool, and 12 students (ages 3 to 5) with moderate levels of mental retardation from a county developmental center. The children came together once weekly at a preschool for integrated music sessions. For 15 sessions following the pretests, the music therapist employed specific strategies to foster interaction. A trend analysis indicated that interaction among the children increased following the music therapy intervention phases. It has often been stated that the mere placement of students with disabilities in the music classroom does not necessarily result in their acceptance by or in positive interactions with their peers (Elliott & Sins, 1981/1982; Sins, 1983). These two studies offer strategies that can be used to foster the social relationships of students with disabilities.

One of the common arguments against mainstreaming is that students with special needs demand excessive amounts of teacher time and, as a result, impede the education and progress of other students (Salend, 1994). This argument was examined in a study by Force (1983). She investigated the extent to which learning in a public school music classroom was affected by mainstreamed students. Students in mainstreamed and nonmainstreamed classrooms were pretested and posttested on their knowledge of rhythm instruments, recognition of instrument timbres, and dynamic levels. Pretest scores differed only on the sound identification subtest. Nonmainstreamed students tended to be more proficient at discriminating among instrument timbres. No significant differences were found between the two groups in pretest to posttest gains. Similar studies are needed to refute or substantiate teachers' beliefs regarding the effect of mainstreaming on students' musical achievement.

Music educators' concerns regarding the musical progress and achievement of their students is understandable. Many ensemble directors and general music teachers are evaluated on the basis of how well their students perform. Adaptive instructional strategies designed for inclusive classrooms are helpful in assuring that all students will make progress in their music study. A study by Colwell (1995) clearly illustrates the benefits of adaptive instruction for students with disabilities. The purpose of her study was to compare the effect of two music lessons (nonadapted versus adapted) on behaviors of two students, one with cerebral palsy and the other with a traumatic brain injury, in the mainstreamed classroom. Two lesson plans were designed for each class; one was not adapted while the other lesson was adapted specific to each students' special needs. Behaviors for videotape analysis were: on/off task, success rate at music tasks, and social interaction with peers. Overall lesson and activity specific data were obtained for each behavior. Results indicated that both students were more on-task, more successful at music tasks, and more apt to interact with their peers and to self-initiate interactions when the lesson had been adapted for their needs. Music educators must receive educational preparation that includes instructional strategies for the mainstreamed classroom—such as adapting lesson plans for students with disabilities. This study is especially important because it highlights the type of information music educators need to successfully integrate students with disabilities into the music classroom.

Music educators' lack of educational preparation for the mainstreamed classroom has been cited often in this review of the research. Smith (1987) addressed this problem by examining whether music education majors who had participated in a 5-day unit on children with disabilities would demonstrate greater ability than would a control group (music education majors with no concentrated instruction on this topic) in generating adaptive teaching strategies in a mainstream context. Subjects were required to apply their knowledge of educational practices by generating instructional adaptations in response to videotaped teaching segments with four different types of students with disabilities (visual impairment, hearing loss, mental retardation, and emotional impairment). Testing took place 3 weeks after instruction of the experimental group. Smith found that students receiving classroom instruction on students with disabilities performed significantly better than students in the control group on the total number of adaptive strategies generated. When analyzed by specific disabilities, both groups produced the smallest number of adaptations for working with behavior disorders. The problem many music educators experience in adapting instruction for students with behavior disorders has been corroborated by other researchers as well. Gfeller et al. (1990) and Frisque et al. (1994) also reported that teachers find students with behavioral disorders as one of the most difficult groups to mainstream into the music classroom.

Wilson and McCrary (1996) were interested in improving music education graduate students' attitude toward children with behavior disorders as well as other disabilities. The purpose of their study was to examine the effect of instruction on the music educators' feelings of comfort, capability, and willingness in regard to teaching children with various disabilities. Participants in the study were enrolled in a 7-week summer course designed to prepare them for teaching music to students with disabilities. Course content included: disability related information, legislative and regulatory issues, differences in segregated and integrated classrooms, videotapes, mainstreaming resources, instructional strategies, and practice teaching. Participants were pre- and posttested using a questionnaire that asked them to respond to given profiles of students with various disabilities in the following manner: "I would feel comfortable interacting with this individual," "I would be willing to work with this individual," and "I would feel capable in working professionally with this individual." For each statement, participants selected a response a 5-point scale ranging from 1 (strongly agree) to 5 (strongly disagree). Results of the study indicate that participants felt more capable to work with individuals who have disabilities after completion of the course, though they felt less comfortable and less willing to do so. These findings have serious implications for the education of students with disabilities. Obviously, we might assume that as music educators gain confidence in their ability to teach students with disabilities that their willingness to do so would also increase. The Wilson and McCrary study is an important one because it reveals that this assumption is not necessarily correct. The findings of the Wilson and McCrary study, however, are similar to other studies reviewed in this chapter that have reported negative attitudes toward students with disabilities. Perhaps attitudinal change strategies should be implemented at a younger age.

A review of attitudinal studies indicated that music students often have negative attitudes toward their mainstreamed peers or others with disabilities (Darrow & Johnson, 1994; Elliott & Sins, 1981/1982). These attitudes are often the result of their lack of experience with students who have been successfully mainstreamed. Students, as well as teachers, are often unaware of the strategies that can be used to make a mainstreaming situation successful or the music potential of many students with disabilities. The purpose of an experimental study by Johnson and Darrow (in press) was to examine the effect of five positive models of inclusion on band students' attitudinal statements regarding the integration of students with disabilities in their music program. Elementary, junior high, and senior high school band students from 15 public schools served as subjects for this study (N=757). A Solomon Four-Group design was chosen for this project. Bands were randomly assigned to one of the following four conditions: (a) pretest-treatment-posttest, (b) pretest-posttest, (c) treatment-posttest, or (d) posttest only. The independent variable for this project was a 30-minute videotape containing five segments which documented students with cognitive, physical, behavioral, or sensory disabilities successfully participating in a band in either rehearsal or performance situations. The dependent variable was a questionnaire comprised of attitudinal statements related to the following subscales: (a) inclusion of students with disabilities in band, (b) degree of comfort with inclusion, (c) efficiency of the band with students who have a disability, and (d) procedural issues involving students with a disability in band. Results indicated that treatment group subjects' attitudinal statements were significantly more positive than attitudinal statements of control group subjects on three of the four subscales. In addition, female students were significantly more positive than were male students on the same subscales. No clear trends were found among the different age groups as have been the case in other studies (Darrow & Johnson, 1994; Elliot & Sins, 1981/1982).

The data reported in this study and the other experimental studies reviewed here support the possibility of effecting positive changes in the learning environment of students in mainstreamed music classrooms. If a research agenda is to be set, it should be to this end. The collaborative research efforts of music therapists and music educators have the potential to make music learning a successful experience for all students.

Conclusions

The studies described in this section reveal little progress in the perceived success of music mainstreaming or in the attitudes of music educators toward mainstreaming. Even recent research reports that music educators are not trained to work with mainstreamed students and often have negative attitudes about teaching them. Since it is doubtful that public education systems will ever go back to self-contained classrooms for most students with disabilities, school music therapists need to explore methods of improving teacher attitudes toward mainstreaming as well as methods of increasing positive interactions between music students with and without disabilities.

As is obvious from this review, more experimental studies are needed. Music educators attitudes toward mainstreaming have been adequately described. It is now time to explore methods of improving attitudes and, more importantly, to examine instructional strategies that will facilitate learning in the mainstreamed music classroom. Mainstreaming studies in general education can give us some direction. By implementing some of the strategies found to be successful in the general classroom and examining their applicability to the music classroom, we should have a research agenda that will take us into the next century and provide us with valuable information. Music therapists, by the nature of their profession, are the likely leaders and researchers to establish this body of literature.

References

Altman, B. M. (1981). Studies of attitudes toward the handicapped: The need for a new direction. *Social Problems, 28,* 321–337.

Amsel, R., & Fichen, C. S. (1988). Effects of contact on thoughts about interaction with students who have a physical disability. *Journal of Rehabilitation, 54,* 61–65.

Atterbury, B. W. (1986). A survey of present mainstreaming practices in the southern United States. *Journal of Music Therapy, 23,* 202–207.

Atterbury, B. W. (1990). *Mainstreaming exceptional learners in music.* Englewood Cliffs, NJ: Prentice-Hall.

Bailey, D. B., & Harbin, G. L. (1980). Nondiscriminatory evaluation. *Exceptional Children, 46,* 590–596.

Baker, J., & Gottlieb, J. (1980). Attitudes of teachers toward mainstreaming retarded children. In J. Gottlieb (Ed.), *Educating mentally retarded persons in the mainstream.* Baltimore: University Park Press.

Barnes, E., Berrigan, C., & Biklen, D. (1978). *What's the difference? Teaching positive attitudes toward people with disabilities.* Syracuse, NY: Human Policy.

Bauwens, J., Hourcade, J. J., & Friend, M. (1989). Cooperative teaching: A model for general and special education integration. *Remedial and Special Education Journal, 1,* 4–11.

Brown, M. C. (1981). *Problems in mainstreaming programs in the Los Angeles Unified School District as perceived by junior high school music teachers.* Unpublished doctoral dissertation, University of Southern California, Los Angeles.

Bryan, T., & Bryan, J. H. (1978). Social interactions of learning disabled children. *Learning Disabilities Quarterly, 1,* 33–38.

Budoff, M., & Gottlieb, J. (1976). Special class EMR children mainstreamed: A study of an aptitude (learning potential) X treatment interaction. *American Journal of Mental Deficiency, 81,* 1–11.

Calhoun, G., & Elliot, R. (1977). Self-concept and academic achievement of educable retarded and emotionally disturbed pupils. *Exceptional Children, 44,* 379–380.

Carlberg, C., & Kavale, K. (1980). The efficiency of special versus regular placements for exceptional children: A meta-analysis. *Journal of Special Education, 14,* 295–309.

Clore, G. L., & Jeffrey, K. M. (1972). Emotional role playing, attitude change and attraction toward a disabled person. *Journal of Personality and School Psychology, 23,* 105–111.

Colwell, C. M. (1995). Adapting music instruction for elementary students with special needs: A pilot study. *Music Therapy Perspectives, 13,* 97–103.

Conway, R. N. F., & Gow, L. (1988). Mainstreaming special students with mild handicaps through group instruction. *Remedial and Special Education, 9,* 34–41.

Damer, L. K. (1979). *A study of attitudes of selected public school music teachers toward the integration of handicapped students into music classes.* Ed.D. dissertation, University of North Carolina at Greensboro.

Darrow, A. A. (1990). Research on mainstreaming in music education. *Update: Applications of Research in Music Education, 9*(1), 35–37.

Darrow, A. A., & Gfeller, K. (1991). A study of public school music programs mainstreaming hearing-impaired students. *Journal of Music Therapy, 28,* 23–39.

Darrow, A. A., & Johnson, C. M. (1994). Junior and senior high school music students' attitudes toward individuals with a disability. *Journal of Music Therapy, 31,* 266–279.

Donahue, K., & Zigmond, N. (1990). Academic grades of ninth-grade students. *Exceptionality, 1,* 17–27.

Donaldson, J. (1980). Changing attitudes toward handicapped persons: A review and analysis of research. *Exceptional Children, 46,* 504–512.

Dunn, L. M. (1968). Special education for the mildly retarded—Is much of it justifiable? *Exceptional Children, 35,* 5–22.

Elliott, C., & Sins, N. (1981/1982). Attitudes and opinions of middle school music students toward the presence of handicapped peers in music classes. *Contributions to Music Education, 9*(5), 48–59.

Evans, J. H. (1976, June). Changing attitudes toward disabled persons: An experimental study. *Rehabilitation Counseling Bulletin, 19,* 572–579.

Evertson, C. M., Sanford, J. P., & Emer, E. T. (1981). Effects of class heterogeneity in junior high school. *American Educational Research Journal, 18,* 219–232.

Fiedler, C. R., & Simpson, R. L. (1987). Modifying the attitudes of nonhandicapped students toward handicapped peers. *Exceptional Children, 53,* 342–349.

Force, B. (1983). The effects of mainstreaming on the learning of nonretarded children in an elementary music classroom. *Journal of Music Therapy, 20,* 2–13.

Frisque, J., Niebur, L., & Humphreys, J. T. (1994). Music mainstreaming: Practices in Arizona. *Journal of Research in Music Education, 42,* 94–104.

Fuchs, L. S., & Fuchs, D. (1986). Effects of systematic formative evaluation: A meta-analysis. *Exceptional Children, 53,* 199–208.

Gavin, A. R. J. (1983). *Music educator practices and attitudes toward mainstreaming.* Ed.D. dissertation, Washington University.

Gearheart, B. R., Weishahn, M. W., & Gearheart, C. J. (1992). *The exceptional student in the regular classroom.* New York: Macmillan Publishing Company.

Gfeller, K., Darrow, A. A., & Hedden, S. (1990). The perceived effectiveness of mainstreaming in Iowa and Kansas schools. *Journal of Research in Music Education, 38,* 90–101.

Gilbert, J. P., & Asmus, E. P. (1981). Mainstreaming: Music educators' participation and professional needs. *Journal of Research in Music Education, 29,* 283–289.

Goeke, R. E. (1994). *Responses among music teachers and principals in the state of Kansas regarding outcome-based public schools' classroom assessment and related curricular topics.* Unpublished master's thesis. The University of Kansas, Lawrence, KS.

Gottlieb, J. (1980). Improving attitudes toward retarded children by using group discussion. *Exceptional Children, 47,* 106–111.

Gottlieb, J. (1981). Mainstreaming: Fulfilling the promise? *American Journal of mental Deficiency, 86,* 115–126.

Graham, R., & Beer, A. S. (1980). *Teaching music to the exceptional child.* Englewood Cliffs, NJ: Prentice-Hall.

Greenbaum, J., Varas, M., & Markel, G. (1980). Using books about handicapped children. *The Reading Teacher, 33,* 416–419.

Gresham, F. M. (1982). Misguided mainstreaming: The case for social skills training with handicapped children. *Exceptional Children, 48,* 422–433.

Guerin, G. R., & Szatlocky, K. (1974). Integration programs for the mildly retarded. *Exceptional Children, 41,* 173–179.

Handlers, A., & Austin, K. (1980). Improving attitudes of high school students toward their handicapped peers. *Exceptional Children, 47,* 228–229.

Haring, N. G., & Krug, D. A. (1975). Placement in regular programs: Procedures and results. *Exceptional Children, 41,* 413–417.

Hawkins, G. D. (1991). *Attitudes toward mainstreaming students with disabilities among regular elementary music physical educators.* Ph.D. dissertation, University of Maryland.

Horne, M. D. (1985). *Attitudes toward handicapped students: Professional, peer and parent reactions.* Hillsdale, NJ: Lawrence Erlbaum.

Humpal, M. (1991). The effects of an integrated early childhood music program on social interaction among children with handicaps and their typical peers. *Journal of Music Therapy, 28,* 161–177.

Idol, L., & West, F. (1991). Educational collaboration: A catalyst for effective schooling. *Intervention in School and Clinic, 27,* 70–78.

Jellison, J. A. (1985). An investigation of the factor structure of a scale for the measurement of children's attitudes toward handicapped peers within regular music environments. *Journal of Research in Music Education, 33,* 167–177.

Jellison, J. A., Brooks, B. H., & Huck, A. M. (1984). Structuring small groups and music reinforcement to facilitate positive interactions and acceptance of severely handicapped students in regular music classrooms. *Journal of Research in Music Education, 32,* 243–264.

Jellison, J. A., & Gainer, E. W. (1995). Into the mainstream: A case-study of a child's participation in music education and music therapy. *Journal of Music Therapy, 32,* 228–247.

Johnson, C. M., & Darrow, A. A. (in press). The effect of positive models of inclusion on band students' attitudinal statements regarding the integration of students with disabilities, *Journal of Research in Music Education.*

Jones, T. W., Sowell, V. M., Jones, J. K., & Butler, G. (1981). Changing children's perceptions of handicapped people. *Exceptional Children, 47,* 365–368.

Kostka, M. J. (1993). A comparison of selected behaviors of a student with autism in special education and regular music classes. *Music Therapy Perspectives, 11,* 57–60.

Larrivee, G., & Horne, M. D. (1991). Social status: A comparison of mainstreamed students with peers of different ability levels. *Journal of Special Education, 25,* 90–101.

Lazar, A. L., Gensley, J. T., & Orpet, R. E. (1971). Changing attitudes of young mentally gifted children toward handicapped person. *Exceptional Children, 37,* 600–602.

Leinhardt, G. (1980). Transition rooms: Promoting maturation or reducing education? *Journal of Educational Psychology, 72,* 55–61.

Leung, E. K. (1980). Evaluation of a children's literature program designed to facilitate the social integration of handicapped children into regular elementary classrooms. (Doctoral dissertation, The Ohio State University). *Dissertation Abstracts, 40,* 4528A.

Lewis, R. A., & Doorlag, D. H. (1991). *Teaching special students in the mainstream.* New York: Macmillan Publishing Company.

Lindsey, J., Burns, J., & Guthrie, T. D. (1984). Intervention grading and secondary students. *The High School Journal, 67,* 150–157.

Litton, F. W., Banbury, M. M., & Harris, K. (1980). Materials for educating handicapped students about their handicapped peers. *Teaching Exceptional Children, 13,* 39–43.

Macy, D. J., & Carter, J. L. (1978). Comparison of a mainstream and self-contained special education program. *Journal of Special Education, 12,* 303–313.

Madden, N., & Slavin, R. (1983). Mainstreaming students with mild handicaps: Academic and social outcomes. *Review of Educational Research, 53,* 519–569.

Madsen, C. K., Smith, D. S., & Feeman, C. C. (1988). The use of music in cross-age tutoring within special education settings. *Journal of Music Therapy, 25,* 135–144.

Marston, D., & Magnusson, D. (1985). Implementing curriculum-based measurement in special and regular education settings. *Exceptional Children, 52,* 266–276.

McCann, S. K., Semmel, M. I., & Nevin, A. (1985). Reverse mainstreaming: Nonhandicapped students in special education classrooms. *Remedial and Special Education, 6,* 13–19.

McLoughlin, J. A., & Lewis, R. B. (1990). *Assessing special students* (3rd ed.). Columbus, OH: Merrill Publishing Company.

Miller, K. J., Fullmer, S., & Walls, R. T. (1996). A dozen years of mainstreaming literature: A content analysis. *Exceptionality, 6,* 99–109.

Myers, J. K. (1976). *The special day school placement for high IQ and low EMR pupils.* Paper presented at the annual meeting of the Council for Exceptional Children, Chicago. (ERIC Document Reproduction Services No. ED 125 197)

Nocera, S. D. (1981). *A descriptive analysis of the attainment of selective musical learning by normal children and by educable mentally retarded children mainstreamed in music classes at the second and fifth grade level.* Unpublished doctoral dissertation, University of Wisconsin, Madison.

Ray, B. M. (1986). Measuring the social position of the mainstreamed handicapped child. *Exceptional Children, 52,* 57–62.

Reynolds, M. C., & Birch, J. W. (1988). *Adaptive mainstreaming: A primer for teachers and principals* (3rd ed.). New York: Longman.

Roberts, C., & Zubrick, S. (1993). Factors influencing the social status of children with mild academic disabilities in regular classrooms. *Exceptional Children, 59,* 192–202.

Salend, S. J. (1994). *Effective mainstreaming: Creating inclusive classrooms.* New York: Macmillan Publishing Company.

Salend, S. J., & Knops, B. (1984). Hypothetical examples: A cognitive approach to changing attitudes toward the handicapped. *The Elementary School Journal, 85,* 229–236.

Salend, S. J., & Moe, L. (1983). Modifying nonhandicapped students' attitudes toward their handicapped peers through children's literature. *Journal for Special Educators, 19,* 22–28.

Shehan, P. (1977). A brief study of music education for exceptional children in Ohio. *Contributions to Music Education, 5,* 47–53.

Shepard, L. M. M. (1993). *A survey of music teachers' attitudes toward mainstreaming disabled students in regular music classroom in selected school districts in Georgia.* Unpublished doctoral dissertation, The University of Southern Mississippi.

Simpson, R. L. (1980). Modifying the attitudes of regular class students toward the handicapped. *Focus on Exceptional Children, 13,* 1–11.

Sins, N. (1983). Mainstreaming the music classroom automatically brings about acceptance by the nonhandicapped. Right? (Wrong!). *Update: The Applications of Research in Music Education, 2,* 3–6.

Siperstein, G. N., Bopp, M., & Bak, J. (1978). Social status of learning disabled children. *Journal of Learning Disabilities, 11,* 1–16.

Slavin, R. E. (1987). Grouping for instruction in the elementary school. *Educational Psychologist, 2,* 107–127.

Smaller, A. G. (1989). *The process of mainstreaming special education students in a suburban elementary school: A case study.* Unpublished doctoral dissertation, New York University.

Smith, D. S. (1987). The effect of instruction on ability to adapt teaching situations for exceptional students. *MEH Bulletin, 2,* 3–18.

Smith, D. S. (1989). A content analysis of music educators' attitudes toward mainstreaming in middle school music classes. *Journal of the International Association of Music for the Handicapped, 4,* 3–20.

Smith, T. E. C., Polloway, E. A., Patton, J. R., & Dowdy, D. A. (1995). *Teaching children with special needs in inclusive settings.* Boston, MA: Allyn and Bacon.

Smith, T. E. C., Price, B. J., & Marsh, G. E. (1986). *Mildly handicapped children and adults.* St. Paul, MN: West Publishing.

Stainback, W., Stainback, S., Courtnage, L., & Jaben, T. (1985). Facilitating mainstreaming by modifying the mainstream. *Exceptional Children, 52,* 144–152.

Stallings, J. A. (1985). *A study of basic reading skills taught in secondary schools. Report of Phase I findings.* Menlo Park, CA: Stanford Research International.

Stephens, T. M., & Braun, B. L. (1980). Measures of regular classroom teachers attitudes toward handicapped children. *Exceptional Children, 46,* 292–294.

Stevens, R. J., & Slavin, R. E. (1991). When cooperative learning improves the achievement of students with mild disabilities: A response to Tateyama-Sniesek. *Exceptional Children, 57,* 276–280.

Stuart, M., & Gilbert, J. P. (1977). Mainstreaming: Needs assessment through a videotape visual scale. *Journal of Research in Music Education, 25,* 283–289.

Swank, P. R., Taylor, R. D., Brady, M. P., Cooley, R., & Freiberg, H. J. (1989). Outcomes of grouping students in mainstreamed middle school classroom. *NASSP Bulletin, 73,* 62–66.

Thompson, K. P. (1986). The general music class as experienced by mainstreamed handicapped students. *MEH Bulletin, 1*(3), 16–23.

Valdes, K. A., Williamson, C. L., & Wagner, M. M. (1990). *The national longitudinal transition study of special education students.* Menlo Park, CA: SRI International.

Walker, V. S. (1974). The efficiency of the resource room for educating retarded children. *Exceptional Children, 40,* 288–289.

Wang, M. C., Anderson, K. A., & Bram, P. (1985). *Toward an empirical data base on mainstreaming: A research synthesis of program implementation and effects.* Pittsburgh: Learning Research and Development Center, University of Pittsburgh.

Wang, M. C., & Birch, J. W. (1984). Comparison of a full-time mainstreaming program and a resource room approach. *Exceptional Children, 51,* 33–40.

White, L. D. (1981/1982). A study of attitudes of selected public school music educators toward the integration of handicapped students in music classes. *Contributions to Music Education, 9*(5), 36–47.

Williams, W., Fox, T., Thousand, J., & Fox, W. (1990). Level of acceptance and implementation of best practices in the education of students with severe disabilities in Vermont. *Education and Training in Mental Retardation, 25,* 120–131.

Wilson, B. L., & McCrary, J. (1996). The effect of instruction on music educators' attitudes toward students with disabilities. *Journal of Research in Music Education, 44,* 26–33.

Zigler, E., & Muenchow, S. (1979). Mainstreaming: The proof is in the implementation. *American Psychologist, 34,* 993–996.

Zigmond, N., Levin, E., & Laurie, T. (1985). Managing the mainstream: An analysis for teacher attitudes and student performance in the mainstream high school programs. *Journal of Learning Disabilities, 18,* 535–541.

MODELS OF SERVICE DELIVERY

Faith L. Johnson

The implementation of PL 94–142 required school districts to develop methods of providing appropriate classroom and support services to students with special education needs. Yet, over the past two decades, there have been significant changes in the way special education services have been designed and delivered. Recent trends seem to indicate that special education will continue to evolve according to student needs and public resources.

In the early years of PL 94–142, school districts had to protect the civil rights of students and parents by providing for due process. Once it was determined that some students would require special services to participate *successfully* in their education, school districts were then obligated to provide those services. Some students with special needs attended regular education classes; others participated in assessments and received specialized services according to the results of the assessment.

Because many students in special education programs had needs that could not be accommodated in regular education classes, the services that were provided for them were regarded as separate or special, and outside the realm of the regular curriculum. These services (e.g., special education classes, a variety of therapies, and other accommodations) were most often delivered through the "pull-out" model, in which students were removed from settings that included their regular education peers. In these separate and often artificial learning environments, students with special needs received special education services since it was assumed that special educators could provide the most appropriate programs for them. In addition, regular education programs were not designed to readily accommodate students' individual needs, or to provide educators with the information they needed about the students.

In keeping with the practices of the time, music therapy was often regarded as different and separate from other educational services, including music education. Music therapists were frequently called upon to provide a different kind of music education (special music education) to students with special needs. In some instances, they were also assigned to provide music therapy services to students with special needs. At times these services were in addition to music education; in other cases music therapy services replaced music education. The typical settings for music therapy, as with other separate special education programs, included self-contained classes, one-on-one therapy, and occasionally a combination program of therapy and education.

In recent years, special education has decreased the number of separate programs and increased programs that support regular education. Students with special needs are now more frequently placed in regular education classes, with special educators, therapists, and other personnel providing support to the regular classroom teacher. Special education is no longer viewed as the only way to provide appropriate services to students with special needs, but rather as a partner to regular education, with each component contributing to the education of the students.

Just as special education has changed, so has the role of the music therapist evolved to a more inclusive model of service delivery. Music therapists have begun to work more in consultant roles, providing support services to staff and parents. These changes have presented music therapists with a variety of working models in which the definition of school music therapist may differ depending upon the interpretation of special education itself.

Direct Services Delivery

When music therapy is provided by a music therapist to a student (or case load of students), this is known as *direct services* delivery. The contact between the therapist and student is immediate. The direct services model, which allows for qualified personnel with specific areas of expertise to work with students toward individual goals, is currently the delivery system for most special education services. Students are taught by a teacher, receive speech therapy from a speech pathologist, or attend adaptive physical education classes with an adaptive physical education teacher.

The Music Therapist as a Member of a Multidisciplinary Team

Philosophy of the Multidisciplinary Model

One model of direct service delivery is through a *multidisciplinary team* approach. In this model, professionals with a variety of backgrounds and areas of expertise work with the student toward the IEP goals. In a school setting, the team includes professionals that are affiliated with an educational facility, such as the classroom teacher(s), an adaptive physical education teacher, and a social worker. Other members of the team are representatives of medical or rehabilitative disciplines, such as occupational therapy and speech pathology, plus parents or child advocates. Each member of the team has direct contact with the student, and contributes to the process through assessment, goal-setting, program implementation, and evaluation. What separates this model from other team models is the separation of team members from each other. Each member of the team develops a separate plan to meet the needs of the student. In addition, team members implement only their individual sections of the plan.

By working within the parameters of a professional discipline, individual team members contribute to the total educational program, yet each discipline maintains a separate identity. Although communication among team members is assumed, it does not always happen. For example, team members meet to set goals, write the IEP, or even meet periodically to compare student progress in each disciplinary area. The success of this communication is dependent on each member's thorough understanding and knowledge of the other disciplines. The lack of visibility of team members to one another, especially in school settings where meeting time for staff groups is negligible, makes it especially important for the music therapist to educate other team members about the uniqueness and effectiveness of music in meeting student needs.

As a member of a multidisciplinary team, the music therapist should emphasize the interrelationships between music therapy and the features of other disciplines. This includes: setting up meetings with other professionals, offering to demonstrate a success story or technique to another team member, arranging a regular time to discuss students with other team members, inviting other team members to attend part of a therapy session, or distributing printed information regarding student progress in music therapy to other team members.

Program Planning and Implementation

For the multidisciplinary team, assessment is completed in separate areas as each discipline looks at the student from a different perspective. For example, the physical therapist usually looks at skills that affect the student's motor abilities, the speech therapist examines the student's ability to effectively use language and communicate, and the classroom teacher collects information about academic and/or functional abilities. Assessment practices are implemented separately, and the results are compiled when all the team members meet to make educational plans.

The lack of standardized music therapy assessment tools should not prevent the music therapist from becoming involved in this phase of the multidisciplinary team process. There is an opportunity to introduce assessment results from observation, therapist-made tools, and other informal methods to the team's review of student needs. Since music therapy is a related service, the interpretation of assessment results are both appropriate and essential to the team process.

The role of parents in the multidisciplinary team process is minimal. Parents meet with individual team members, each of whom discusses the needs of the student in terms of a specific area of need (motor, cognitive, language, etc.). It is often difficult to get parents involved in team decisions. At the team meeting, assessment results are discussed by all the disciplines represented on the team, and student goals are written in terms of each individual discipline, based on student needs in that area. The occupational therapist sets the fine motor goals, the classroom teacher addresses academic or classroom goals, and the music therapist establishes goals within the music experience. Musical goals address the musical or music education needs of the students, while nonmusical goals can be coordinated with the goals of other disciplines, namely, motor, communication, cognitive, and social needs of the student. For example, if a student needs to develop more appropriate group skills (e.g., sitting next to peers during a group activity), the music therapist addresses this goal within a music group experience. The goal is nonmusical, but the learning environment is a musical one. In addition, the music therapist can also address a goal that comes from the music education curriculum, such as vocalizing with the group during a singing activity. Working toward musical goals and nonmusical goals can occur simultaneously.

It is at the goal-setting level that the student's educational program is coordinated into a single document, the IEP. While goals are written in terms of the discipline itself, there remains a sense of teamwork in working with the student on a daily basis. For example, a physical therapy goal might focus on developing mobility around the school building; the classroom teacher writes goals related to academic ("classroom") development in the areas of reading, math, and language development; the music therapist establishes goals so the student can develop in a variety of ways via the medium of musical involvement. While the goals are particular to each professional discipline, they are written in an atmosphere of cooperation.

Following the team's review of assessment results and student goals, implementation of the student's educational program is enacted by professionals who work in relative isolation from each other. Each discipline is part of the educational team, but the program is a sum of many different parts. Among the advantages of the multidisciplinary team approach is the spirit of coordination and cooperation among the specific services in meeting the student's needs. While mutual respect and responsibility among the disciplines is a desirable outcome of the multidisciplinary team process, the resulting fragmented approach to education is also one of its disadvantages. The student seems to receive services in parts, with each discipline addressing a specific area of need. With this method of service delivery, services are often duplicated or overlapped, and it becomes difficult for the student's program to be integrated into a whole.

Staff Development

In the multidisciplinary team model, staff development is independent of the team concept. Each discipline participates in inservice training or continuing education according to that particular discipline's territorial boundaries. For example, a speech pathologist would not necessarily need to be familiar with the work of the music therapist, the influence of music on behavior, or the role of music therapy in the total education of the student. In the multidisciplinary team model, the speech pathologist would be primarily concerned with speech and language development.

The Music Therapist as a Member of an Interdisciplinary Team

Philosophy of the Interdisciplinary Model

In the interdisciplinary approach to education, professionals provide services in a variety of disciplinary areas, just as they do in the multidisciplinary model. However, team members on the interdisciplinary team share their IEP goals and implementation plans with each other. Each member of the team knows how every other member intends to provide services to the student. However, team members implement their own sections of the plan; there is no crossing or blurring of professional boundaries.

Program Planning and Implementation

Assessment takes place in separate disciplines, although the results are shared with the other team members. Parents meet with the team as a group, providing for the possibility of a more coordinated program than in the multidisciplinary approach. The team plan incorporates all the disciplines. In this model, the music therapist has an opportunity to educate the other team members about music therapy, although this is not an essential element of interdisciplinary teams. Still, there is a greater chance for including music therapy as a legitimate service than in the multidisciplinary approach.

The IEP is developed and implemented by the group, but there is little or no crossover of objectives between professional disciplines. What occurs in the classroom is different from what occurs in physical therapy, which in turn is different from the activities in speech and language. The music therapist can fill a unique role on the interdisciplinary team by demonstrating how boundaries can be changed or eliminated through an all-inclusive pursuit such as music. For example, music therapy goals can reflect classroom goals by working on readiness, academic, or functional skills. Physical therapy goals can be practiced in the music therapy setting through mobility activities, while speech and language goals can be met in an additional setting through opportunities for self expression.

Staff Development

Just as is the case in the multidisciplinary team approach, staff development occurs within each discipline. However, because of the team sharing that takes place at least at the program planning stage, individual professionals often seek additional information or training in other areas.

The Music Therapist as a Member of a Transdisciplinary Team

Philosophy of the Transdisciplinary Model

A *transdisciplinary team* includes members with backgrounds in a variety of fields, but the work of the team surpasses individual professional identities and coordinates all its efforts on behalf of the student. In addition, parents are an integral component of the team. As a result of this approach, all team members are responsible for how the educational plan is implemented. Often, IEP goals are met in a number of settings, with team members truly working together throughout the entire process.

In the transdisciplinary model, the student is not regarded as a set of problem areas or deficient skills, but as a complete person who is capable of functioning within the school setting and society as a whole. Therefore, team members (including parents) plan a coordinated program for the student based on needs, resources, and educational priorities. Rather than working independently of each other, disciplinary lines become blurred or eliminated because the emphasis is for the student to perform functional activities in meaningful contexts. In other words, students learn to complete whole tasks in real school or community settings. For example, instead of learning a fine motor skill in occupational therapy and being expected to transfer that skill in another situation, the student and teacher are instructed by the occupational therapist in how best to complete tasks that use fine motor functions. Rather than doing isolated activities that "drill" hand skills, the teacher uses the knowledge of the skill in daily activities that occur in the classroom to instruct the student in picking up crayons to place them in their appropriate container, or returning a book to its shelf.

In the transdisciplinary model, team members plan, implement, and evaluate the students' educational programs together. Each staff person involved with the student works on instructional tasks that include motor, sensory, communication, cognitive, and social components. Therefore, a group of students with needs in the area of motor development might work with an occupational therapist, an adaptive physical education teacher, and a music therapist, since each can design activities that will help meet this goal. In this group, each professional provides the expertise of a disciplinary field, but works cooperatively to provide the most meaningful experiences for the students. The music therapist has an important role in the transdisciplinary approach because music experiences typically provide for the integration of a number of motor, cognitive, communication, sensory, and social skills.

Assuming that a student needs experiences that will train the neurological system to adapt to different kinds of movement, the occupational therapist and physical therapist might recommend supervised spinning on a scooter board. With the input of the classroom teacher, who wants to involve as many students in the group as possible, a game is designed in which each individual student is spun on the scooter board inside a circle of students. As the music therapist becomes involved in the design of the activity, music is added to assist in making the activity more fun and more meaningful for the student. The music reflects the character of the activity; it stops when the student stops spinning. The music provides a language base for what is going on in the activity. In addition, the other students remain involved in the activity as they wait for their turns.

For the transdisciplinary approach to be effective, the following conditions must be present: (a) all staff must assume responsibility for the total educational program of the student; (b) staff must be prepared to address the concerns of parents that students receive less direct service; (c) the issue of liability for services provided by other disciplines must be resolved; (d) communication, cooperation, and flexibility among all staff members must be present; and (e) staff must accept a change in traditional roles (Peterson, 1987). In addition, this method requires an effective group process among team members, goal identification according to the needs of the student (rather than along traditional disciplinary lines), and procedures for solving problems.

The transdisciplinary approach has been shown to be effective in meeting the needs of students with severe needs, and in developing an atmosphere in which there is an innovative exchange of ideas among professionals (Beninghof & Singer, 1992; York & Vandercook, 1991). A music therapist working on such a team has the opportunity to demonstrate first hand how music can meet student needs. Professionals in other disciplines also become familiar with music experiences and are able to recognize the advantages of using music to address a variety of goal areas.

Program Planning and Implementation

In the transdisciplinary team model, students are assessed in terms of whole entities: the student is a person who engages in integrated, functional activities (as opposed to individual skills) which require the interplay of motor, cognitive, sensory, social, communicative, and emotional areas. The purpose of assessment is to gather information which will lead to instructional practices. By focusing on the student holistically, the transdisciplinary assessment often reveals more specific information than do more traditional assessment tools. In addition, time is not wasted assessing skills that are not essential to the educational program. This approach places the needs of the student first, and is not dependent on typical disciplinary approaches. At the assessment level, the transdisciplinary model provides an excellent opportunity for the music therapist to become directly involved with the team at this early stage.

Goals for each student are written in terms of prioritized needs, determined by the team, with each disciplinary area regarded as a strategy toward goal attainment, rather than *the* one-and-only way for the student to learn skills. An emphasis is placed on age-appropriate, functional goals, and therapy-related objectives are integrated into everyday classroom situations.

In addition to working together in the assessment and goal-setting parts of the transdisciplinary process, members of the team work cooperatively with students throughout the school day. For example, students with sensorimotor needs might be involved in activities planned and led by an occupational therapist, a music therapist, and a classroom teacher. Likewise, a community-based experience can involve a speech/communication specialist, a classroom teacher, and an educational assistant working with students whose needs are coordinated into one activity. In the implementation of the program, professionals not only interact with students, but also teach their peers in other disciplines. As professionals work and communicate with each other on a regular basis, information is exchanged, observations are made and validated by other staff, and the students remain at the center of the discussion. This process of crossing professional boundaries is essential to the team building process. Rather than receiving traditional direct services two or three times per week, or during a specific time during the school day, the student's program is coordinated into each instructional area over the course of the entire school week. As a result, the services a student receives are more in the realm of indirect or consultant services, rather than traditional direct services.

In order for the transdisciplinary model to be successful, professionals must meet regularly and each team member must remain accountable for the student's total program. In the interest of cost-effective educational programs, more than one professional working with even a group of students can be regarded as duplication of energy or an unaffordable ratio of staff to students. Yet, in the long run, students receive a more complete and relevant package of services, since each student's program is integrated at the instructional level. The student's needs remain as the primary focus through all phases of the educational process. Each professional discipline is recognized as an important contributor to the development of the whole student, and, in the case of a lesser known discipline like music therapy, there is the opportunity for promoting the field as a viable and effective way to meet student needs.

Staff Development

Staff development in the transdisciplinary approach is an integral component. Team members learn informally and through formal training about the techniques and strategies that comprise the student's educational program. Team meetings have staff development as a central component, as professionals work across disciplines. The music therapist is an equal partner in the implementation of the plan, and has a prime opportunity to educate other professionals (and parents) about music therapy.

Traditional Direct Services

A *traditional direct services model* is often referred to as "pull-out" therapy, since music therapy services are delivered to the student outside the classroom setting. The student is removed from the school activity, taken to another location for therapy, and then returned to the classroom.

The "pull-out" model allows for intense, individualized work toward educational goals. Often, multiple functions are incorporated into the musical experience, as the music therapist works in many goal areas simultaneously. Whatever amount of time is spent in music therapy, the total amount belongs to the music therapist and the student, allowing the musical experience to be focused entirely on the needs of the student.

This model has some potential disadvantages for both the therapist and the student. Removing students from the classroom routine reduces the communication among the professionals involved with the student. It is difficult to relay the work that is accomplished in therapy to other members of the educational team when the therapist works in relative isolation. Working in this manner, there is also little opportunity for the music therapist to engage in a professional exchange with other disciplines. In addition, the "pull-out" model sets students apart from their peers because they are removed from the classroom. Since there is little or no opportunity to learn skills in a real life situation, it is assumed that the transfer of skills from the therapy setting to school, home, and community will occur. Furthermore, the musical experience associated with music therapy in the "pull-out" model appears to the outside observer to be similar to music lessons, music education class, or recreational music. While activities that take place in music therapy resemble typical musical endeavors, the underlying reasons for involving the student in these experiences are quite different. Music lessons are intended to teach a student mastery of the voice or an instrument; in music therapy, the lesson format is often used to help the student achieve nonmusical goals, such as increasing vital capacity, facilitating inclusion, or developing skills in appropriate nonverbal expression. The purpose of the music education class is to provide students with fundamental skills in music upon which they can build a lifetime of musical involvement; a music therapist provides music class experiences for a student to develop individually, to increase language, or to practice motor patterns that are used in daily living. Although music therapy may look on the surface like recreational music, it is primarily used to help the student develop leisure time skills, to provide an appropriate outlet for feelings, and to offer an alternative to standard recreational activities.

Working in Self-Contained Classes

In many educational facilities, classrooms for students with special needs are self-contained units. Providing music therapy services for students within classroom settings is often difficult since music is an auditory medium that distracts the students who are not working with the therapist. On the other hand, the "spillover" effect may be beneficial for students who receive indirect instruction while the therapist concentrates on the students receiving direct attention.

In self-contained classes of students with severe needs, one approach is to use a "round robin" process, since it can be implemented in a variety of ways. During a class period, the music therapist works with one or two students at a time, while other students are engaged in other activities with other classroom staff. For example, one student might be practicing self-care skills, another student is learning a work strategy, and other students are involved in an interactive story. The therapist completes the work with the first small group, and then moves on to the next designated students until all students have received direct services. There are several advantages to using this method. Students receive individual attention from the therapist, and the learning atmosphere for the total time period contains a musical element. For students who need some preinstruction before receiving direct services, the "round robin" method provides students with a preparatory phase. This model is also effective for half-day classrooms where students have a limited time to complete their instructional activities. Finally, this method can be a nonthreatening way to introduce classroom staff to the implementation of music therapy services.

Another in-class model for self-contained classrooms places the music therapist in the role of instructional leader for the entire class. Classroom staff (teachers, educational assistants, aides, parent volunteers) become directly involved in the session through hands-on work with individual students. With this method, each student participates in all activities, group cohesiveness is established, and classroom staff become familiar with the process of music therapy. To get everyone involved in the learning experience, classroom staff can be assigned musical accompaniment parts, such as strumming the autoharp or playing an ostinato on the bass chime bars. This arrangement can serve as an excellent role model because students see familiar people engaged in and deriving pleasure from music experiences. This in-class model also serves to train classroom staff in the implementation of activities to be repeated at times when the music therapist is not present. As the music therapist and staff work together, there is an exchange of ideas for providing effective instruction to students. Using this model, classroom staff witness firsthand the positive responses and the progress of their students to music.

Working in Inclusive Classes

With the trend toward inclusion, delivering services such as speech, occupational, and physical therapies to students in the traditional "pull-out" model is being increasingly challenged. Inclusion typically means educating all children with disabilities in regular classrooms regardless of the nature of their disabling conditions (The Association for Persons with Severe Handicaps, 1994). Educational services are provided within regular schools, and often within the regular classroom. Friendships between nondisabled and disabled students are encouraged, and the emphasis is on an educational program that is appropriate to students' lifelong needs. In some studies of inclusive settings, improved self-esteem and increased social skills of special learners (Conway & Gow, 1988; Dickinson, 1987), increased participation in age-appropriate levels of classroom activities (Killoran, 1987) and a reduction in the number of students identified as needing special education services (Adamson, 1989) have been reported. Advocates for inclusion see it as a way to change attitudes about students with disabilities, promote teamwork among teachers and staff, and develop interpersonal skills among diverse groups of students.

Students are often placed in inclusive arts and physical education classes before they are included on a regular basis in academic classes. In these cases, the music therapist who provides direct services is in a position to not only affect the student's ability to participate in music education, but also lay the groundwork for successful inclusion practices for the classroom setting as well.

In a model of inclusion, therapists are encouraged to work with students within the classroom and other typical school settings, rather than taking students to isolated therapy rooms for treatment two or three times a week. For example, an occupational therapist might work on fine motor skills with a student in an inclusive home economics class, a physical therapist may assist a student in balance activities during a bowling game in PE class, and the speech therapist can train a student to use a communication device during class discussion. This model of service delivery works toward two main objectives: (a) to diminish the isolation of the student with special needs by providing services in a natural setting, and (b) to provide "spillover" effect in which the work done with the special student also enhances the education of the other students in the group.

Implementing music therapy in the inclusive classroom is often more difficult than in a self-contained class. The sound generated by music and the activity of the students can be distracting for students engaged in other classroom activities. However, there are some options for delivering music therapy in an inclusive setting. For example, the music therapist could involve the entire class in an activity which will serve to benefit all students (IEP goals for the targeted student(s) and other goals for the students receiving indirect instruction). Another way to provide services is through reverse inclusion, in which regular education students are integrated into the classroom activities of students with special needs. A third alternative for providing music therapy in an inclusive setting is to use audio equipment that can accommodate headphones. Electronic instruments (keyboards, guitars, MIDI instruments) involve students in live music experiences, but keep distractions for other students to a minimum.

One of the most effective ways to deliver music therapy services within an inclusive class is to work with the targeted student in music education class. This method not only provides the student with direct instruction, but also supports the music educator with on-site consultation services. In the general music class, the music therapist and the music educator can work as coteachers. In this situation, it is important for goal-setting, planning, and implementation to be completed by both professionals in the spirit of inclusion. It would be inappropriate for the music therapist to concentrate only on the students with special needs, and the music educator to teach only the students in general education, since this will only serve to divide students into separate groups. The purpose of having the music therapist in the class is to meet the needs of a diverse group of students and to promote cooperation. Therefore, the music therapist needs to be cognizant of the school district's philosophy of inclusion and the rationale for including students in regular music classes. Providing music therapy services within the general music class helps reduce the frustration felt by many music educators who assume they must adapt every lesson to a wide variety of individual needs.

Similar strategies are used in inclusive performing groups. During rehearsal of an instrumental or vocal group, the music therapist can provide on-site assistance to the student and teacher by: (a) observing the student's ability to function in the performance group and working with the music educator to set realistic goals, (b) adapting the instructional environment for the student so the rehearsal can proceed, and (c) providing on-site inservice training to the music educator and demonstrating accommodations that can be made. In addition, the student who needs additional practice/lesson opportunities can work with the music therapist in a lesson format. Lessons are structured in conjunction with the student's regular music lesson with the music educator, and are not meant to replace the inclusive lesson experience.

The Use of Technology in Direct Service Delivery

Music therapists use a variety of tools in their work; the elements of music are manipulated and adapted, and the therapist applies appropriate materials and equipment to the musical experience. If music, instruments, and music activities are the tools of the music therapist's trade, technological devices are additions to this arsenal of tools. Electronic instruments, music applications for the computer, speech synthesizers, and adaptive devices continue to be produced and refined, and many of these are appropriate to music therapy practice. Yet, even with the daily advancements in the variety and range of technological devices available to music therapists, these implements must still be used according to established standards of clinical practice.

Depending on student needs, equipment availability, and the level of comfort of the music therapist in using technological devices, there are a multitude of applications in clinical practice. For example, a touch-sensitive keyboard is a development which has provided persons with limited hand strength and finger dexterity the opportunity to play a keyboard instrument. Instruments that can be powered by batteries provide students access to portable leisure time activities. Composition programs for the computer make it possible for students with limited cognitive understanding of the fundamentals of music to have a means for self-expression and a creative outlet. In addition, many of these technological devices can be utilized to facilitate inclusion by providing students with disabilities with an equal footing with their regular education peers.

Assistive Technology

One segment of the comprehensive field of technology is *assistive technology* (AT), which is defined as the use of devices and services that help people with disabilities of all ages in their daily lives. The definition is broad for a reason, so that programs related to providing assistive technology to people who need it do not restrict themselves to dealing *only* with computers. There is much more to AT than computer technology, although this is a significant and very fast-growing part of the field. Devices that fall under the heading of AT may include computers, as well as such things as a remote control to operate a television or CD player, an amplifier for the earpiece of a telephone, or a remote switch that will turn an appliance on and off. Assistive technology services include evaluation of individuals to determine a need for technology, instruction in the use of AT devices, and inservice training for staff to more effectively work with people.

Assistive Technology in the Law

One piece of legislation that specifically addresses assistive technology is the Technology-Related Assistance for Individuals with Disabilities Act (PL 100–407). The purpose of the Tech Act, as it is called, is to extend the availability of assistive technology to individuals with disabilities and their families. Funds were appropriated to develop a consumer-responsive statewide service delivery system for each state. For example, Wisconsin's response to this law was the creation of WisTech, which has outreach sites at eight independent living centers across the state. WisTech is available to citizens with disabilities of all ages and provides evaluation services, a demonstration lab for trying out assistive technology devices, and other assistance to individuals and families. School-age children, adults in independent living situations, and persons providing services at extended care facilities are all eligible to utilize what WisTech has to offer.

Another law that relates to provision of assistive technology devices and services is the IDEA: Individuals with Disabilities Education Act (PL 101–476). This 1990 revision of the Education of the Handicapped Act (PL 94–142) of 1975 includes definitions for assistive technology devices and services. Under this law, AT may be provided as part of special education, as a related service, or as a supplementary service.

Assistive Technology in Music Therapy

Just as music therapists work in a variety of settings to meet a multitude of individual needs, so are there numerous applications of assistive technology in the field of music therapy. In many cases, the tools themselves may be the same or similar across populations, but the applications vary according to the setting. For example, computer programs (including any music applications) can be adapted so that a student can independently operate the software using a simple switch, an adapted keyboard, or a standard computer keyboard that has been reconfigured to meet the student's specific needs. These adaptations may be used with students with physical disabilities, cognitive or sensory limitations, or attention disorders. In addition, there are devices that are not related to computers that have been designed to provide students with special education needs greater access to their education. One example of such devices is the use of a simple switch to operate the chord progression feature of the Omnichord™. The Suzuki Corporation actually developed this feature so that the chords of a song could be changed with the use of a footswitch, enabling the player to play a song without having to search for the right chord button at a given time. But for students with limited physical abilities, but developed *musical* abilities, this feature is advantageous for developing independence and skill. When the chords of the song are fed into the memory feature of the Omnichord, the student can change the chords of the song at the appropriate times with the simple touch of a switch. This device has also assisted teachers in discerning musical skill in students who were previously unable to demonstrate an understanding of the concept of chord progression.

Technology Training

Just as there are daily developments in new technologies that hit the market, so are there an increasing number of opportunities for applied training. Local school districts have placed great importance on technological literacy, and training resources have geared up to meet those needs. Classes, workshops, and seminars provide participants with background information and usually hands-on work with the equipment itself. In the area of music for students with special education needs, staff training has at least two major components: teachers and therapists are called upon to become familiar with technological developments in the area of *music* (composition, sequencing, synthesizing, recording, sampling, etc.) as well as the area of *assistive technology* (adaptive devices, adapted software, low-tech or high-tech uses, etc.).

Music therapists who utilize technology in their daily work can serve as excellent resources for information, training, and product development. Many of those who incorporate technology in their practices are self-taught individuals who worked with particular devices until they became skilled in using them. Once familiarity was established, these individuals made the transition from personal use to use in their professional endeavors.

Case Studies: Direct Service Delivery

"Carrie," a student with cognitive and language disabilities, attended a regular K–5th grade school, and was a member of the school chorus. At the music teacher's request, the music therapist rearranged the choral music so that Carrie could follow the printed page and keep up with the rest of the group. In addition, the therapist worked with Carrie for 30 minutes every week to practice the music individually, and to work on any parts that needed attention. In this setting, Carrie was able to articulate which passages were difficult for her, and she and the music therapist were able to practice strategies for overcoming the musical obstacles she encountered. Carrie was able to rehearse and perform the music with the chorus without any other intervention.

Another student, "Jim," signed up for trombone lessons and band at the high school he attended. Because of his physical limitations, progress was very slow, but steady. Jim had difficulty keeping up with the pace of the band, and no matter how much he practiced at home, the group lessons continued to present a challenge to him. The music therapist was contacted by the band director, who valued Jim's positive attitude and determination, and wanted him to be able to continue in the program. Jim's band music was reconfigured to allow him time within the context of the music to make necessary note changes, and the music therapist also provided one-to-one lessons to help Jim develop new playing strategies. Jim continued to participate in all band and lesson activities, including marching season, a trip to the state basketball tournament, and several concerts throughout the year.

"Mike" was a student in an inclusive general music class in an elementary school. Mike was especially responsive to music, but because of severe behavioral difficulties, was not able to make a satisfactory transition from his class to the music class. The time it took for the teacher to settle the students and get the class started presented an obstacle to Mike's success. The music therapist provided direct services to Mike by assisting him with a transition program. In addition, the therapist worked with the music educator to develop effective strategies for working with a class in which students had very diverse needs. This program helped reduce the number of variables with which the music educator had to cope, and the therapist was able to provide support and on-site assistance to both Mike and the teacher. Mike's success in going from class to music class and back to his regular class carried over into the rest of his educational program.

Direct Service Delivery in the Home

In some school districts, the role of a music therapist includes providing direct services to students who are confined to their homes because of medical reasons. For students who are recuperating from surgery or the effects of a traumatic injury, home schooling is sometimes necessary. In these cases, music therapy services provide an important link between the home and the school, and help alleviate a student's physical discomfort or feelings of isolation and fear. The goals of music therapy in the home are a continuation of the student's IEP program; if music therapy is introduced to the student's program because of medical needs and a home-bound program, the goals should be clearly identified in terms of educational need.

The School Music Therapist: Education or Therapy?

Parents and student advocacy groups have worked diligently for many years so that the educational community will regard students with special needs as a diverse population of *learners*, rather than children with conditions that need to be "fixed" with therapy. Some school districts have moved away from terminology such as "therapist," "therapy," or "treatment" to words that are centered in educational language. In fact, in some states, services can be provided by the local school district only if they are "educationally necessary." Services that have a medical basis (as "therapy" does), must be provided by other agencies. Therefore, if a student receives physical therapy, occupational therapy, nursing services, or music therapy in a school, it should be for educational reasons.

Music therapy in a school setting does not replace music education or recreational music opportunities, but joins these programs as another option for meeting IEP goals. Since music therapy is regarded as an instructional support program, it *is* compatible with the educational model. School music therapists must be prepared to fill the roles of teachers, consultants to teachers, and instructional team members. The result is a blend of education *and* therapy that assists students with special needs in using their strengths to minimize their disabilities and maximize their potential.

The Music Therapist as a Consultant

Music therapists are often assigned to provide consultant support to teachers and additional school personnel. The consultant role is quite different from that of providing direct music therapy services to students. Whereas direct services involve immediate contact with students on a regular basis, consultant services are provided to other individuals who work with the student (namely, teachers, parents, administrators, and other school personnel), and may range from a single meeting to regularly scheduled contacts throughout the school year.

Consulting to Facilitate Inclusion

In some school districts, the music therapist fills the role of consultant in order to facilitate the practice of inclusion. According to The Association for Persons with Severe Handicaps (TASH), inclusion means "providing necessary services within the regular schools" and "supporting regular teachers...by providing time, training, teamwork, resources, and strategies" (1994). The support that is provided should not only be for the regular education classroom teachers, but also for music teachers who work with inclusive groups of students. To design and provide appropriate educational activities for students with special needs, a music therapist works with regular education teachers from planning through the implementation stage. The music therapist is qualified by credentials and background to address the unique role music plays in the education of students with disabilities. Dual certification (such as a teaching license in music education) is an additional asset in the area of inclusion and gives the music therapist credibility in dealing with special education as well as regular education personnel.

Consultation to Facilitate Music Education

Music educators working with special education classes should have access to trained professionals for the purpose of consultation. Although the similarities between music education and music therapy are numerous, some music teachers regard the music therapist as being concerned only with students with special education needs. If the music therapist remains sensitive to the music educator's complete teaching assignment, consultant work on behalf of students with special needs will be more effective. In addition, the therapist will have to work at making music therapy part of the educational setting and school life. Rather than becoming a threat to the educator's effectiveness as a teacher, the therapist needs to be aware of the complex educational and societal issues facing school staffs. The music therapist filling a consulting role is most effective when maintaining a peer relationship with the educator on behalf of students with special needs. Music therapy services have a different goal emphasis than music education, but should not be portrayed as superior to, or as a replacement for, music education. All students need music education. Some students with special education needs also need music therapy services.

As described in previous chapters of this book, music educators typically report having a lack of information regarding the handicapping conditions of students in their classrooms and limited input into the IEP development process. In addition, music teachers have reported that their own participation in the process of making decisions about appropriate music programming for students with special needs is more important than knowing about modifications to the program itself (Myles & Simpson, 1989). Music educators who teach hundreds of students per week, including students with special needs, find it difficult, if not impossible, to become involved in the planning and implementation process of special education programs for individual students.

With the introduction of National Standards for Music Education (Music Educators National Conference, 1994), music educators are looking at the components of quality music education programs from a more unified perspective. They will need support to design appropriate programs that assist students with special education needs in reaching the following standards that have been established:

1. Students will be able to sing, alone and with others, a varied repertoire of music;
2. Students will be able to perform on instruments, alone and with others, a varied repertoire of music;
3. Students will be able to improvise melodies, variations, and accompaniments;
4. Students will be able to compose and arrange music within specified guidelines;
5. Students will be able to read and notate music;
6. Students will be able to listen to, analyze, and describe music;
7. Students will be able to evaluate music and music performance;
8. Students will be able to understand relationships between music, the other arts, and disciplines outside the arts;
9. Students will be able to understand music in relation to history and culture.

(Music Educators National Conference, 1994)

School music programs that are able to meet these standards must also address the individual needs of all students. The music therapist who works as a consultant to music educators must become familiar with the MENC National Standards, as well as the state or individual school district's plan for implementing those standards. Students with special education needs can work toward achieving each standard, but the educational opportunities and techniques may be in sharp contrast to what is currently offered. Music education in some districts will have to undergo systemic change in order to accommodate the needs of all the students at all grade levels.

In each area of musical response, singing, playing, moving, and listening, there is a range of ways students can participate. For example, "singing" is not the only vocalization response there is that relates to a musical experience (see Figure 1). Some students, when music is heard, will start to produce vocal sounds, including humming, cooing, or "playing" with the voice. This appears to be an attempt to join the musical experience, and is considered to be a "singing" response. Among the additional responses that fall into the singing category are: (a) repeating vocal sounds; (b) imitating the contour of sounds (moving up or down in pitch relative to what is heard, duplicating the rhythmic feel of the music, etc.); (c) joining the music at key vocal phrases (such as a repeated word, the ending of the verse, the chorus, etc.); and (d) singing to one's self. Many students who are nonverbal make responses to music within the singing category that should be considered as legitimate "presinging" reactions. For example, some students breathe more deeply and smoothly when the music is happening. The music has a physiological effect on them, and since breath control is a necessary component of singing, this physical response falls into the singing category.

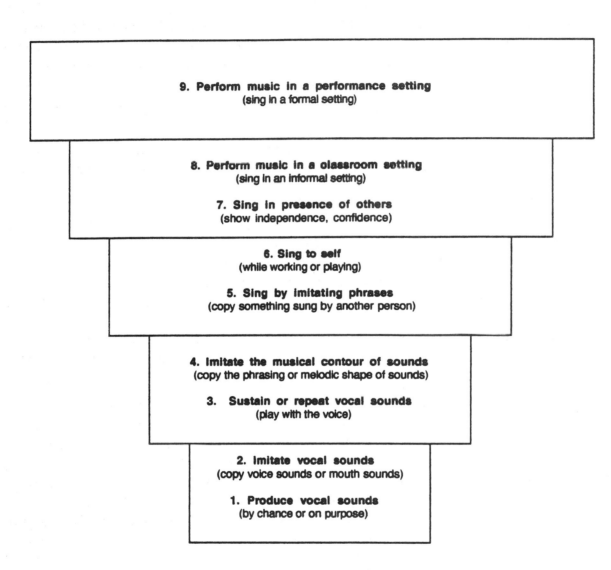

Figure 1. Range of Singing Responses

Another classification of musical participation is "playing" body rhythms or classroom and performance instruments. Once again, there are many items in the range of playing responses that can be considered to be intentional musical responses on the part of students (see Figure 2). Performing musically on an instrument is one way to play, but other responses include: (a) getting out and putting away an instrument; (b) choosing a preferred instrument; (c) exploring the sounds made on an instrument or with body rhythms; (d) repeating an action to make a sound; (e) participating in a playing experience for part of the time; (f) being tolerant of a variety of sounds produced by several instruments; (g) changing tempo, style, volume, rhythm, etc.; and (h) practicing. There are also physiological "preplaying" responses to be included. For example, some students' muscle tone is improved when music is heard. The music positively affects their posture and strength, which are components of the ability to play. Therefore, these very basic responses also are included in the playing category.

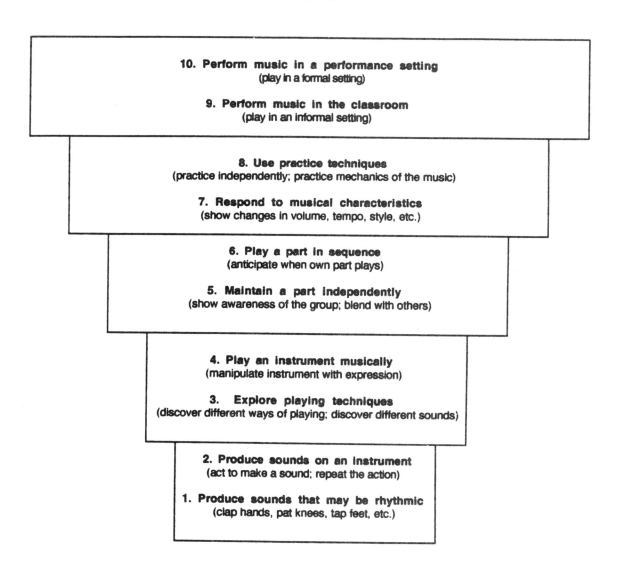

Figure 2. Range of Playing Responses

Similarly, "moving" and "listening" to music include a wide range of responses which are acceptable for considering how a student is participating in music experiences (see Figures 3 and 4). For example, moving to music refers to rhythmic and stylistic action, but can also include (a) turning or moving toward the music source, (b) imitating the movements of others in relation to the music, and (c) coordinating purposeful movements in response to music. In addition, physiological responses of changes in muscle tone and posture are "premoving" reactions that are within the realm of movement to music. In the category of "listening," a student may respond by (a) regarding sounds/music, (b) acting to repeat the sounds, (c) developing simple discrimination skills and preferences, (d) selecting music as a free time option, (e) and practicing appropriate audience skills.

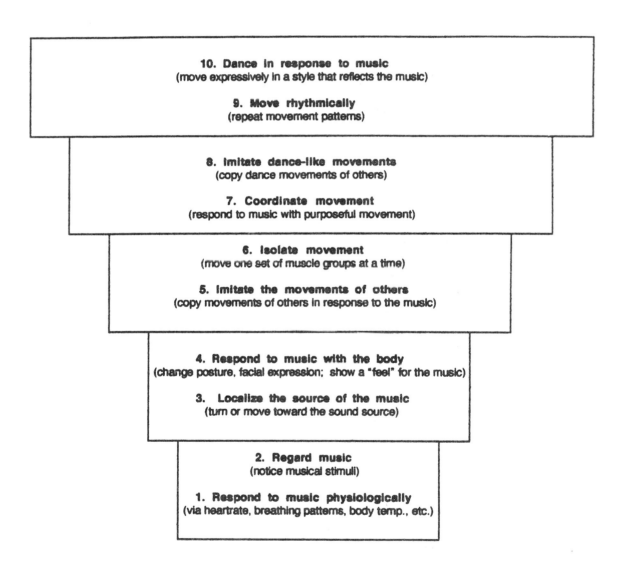

Figure 3. Range of Movement Responses

The frustrations, concerns, and questions of music educators who teach students with special needs are occasionally beyond the scope of the music therapist's role as a consultant. When this happens, the music therapist acts as a resource person, and steers the educator toward appropriate services that can help. Sometimes educators seek further training, and the music therapist is in a position to either provide inservice training in specific areas, or to recommend workshops or college courses that will be beneficial to music educators.

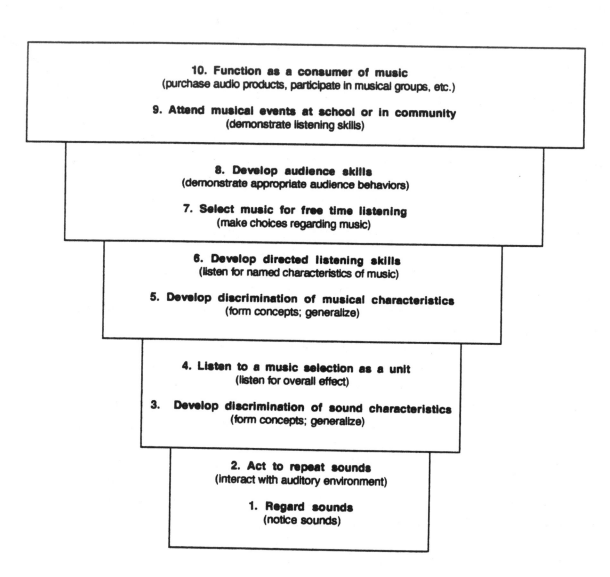

Figure 4. Range of Listening Responses

Consulting to Facilitate Musical Performance

When working in a consultant role with performance group teachers, the role of the music therapist is more specifically designed than in general music classes, where a variety of music experiences is available to the music educator. In the general music class, the learning process can be seen as more comprehensive, appearing to make it easier for the music educator to design appropriate activities that will meet the needs of all students in the class. But in performance groups, the ability of the student to contribute to the expectations of the class will be the main concern of music educators. Some performance group teachers will question how or why a student came to be in the band, orchestra, or choir. The role of the music therapist consultant is to help identify and interpret district policy for placement of students in performance groups. District policy should reflect federal and state guidelines for special education services.

One of the most difficult aspects of consulting with performance groups, especially in school districts that have long histories of musical performance, is to keep the focus on process over product. The award-winning band that suddenly includes a student with a physical disability in the percussion section, or the madrigal group into which several students who are nonverbal are scheduled are not uncommon occurrences in these times of inclusivity. Yet these scenarios, and others like them, create challenges and questions for music educators, who often begin to doubt their abilities to accommodate the needs of students with special needs. Music educators, however, are well aware of the influence that music has on young lives, and are interested in providing music experiences that will benefit all students for a lifetime.

In performance classes, the music therapist assumes the position of helping the student function within the parameters of the performance group. The main focus for the therapist is the student, although it is also necessary to work with the music educator to expand the mission of the band, orchestra, or choir to a more inclusive one. As the music therapist explores options with the music educator, it is necessary to remain aware of and sensitive to the role that the music educator plays in the educational program.

The music therapist must be prepared to provide real support. Rather than talking about options, the therapist should be ready to assist in implementing as many options as it takes to help accommodate the student. Since physical presence is a major component of good consultation services, the music therapist should attend rehearsals on a regular basis, observing the entire group, as well as the student with special education needs. If the written music is a major obstacle to the student's participation, the music can be rewritten by enlarging or rearranging so it is easier to follow (keeping in mind the copyright laws!). Another option is to make rehearsal tapes so the student can work on the music at home or in the classroom. Or a combination program can be developed in which the student participates in the performance group, but also receives direct services in the form of specialized lessons or extra help.

When typical performance groups do not meet the needs of all the students who would like to be involved in musical performance, non-traditional groups can be developed. These include, but are not limited to, percussion ensembles, Orff groups, guitar classes, bell choirs, or singing groups that perform pops literature as a community service. The role of the consultant music therapist in these groups is much the same as it is in the traditional school musical groups. However, the music therapist is able to offer valuable assistance in getting nontraditional performance groups started and in training the music educator in techniques, methods, and identifying appropriate performance goals and objectives.

Consulting with Nonmusic Education Staff

In some districts, the music therapist provides consultation services to staff besides music educators. Classroom teachers (both regular education and special education), teaching assistants, and other school personnel are recipients of such services. In these cases, the music therapist provides support in the following areas: (a) designing appropriate music activities to meet IEP goals, especially in the areas of leisure skill and social skill development; (b) training classroom personnel to implement basic music activities; (c) teaching classroom staff simple accompaniment techniques or other skills that will assist in implementing appropriate music activities; (d) collecting and providing appropriate music resources in the form of songsheets, songbooks, recordings, and instruments; (e) providing in-class demonstration of appropriate music activities and appropriate expectations for the students; and (f) providing other assistance that supports classroom instruction.

Consulting Guidelines

The following guidelines have been used to provide beneficial consultation services to music educators and classroom teachers at the elementary, middle, and high school levels:

1. Keep a schedule that is flexible and allows the music therapist to be available when the students and teachers need assistance;

2. If teachers are reluctant to ask for assistance, seek out their input with surveys, phone calls, and other communication techniques;

3. To efficiently determine what the teacher needs/wants, use a simple checklist or flow chart to help the teacher better utilize resources that are already available in the school;

4. Instead of providing quick solutions to every problem, work through the problem-solving process with the teacher to identify some reasonable options and strategies;

5. Develop options that fit the situation, including the teacher's current comfort level and background, the profile of the class, time constraints, district goals, etc.;

6. Encourage the teacher to keep trying a chosen strategy; demonstrate the strategy and show that sometimes a solution needs to be tried over and over again before it is successful;

7. Remain visible and accessible; attend meetings, send memos or mailings, make phone calls, provide inservice offerings, etc.; sometimes teachers will know that a support person is available, but will only let the therapist know there is a concern if the therapist makes the contact;

8. Let administrators know what consultant services have been provided for the students and teachers in a particular school;

9. When developing strategies to address a concern, give teachers examples of other teachers that have been in similar situations, and the options that were tried in those instances (team teaching, sample lessons, resource equipment, networking assistance, etc.);

10. Target the teachers new to the district for extra attention throughout their first year, even if they seem to be working effectively with the students;

11. When providing inservice training, make topics specific; teachers want specific information about behavior management, students with severe multiple disabilities, how to play the guitar, etc.;

12. Give teachers an opportunity to vent frustrations, concerns and problems without responding with a judgment call or an easy answer;

13. Know the limitations of the consultant position, which is that of an outsider.

Resource and Equipment Distribution

In some districts, there is a central supply of music materials and equipment that teachers can borrow. Usually these materials are for music educators, but more and more districts are making them available to classroom teachers as well. As a consultant, the music therapist is responsible for recommending appropriate equipment to be ordered, either at the district or the school level. To accomplish this task effectively, it is often possible for the music therapist to get equipment on a trial basis. Once equipment has been procured, the therapist can ask for teacher input regarding the usefulness of specific items. Regular communication with school staff is necessary in order to let them know what materials are available, as well as what materials have been added to the supply. By dividing equipment into areas of application, such as materials appropriate for early childhood, accompaniment instruments, technological equipment, or multicultural instruments, the therapist is able to keep materials easily organized for functional use.

In addition to keeping track of equipment that is available, ordering appropriate materials to have in the resource library, and evaluating quality of materials used, the music therapist is also responsible for demonstrating how the materials can be used most effectively. One way is to demonstrate the materials with actual students in the classroom or music setting. Besides showing the students how to use the equipment, the therapist should also familiarize staff with the appropriate way to use, play, store, and care for the equipment.

Music Therapy and the IEP

According to PL 94–142 and IDEA, students with exceptional education needs are entitled to the same educational opportunities as their regular education peers. This includes the area of music education, in which both general music and performance opportunities should be provided to accommodate the needs of all students of school age.

For some school districts, the provision of appropriate music education experiences involves support services for music educators in the form of inservice training and consultation by music therapists or special education personnel. In other districts, designing music education services that meet individual needs of all students, including those with disabilities, will require systemic change and a reexamination of the music education program for all students.

The Individual Education Plan (IEP)

The IEP Process

For students in special education programs, the Individual Education Plan (IEP) should be considered to be more like a process rather than a product. The IEP is developed by the group of individuals who have been in contact with the student, including staff as well as family members. It is a yearly process and serves to determine appropriate goals, objectives, and educational services. The IEP is not the plan itself, but the dialogue and assessment that occur on behalf of the needs of the student. The IEP identifies services that are necessary to address the needs of the student, and includes the following components: (a) the current abilities and needs of the student; (b) the long-range (yearly) goals and the short-term objectives for achieving those goals; (c) what educational services are required to meet the goals; (d) the strategies that will be used to reach the objectives, including any modifications that will be made; (e) the professionals who will implement the strategies, or the domains in which the learning will take place; (f) criteria for evaluating progress; and (g) dates for completion of objectives.

Most special education programs rely on a team approach. For an integrated program to be effective, teamwork among staff and parents is critical. The implementation of the IEP is dependent on cooperation and communication among teachers, support personnel, parents, and peers of the student.

The following is a brief explanation of the most common team models (refer to the Models of Service Delivery section in this chapter for more detailed information):

1. *Multidisciplinary*, in which communication between team members is unidirectional and limited; in this model, the focus of service delivery is discipline-centered; assessment of students is done in isolation from other disciplines; IEPs are developed with minimal group input from team members; service delivery is isolated within each discipline;

2. *Interdisciplinary*, in which communication among team members occurs at the IEP planning stage; in this model, the teacher works with each individual discipline to reach decisions; assessment of students is done in isolation, but results are shared with other team members; IEPs contain portions contributed by each discipline; and

3. *Transdisciplinary*, in which communication among team members is multidirectional and frequent; parents are an integral part of the team, and decisions regarding the student are reached by consensus; the focus of service delivery is child-centered; assessment, IEP planning, and service delivery are integrated and holistic (Beninghof & Singer, 1992).

Professional identities and territories can become entangled in the course of setting priorities for the student (York & Vandercook, 1991). However, if IEP development is viewed as an ongoing process, the team will be able to provide appropriate services according to what he student really needs. Professionals who remain committed to making the IEP student-centered can design an integrated educational program for the student. Strategic development of an integrated IEP includes the following steps in the process: (a) examine the student's current abilities to identify strengths and needs; (b) determine priority areas; (c) to the maximum extent possible, integrate the student into regular class environments *first*; and (d) revise and implement IEP priorities as needed, including providing special services.

Music Therapy in the IEP

The inclusion of music therapy in the IEP process is sometimes a controversial practice. If music therapy is named specifically as *the* way to achieve goals, school districts are obligated to provide music therapy services. On the other hand, if music therapy is listed as *a* way for achieving goals, it is regarded as one of many possible services that could assist the student. For example, a goal that focuses on motor development of a student, specifically mobility over a variety of floor surfaces, can be addressed in physical education class, in physical therapy, in the classroom, and in music therapy. In this scenario, music therapy is a strategy for achieving a goal which is also being met in other locations under the direction of other professionals.

If the general education (regular education) curriculum is adapted to meet the exceptional education needs of the student, this information must be included in the IEP. When a music education program requires adaptation, it does not automatically imply that music therapy services, or the expertise of a music therapist, are needed. These adaptations can be implemented by music educators who have a history of teaching students with diverse needs. Adaptations to the music education program can be curricular in nature, or designed to provide the student with physical access to materials and equipment used in class. For instance, to help a student develop an understanding of musical form, picture representations are matched with the aural material, or examples are used that involve touch or movement. This is an example of a lesson modification. On a curricular scale, a student might be involved in activities which promote appropriate audience behavior at musical events. An example of a physical modification might be an adaptive mallet for playing the drum or placing a mallet instrument to the side of a student in a wheelchair for easy access. Modifications to the music education program are known as *special music education* or *adapted music education*.

When it is determined through assessment that a student does require music therapy services, specific information about the nature and delivery of these services is included in the IEP. Depending on the level of involvement of the music therapist working with special education programs, assessment is completed at the intake level (if the music therapist is a member of the standing assessment team), the programming stage (if there is a determination to be made between music education or music therapy), or at the IEP development phase, in which programming is determined. Many music therapists utilize standardized assessment tools to determine the appropriateness of music therapy services for individual students. In addition, many music therapists have developed effective assessment tools that are specifically designed to meet their assessment needs. The way in which music therapy is included in the IEP depends on how the IEP itself is constructed, which, in turn, depends on the type of educational team that is assembled to provide a coordinated program.

For example, if the music therapist is working within a model in which all phases of the student's educational program—assessment, planning, and implementation—are done together with the other members of the team, music therapy is more likely to be an integral element in the IEP. This is because, in an integrated program, the other members of the team are more likely to gain a better understanding of the value of music therapy services in achieving IEP goals. Furthermore, an integrated IEP deals with the student holistically, and team members are more inclined to disregard strict disciplinary definitions in favor of what is the most effective program for the student. On the other hand, if the music therapist is part of a team in which all phases of the student's program are implemented separately, according to specific disciplinary boundaries, then music therapy is more likely to be isolated from the progress that is made in other areas.

Developmental vs. Functional Music Activities

Many educational assessment tools measure a student's abilities, such as motor, cognitive, and social skills, in terms of developmental age. Developmental skills are those milestones that are reached at typical ages for most infants and children. They are norms of development, or ways of measuring the developmental process for the average person.

Since assessment results are stated in developmental terms (age equivalents), special education programs are designed to increase the student's age equivalent in each area where a discrepancy exists. For example, a 5-year-old student who uses a grasp typical for a 2-year-old receives educational support services to develop this fine motor skill to a level that is more commensurate with the student's age. In the area of music education, a student in a similar early stage of the primary level works on the skill of determining whether, in a recorded or live example, the voice is that of a woman or a man. A child who has not yet acquired this discrimination ability presumably receives additional attention in this area to make the responses to music more in keeping with the chronological age.

Programs based solely on developmental ages present a major drawback for students with severe disabilities as well as for students with special education needs who are older than the primary years. The problem with such programs is that, as the student gets older, the discrepancy between the actual chronological age and the age equivalent of skill development becomes greater. It is difficult to provide age-appropriate educational programming for students when only their developmental skills are considered.

During recent years, special education programs have incorporated a functional skill approach to educational planning and service delivery. Functional skills are those tasks which relate to everyday living in the present and in the projected future. Examples of functional skills include taking care of personal needs (eating, dressing, toileting), performing work-related tasks (cooperating with others, completing a job, being on time for a job), getting along in the community (shopping for needs, using transportation), and using free time productively (pursuing special interests, developing hobbies).

Among the functional skills associated with the music education class are selecting/obtaining an instrument from among a group of choices, participating in singing by vocalizing during a portion of the song, and starting/stopping a motor response according to musical cues. While these activities involve skill development that is typical at certain ages, each activity is regarded as a unit of effort that requires a combination of skills in different areas to be meaningful. The activity takes place in the context of a real setting under real circumstances.

In a music education setting the developmental age of a student with special needs is often quite different from the chronological age. For example, if the student is 7 years old, but the developmental assessment provides a functional age of 9 months, it is considered best practice to provide music activities appropriate for a 7-year-old student. Developmental ages are considered only as a frame of reference, rather than to determine the curriculum content for the student. It is not unusual for a discrepancy of 2 years or more between the developmental age and the chronological age to remain as a discrepancy throughout the student's life. Rather than becoming "stuck" in the area of developmental skills (which fall strictly into the social, motor, cognitive, communication, and sensory areas), the student would be better served working toward goals in functional areas (life experience areas). Therefore, a recommended practice is for the music educator/music therapist to work on developmental objectives during the chronological years when childhood development occurs (through approximately age 7). After this age, the student's program should be centered around goals and objectives that will help the student function more effectively within the school environment, the home setting, and throughout the community.

All people progress through several stages of growth in music experiences (see Figure 5). The first stage, *exploration*, is the stage in which individuals get to know the materials, try things out, and gain some preliminary experience in the medium. In the *control* stage, the person has enough early experience with the materials or activity to gain some basic-to-advanced control over the activity or materials. This enables the person to participate more fully in the group experience and have access to additional activities and materials through prior knowledge.

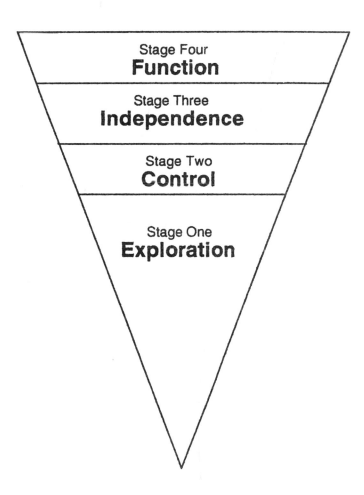

Figure 5. Stages of Growth in Musical Experiences

The next stage is the development of *independence*. The person is able to be a musician and carry a part within a group, or use fundamental skills to create music. In the final stage, the *functional* stage, the individual uses the medium of music vocationally, avocationally, for further study or refinement.

An example of a student operating within the *exploration* stage is in the area of playing classroom instruments, such as the autoharp, tambourine, or drum. A student in this stage of development would look at, touch, pick up, and explore the instrument by experimenting with ways to make a sound, ways to hold the instrument, and how the student acts upon the instrument. Many students proceed through this stage very quickly, but some students spend a longer period of time investigating what makes the instrument "tick."

In the *control* stage, the student is able to have some command over the instrument. By this point, the instrument is familiar to the student, and the exploration that took place before is incorporated into the playing of the instrument. The student is able to consistently start or stop playing, change tempo, volume, or style of playing, and achieve a level of mastery over the instrument. Many students spend a long time in this stage, depending on the inherent difficulty of the instrument itself.

The *independence* stage occurs once a student has achieved a certain level of musicianship. In this stage the student is able to participate with a minimum of outside intervention, and can follow the guidance of a leader or members of the group. Because of the independence that is developed, a student is able to proceed to the next stage, that of *functional* use of the instrument in recreational or vocational experiences. The student is able to play in a school group, perform for an audience, practice independently, maintain a part within an ensemble or on a solo basis, and be involved in music for personal pleasure or as a service to others.

Music Therapy in Various IEP Team Models

The Multidisciplinary IEP

Because of the separateness of individual members of the *multidisciplinary team*, this model often isolates the work of the music therapist from the work of other professionals. In some cases, goals are generated that (a) are not related to other IEP goals, or (b) do not reflect a specific *need* for music therapy. For example, if the IEP team has determined that finger strength is less of a priority than other issues for the student, a music therapy goal of "increasing finger strength by playing a keyboard" is clearly not related to the IEP process . In addition, the goal of playing the keyboard does not show a need for music therapy services unless prior assessment has indicated that music therapy could capitalize on the student's motivation and abilities, provide appropriate adaptations for the student, and offer an efficient and effective way to meet the student's goal. The responsibility lies with the music therapist to demonstrate to the rest of the team that music therapy is a unique and legitimate related service. For example, in addressing the aforementioned goal regarding finger dexterity, the needs of the student can be better served if the music therapist works with the occupational therapist to determine what functional hand skills need attention. Then the music therapist can design an appropriate program that will work on those hand skills, such as reaching all parts of the keyboard, isolating finger movement, and developing finger strength that in turn can be used in feeding, dressing, and other functional hand activities.

The Interdisciplinary IEP

In the *interdisciplinary team* model, individual members share their evaluations, goals, and implementation plans with each other. Therefore, the music therapist encounters more opportunities to educate other professionals about the benefits of music therapy. Because team members share assessment results and program plans with each other, there is increased opportunity for communication. One disadvantage similar to the multidisciplinary model is that the need for music therapy services is often determined without the benefit of standardized assessment tools. Therefore, input by the music therapist can be regarded by other team members as self-serving.

Music therapy in the interdisciplinary IEP can be included as a separate disciplinary area, with goals and objectives that are particular to the music setting. Another way of including music therapy is as a strategy for achieving goals that have been determined by other members of the team. For example, the music therapist can incorporate into music therapy the motor goals articulated by the adaptive physical education teacher, the fine motor goals identified by the occupational therapist, and the speech and language goals listed by the speech pathologist.

The Transdisciplinary IEP

The *transdisciplinary* model, like the other models, is used for planning the IEP. The team identifies student needs, prioritizes goals and objectives, and determines how the services of each education professional will be coordinated into a team concept. Team members cooperate to plan instructional experiences that require the expertise of all staff involved. This model of IEP development is also known as "integrated IEP" construction. In this model, music therapy is regarded as "a way," but not necessarily "the way" to accomplish goals. To diminish this negative side effect, it is imperative that music therapists working in the transdisciplinary model contribute to the goal-writing process with a knowledge of specific student responses to music and the ability to see music as an *integral* part of instruction.

In some transdisciplinary or integrated IEPs, goals are "domain-based," developed from the educational perspective that people function in a variety of locations, territories, or domains. For example, when people are at home or involved in home-related situations, they perform domestic tasks, in the vocational domain they work at a job or train to work at a job, when they are anyplace but home and work, they function in a community domain, and during their leisure time, they participate in leisure activities. For goals that relate to the domestic domain, the music therapist teaches the student to get materials to be used in the music activity and then return them to their appropriate containers. The community domain includes activities which expose the student to community music activities and train the student in the exercise of appropriate audience skills. For vocational skill development, the music therapist addresses the areas of task completion or the acquisition of computer skills that assist the student in the creative process. Leisure skill development includes choosing activities that are pleasurable and rewarding to the student and that will occupy the individual's free time.

Since the *transdisciplinary* model is based on crossing disciplinary boundaries, it is recognized that students function in different domains or settings, and perform a variety of tasks that go together to form complete activities. This is different from the other models because students are involved in real settings with real activities, rather than in the occupational therapy room as an occupational therapy client, or as a student on the Speech/Language caseload.

Music therapy most often relates to domain-based goals in the area of "leisure skills." For example, listening to music for pleasure, learning to play an instrument as a hobby, or attending concerts in the community are activities which people choose to do in their spare time. However, when music therapy services are delivered, the goals in the other domain areas are also addressed, providing an integrated instructional setting. Music therapy that addresses the domestic domain involves any self-help skills, such as getting equipment out and putting it away, taking care of materials, and operating home-based music equipment. In the vocational domain, music therapy addresses goals in the area that relate to the world of work: namely, work habits, attitudes, and the completion of a variety of tasks. The community domain includes such music therapy goals as independence during community events, becoming aware of opportunities in the community, and practicing appropriate behaviors.

Other Team Models

In some cases, the music therapist works with students whose instructional program is not determined by the IEP, such as students in general (regular) education classes who have been determined to be at-risk and students who qualify for services under Section 504. Typically, these students do not meet the criteria needed to receive special education services but are in need of support services which include music therapy. In these cases, the music therapist functions as a member of student services team (or Sec. 504 team), which meets on a regular basis to ensure that appropriate services and resources are provided for each student.

Music therapists are assigned to provide services according to a number of different models, depending on who employs them. For example, music therapists (a) work out of centralized county, state, or multidistrict systems; (b) are employed by local private or public school districts; or (c) receive contracts through a service provider structure. In any of these employer models, music therapists are assigned on a departmental, school-assignment, or district-wide basis. Each of these models has an internal team structure to which the music therapist contributes.

One school operation model that is currently being explored in school districts nationwide is Site-Based (or School-Based) Management (also known as Shared Decision-Making), in which the local school staff has control of the budget, staff allocation, hiring practices, program direction, and provision of necessary services for the students attending that school. A music therapist working in a Site-Based Management (SBM) school faces both an opportunity and a challenge. The opportunity is to participate as a member of an SBM team and to demonstrate the effectiveness of music therapy for students with special needs, regardless of whether the school district provides music therapy services. Under Site-Based Management, the opportunities for employment of music therapists in school settings are increased. Site-Based Management demands greater accountability at the local school staff level, and music therapists who are members of SBM teams need to provide documentation that their services are necessary to the student population.

References

Adamson, D. R. (1989). Collaboration/consultation: Bridging the gap from resource room to regular classroom. *Teacher Education and Special Education, 12*(1–2), 52–55.

The Association for Persons with Severe Handicaps. (1994). *Inclusion in education: A choice for your child* [Brochure].

Beninghof, A. M., & Singer, A. L. T. (1992, Winter). Transdisciplinary teaming: An inservice training activity. *Teaching Exceptional Children,* 58–60.

Conway, R. N. F., & Gow, L. (1988). Mainstreaming special class students with mild handicaps through group instruction. *Remedial and Special Education, 9*(5), 34–40, 49.

Dickinson, V. J. (1987). *Attitudes and practices of special day class teachers concerning least restrictive environment.* Unpublished master's thesis, San Diego State University, San Diego, CA.

Killoran, J. (1987). *Grouping handicapped and non-handicapped children in mainstream settings.* Report of the Functional Mainstreaming for Success Project, State of Utah, Salt Lake City..

Music Educators National Conference (1994). National standards for music education. Reston, VA: Author.

Myles, B. S., & Simpson, R. L. (1989). Regular educators' preferences for mainstreaming mildly handicapped children. *Journal of Special Education, 22*(4), 79–91.

Peterson, N. L. (1987). *Early intervention for handicapped and at-risk children: An introduction to early childhood social education.* Denver, CO: Love Publications.

York, J., & Vandercook, T. (1991, Winter). Designing an integrated program for learners with severe disabilities. *Teaching Exceptional Children,* 22–28.

INSERVICE TRAINING: A MAJOR KEY TO SUCCESSFUL INTEGRATION OF SPECIAL NEEDS CHILDREN INTO MUSIC EDUCATION CLASSES

Carol Culton Heine

CONTAINED within this book are many activities, suggestions and approaches for the use of music in mainstreamed music education settings. These ideas and methodologies will assist both music educators and music therapists plan effective educational and instructional strategies for mainstreamed students. But are these enough? In addition to helpful hints and strategies for musical activities, what do music educators and music therapists need to meet the creative challenges that mainstreamed music classes present? Current studies and surveys indicate that music teachers who work in mainstreamed music settings need: (a) a positive attitude toward mainstreaming (Darrow, 1990b; Thompson, 1986; White, 1981/1982); (b) inservice training beyond the preservice, college curriculum (Frisque, Niebur, & Humphreys, 1994; Gfeller, Darrow, & Hedden, 1990; Gilbert & Asmus, 1981; Stein, 1983); (c) inservice providers who recognize the importance of the teacher-participant; and therefore, (d) inservices with content and format based on the needs and the strengths of the teacher-participants (Hutson, 1981; Powers, 1983).

The Music Teacher is the Key

Special needs students are routinely placed in elementary general music classes (Atterbury, 1986a, 1990; Damer, 1979/1980; Gavin, 1983/1984; Gilbert & Asmus, 1981; Graham, 1988; Nocera, 1981; Sideridis & Chandler, 1995), and as such, it is the music teacher who is responsible for providing opportunities for children to learn, participate, and create enjoyable, reinforcing, and meaningful musical experiences. It is the music teacher who, with a realistic but positive attitude, will determine each day's success (Schultz & Turnbull, 1984) and will stimulate and promote positive attitudes and interactions among all children (disabled and nondisabled) in the mainstreamed music education setting.

In addition to a positive attitude, it is imperative that music educators have proper training, skills, and support to accomplish the tasks and meet the challenges of the mainstreamed setting willingly and with confidence and security. It cannot be denied that the process of mainstreaming requires music educators to develop new and more specific knowledge and skills not generally acquired in preservice college curricula (Atterbury, 1990; Gfeller & Hedden, 1987; Gilbert & Asmus, 1981; Stuart & Gilbert, 1977). However, many music educators continue to receive limited or no extensive or formal training to enable them to work with special needs children in either integrated or self-contained classes (Frisque et al., 1994; Gfeller et al., 1990; Goldsmith, 1984/1985; Stein, 1983; Stuart & Gilbert, 1977). This means that, "Most music educators are attempting to meet the educational needs of handicapped students with little or no educational preparation" (Gfeller et al., 1990, p. 99). As a result, many music teachers feel unprepared to teach students with special needs within their integrated classes and continue to indicate a desire to have additional training that addresses their special and specific needs (Atterbury, 1990; Frisque et al., 1994; Gfeller et al., 1990; Pratt, 1986; Thompson, 1990).

For many teachers, this lack of information and preparation may contribute to feelings of inadequacy, frustration, and negativism (Hawkins, 1991/1992), and, undoubtedly, affect teachers' attitudes towards mainstreaming and special needs children. Clearly, this indicates a great need for effective inservice for music educators teaching in mainstreamed situations.

Inservice

Definition

Inservice is a developmental activity provided to teachers who engage in professional practice. Inservice provides: (a) training to improve present levels of skill and knowledge, (b) opportunities to learn new teaching methods and strategies (Joyce & Showers, 1980), and (c) self-renewal for teachers and schools within a supportive and positive climate (Dillon-Peterson, 1981). According to Fresko and Ben-Chaim (1986), "Inservice education has become the main vehicle to meet the needs of teachers currently working within the school" (p. 205), and, in fact, according to some experts, inservice is a critical factor in successful mainstreaming (Tymitz-Wolf, 1982; Williams, 1988).

What Is Good Inservice?

There are several criteria that make up what can be labeled as "best practices" in inservice training. A list of best practices for inservice in music and mainstreaming appears at the end of this chapter. However, three essential issues critical to effective inservice must be addressed as they relate to inservice for music educators: (a) teacher attitude, (b) needs-based inservice content, and (c) evaluation. The following sections of this chapter focus on these three essential components of successful inservice.

Attitude

The first critical component of effective inservice is attention to participant attitude. Teacher attitude is an important factor in the successful integration and learning success of students with disabilities in music classes (Damer, 1979/1980; Darrow, 1990b; Elliott & Sins, 1981/1982; Sideridis & Chandler, 1995; Smith, 1989; Thompson, 1986; White, 1981/1982). Student productivity, student responses, and successful implementation of instructional strategies are influenced and often dictated by teacher expectations and attitudes (Darrow, 1990a; Gavin, 1983/1984). Positive teacher attitude helps to encourage positive responses, enthusiastic involvement, motivation, enjoyment, and participation among special needs children in music classes as well as other children.

While attitude is recognized as an especially important issue in facilitating successful integration of students with disabilities into music classes, information on how music educators feel toward mainstreaming is scant (Hawkins, 1991/1992). Some studies suggest that educators support the principle of mainstreaming and feel positive toward mainstreaming of special needs children into music classes (Hock, Hasazi, & Patten, 1990; Jellison, 1992; Sideridis & Chandler, 1995; Sins, 1983), while other research reveals that this support is only moderately favorable (Gfeller et al., 1990; Gfeller & Hedden, 1987; Hawkins, 1991/1992). Ambivalent or negative attitudes among music educators toward mainstreaming may stem in part from several factors including: (a) lack of input into the placement decision, (b) lack of information about the unique characteristics and needs of the student, and (c) lack of teacher preparation and training.

Lack of Input Into Placement Decisions

While PL 94–142 does not specifically mandate mainstreaming into music classes, music educators have traditionally been among the first to provide classroom settings for special needs students (Hock et al., 1990). Unfortunately, many educational personnel view the "least restrictive environment" clause as blanket permission to include all children with disabilities in music classes (Atterbury, 1986a), and placement in music classes is often perceived as one means of meeting the intent of PL 94–142 (Goldsmith, 1984/1985). Thus, students with disabilities may be placed in music classes, especially in elementary school (Atterbury, 1986a; Gilbert & Asmus, 1981; Sins, 1983), out of expediency rather than because the music class is the best educational setting for mainstreaming. In addition to inappropriate placement (Goldsmith, 1984/1985), music educators often report limited participation in the placement process (Frisque et al., 1994; Gfeller et al., 1990) or exclusion from curricular and placement planning meetings regarding the special needs students mainstreamed into their music classes (Wilson & McCrary, 1996).

It is clear that music educators face unique problems concerning the placement of special needs children into music classes. The fact that general music educators may see as many as 700 to 1,000 regular students in class each week (Atterbury, 1986b) is quite an instructional challenge in and of itself. Now, as a result of PL 94–142, many music teachers are faced with the addition of significant numbers of special needs students who bring unique instructional demands to the music classroom.

Lack of Information About Individual Students

In addition to placement issues, there are other factors that may influence the attitudes of music educators working in mainstreamed settings. Music teachers may have less contact with children with disabilities and less opportunity to become aware of specific problems (Goldsmith, 1984/1985). Often they are not given any information regarding the specific disabilities of the children mainstreamed into their classes (Wilson & McCrary, 1996), and they experience a lack of educational and instructional support and resources, e.g., lack of preparation time, aides, and consultation (Gfeller et al., 1990).

Lack of Teacher Preparation and Training

Another problem that interferes with teacher attitude toward integrating children with disabilities into mainstreamed music settings is the lack of teacher preparation and training. This lack of preparation exists not only at the undergraduate, or preservice level, but also at the professional, or inservice level.

In terms of preservice preparation, music educators may not have much previous educational preparation for dealing with the challenges of mainstreaming. This lack of preparation may lead to feelings of uneasiness. Stuart and Gilbert (1977) found that preservice music education students were less comfortable and less willing than preservice music therapy students in working and interacting with persons with disabilities. With mainstreamed music classes a reality of the not too distant future, this 1977 study heralded the importance of concerns and attitudes of music educators. In light of these concerns, Stuart and Gilbert (1977) recommended more attention to inservice training.

However, little change has apparently occurred since the Stuart and Gilbert report was published. In a national survey, Gilbert and Asmus (1981) found that 63% of music educators were involved in mainstreaming, but few felt adequately prepared to work with students with disabilities. In another survey to investigate, among other things, music educators' opinions about working with students with mental and learning disabilities (Stein, 1983), music teachers reported that they lacked foundation, understanding, or skills to undertake appropriate planning or adaptations necessary for successful education in mainstreamed music settings. Indeed, of the music teachers surveyed by Stein, over 56% of the respondents had not taken any post-baccalaureate educational courses, and only 19% had taken a course on mainstreaming in college. Sixteen percent had participated in workshops, 3% had taken a workshop in special education, and 12% had taken some inservice training.

Similar findings were reported in four recent surveys. Gfeller et al. (1990) examined the perceived status of mainstreaming among music educators in two Midwestern states. Results of the survey indicate that teachers continue to receive little preparation in terms of coursework pertinent to working with mainstreamed students. In fact, only 25% of the survey respondents had taken even one college course related to teaching students with disabilities. Hock et al. (1990) surveyed a cross section, albeit small sample (N=27), of music teachers in Vermont. Consistent with other surveys, they found that although 92% of the respondents taught in mainstreamed music settings, only 37% reported any special training, which typically consisted of one or two inservice workshops.

Similar results were reported by Jellison (1992) and Frisque et al. (1994). Jellison conducted an investigation of the experiences, attitudes, and perceptions of 149 Texas music educators. She found that the majority of respondents reported little (only a few hours of workshops or inservice) or no formal education or inservice training. Frisque et al. (1994) obtained information from a random sample of elementary music teachers (N=107) in Arizona. Their data (p. 98) reveal that while 84% of the respondents were currently responsible for teaching in mainstreamed settings, more than 40% had no formal training and another 20% reported limited inservice and workshops. In addition, opportunity for inservice was rare, with 34% of the responding teachers receiving inservice training only upon request and 44% receiving none at all.

In addition to these four current surveys, two recent studies substantiate the lack of appropriate educational preparation in the area of special education, disabilities, and mainstreaming (Wilson & McCrary, 1993, 1996). Using Stuart and Gilbert's 1977 study as a benchmark, the Wilson and McCrary study (1993) found that nothing has changed in terms of preparing teachers for mainstreamed music settings. Their study revealed that, among other things, preservice music education students continue to report minimal college coursework in special education and experience with special needs students. Of the 31 music education and music therapy preservice students responding to this survey, 11 (35%) reported having no special education preparation, 10 (32%) had taken one special education course, 13 (42%) reported having only minimal experience with special needs children, and 8 (26%) reported extensive experience.

The other study by Wilson and McCrary (1996) reported a similar lack of training and preparation for special education or mainstreaming. The participants (*N*=18) were music educators enrolled in a graduate course focusing on music for the special learner. Thirteen (72%) of the participants reported having no previous special education training, 3 (17%) had taken either one workshop or college-level course, and 2 (11%) had taken more than one college-level special education course.

Music educators have indicated a more willing attitude to participate in mainstreaming if provided additional training and support (Damer, 1979/1980; Sideridis & Chandler, 1995; Stein, 1983). Damer found that teachers expressed more willingness to teach a wider spectrum of children with disabilities if they had additional support and inservice training. When she surveyed the same sample of teachers 5 years later she found that: (a) there was an increase in the number of special needs students in mainstreamed music settings, and (b) attitude toward mainstreaming had deteriorated significantly (White, cited in Atterbury, 1990). She believed that the primary reason for this decline in teacher attitude was related to a lack of continuing support and training.

In her descriptive survey to study the efficacy of curriculum in meeting the needs of special area teachers (music, art, and physical education), Stein (1983) found that teacher attitude was a key factor in willingness to teach in mainstreamed music settings. Sixty percent of the music teachers surveyed (*N*=62) stated that they would be willing to attend workshops, and over 60% said they would welcome opportunities to interact and talk with other music educators who faced similar challenges. Similar results were obtained by Sideridis and Chandler (1995), who surveyed 54 music teachers in Kansas and found that participants in this study were "willing to attend workshops that pertain to the teaching of children with disabilities in an effort to become more effective teachers" (p. 14).

Conclusions

Concerns regarding lack of preparation for music educators in the area of mainstreaming special needs students have been reiterated through the 1980s and into the 1990s, and the need for additional college and on-the-job inservice training has been identified (Frisque et al., 1994; Gfeller et al., 1990; Gilbert & Asmus, 1981; Stuart & Gilbert, 1977; Wilson & McCrary, 1993, 1996). Unfortunately, while many music educators continue their efforts to meet the challenges in the mainstreamed music classroom, there seems to be little opportunity to receive on-the-job training (Gfeller at al., 1990). In addition, Goldsmith (1984/1985) suggests that because music educators may teach in more than one school, they may not have opportunities to participate in available inservice. Needless to say, without continued support and opportunities for additional training, Goldsmith fears that the attitudes of these teachers will continue to suffer. He recommends that, because of the frequent placement of special needs children in art, music, and physical education classes, meeting the needs of these teachers through inservice training should be a priority. It seems reasonable to conclude that music educators require educational and inservice opportunities that provide knowledge and skills necessary for integrating the special student.

Inservice Content

The second component of quality inservice training is needs-based content. In fact, for inservice to be useful to music teachers, the content must address the needs and concerns of the teachers (Broadwell, 1986; Hayden, 1989/1990; Hutson, 1981; Powers, 1983). We cannot assume we know what music teachers need or want, because, as all adult learners, they bring to the learning environment many different experiences and levels of knowledge and skills. When planning inservice training and educational opportunities for teachers, the approach should not be a deficit-oriented one, but rather one in which the strengths and needs of the teachers are seen as guideposts for determining inservice content and format.

Inservices must provide teachers with specific information (Spanier, 1987) that, in turn, may help them acquire new teaching methods and strategies to "improve the conditions for learning and teaching" (Miller & Wolf, 1978, p. 141). In short, effective, well-planned inservice programs provide music educators with the knowledge and skills necessary to work effectively and positively within mainstreamed settings, thereby enabling these teachers to become a positive and effective force in the education of children with disabilities.

In addition to offering topics deemed important by the educators themselves, the literature on "best practices" (Hutson, 1981; Powers, 1983) recommends that inservice content incorporate an approach and format practical and useful to the participating teachers. In addition, content should be practical, be directly applicable, emphasize instructional activities, focus on specific difficulties in the classroom, and reflect teacher needs. In short, it should translate theory into practice and be reality-based.

This is especially true of music education inservice. In a survey of music educators, Gilbert and Asmus (1981) found that teachers desired practical information about methods and techniques and lacked information about or access to new and adaptive materials and pedagogical strategies. Similarly, the teachers surveyed by Sideridis and Chandler (1995) reported having inadequate instructional materials and funds.

In summary, it is important to determine the needs of music teachers prior to providing an inservice program. It should provide content that: (a) is based upon perceived needs of the participants; (b) brings to music educators current research and trends in methodology and pedagogy; (c) provides music teachers with pragmatic, applicable materials; and (d) is presented in a sensible and enjoyable manner, providing opportunities that encourage and enhance participation and group discussion.

Needs Assessment

The most important factor in determining inservice content and, indeed, the success of inservice training, is assessment of participant needs. In fact, in music education, several researchers have indicated that a needs assessment is essential to successful and effective inservice (Brown, 1985; Stuart & Gilbert, 1977). According to Hutson (1981) and Powers (1983), a needs assessment must focus on three specific areas: knowledge, skills, and attitudes. In terms of developing better attitudes and successful classroom experiences for both music teachers and their mainstreamed students, it is essential to employ a needs assessment that can be used for the following: (a) identification of teacher needs; (b) identification of inservice content and format that are perceived by music educators as necessary and relevant to their instructional settings; (c) measurement of pre-to-post inservice changes in attitude and knowledge as it relates to perceived need for inservice; (d) evaluation of changes in felt needs, attitude, and knowledge gain; and (e) determination, if desired, of the long-term effectiveness of the training.

Needs assessments help identify content relevant to music teachers. Music teachers, as all adult learners, have varying levels of knowledge, attitudes, competencies, concerns, experiences, and backgrounds, and as such, their training needs are both numerous and diverse. Listening to the needs of music educators can lead to the creation of specific inservice programs designed and modified to meet the needs of each group. Therefore, to be relevant, inservice content must focus upon topics considered important to the teachers themselves, providing insight into teacher perceptions regarding their abilities to adapt curriculum and use support services (Hesse, 1977/1978), as well as a relatively accurate view of current competency levels and needs for additional training (Nevin, 1979). A needs assessment instrument has been developed by Heine (1996) to assist inservice trainers with determination of music educators' needs for specific topics and skills perceived as necessary to enhance their teaching in mainstreamed music settings. This needs assessment is discussed later in this chapter.

Needs assessments can help evaluate inservice effectiveness. A needs assessment can be used to examine pre-to-post changes in felt needs, attitudes, skill levels, and knowledge base of teachers as a result of inservice training (Haire, 1976; Waggoner, 1976/1977). Parker (1990/1991) used a needs assessment as pre- and posttreatment evidence of improved attitude and knowledge of disabilities, instructional strategies, and behavioral management techniques. Parker used several pretest assessments of knowledge, skills, and attitudes, as well as topics and skill-areas identified in the general education literature to help to determine the instructional content of her inservice program. Inservice effectiveness was determined not only through participant evaluations, but also by statistical evaluation of pre-to-post knowledge gains and attitude changes. Parker (1990/1991) was able to demonstrate positive changes in attitude, as well as significant ($p<.05$) pre-to-post gains in knowledge.

Needs assessments may influence long-term inservice benefits. A study by Rappa, Genova, and Walberg (1983) suggests that using inservice content based on a needs assessment has important implications for the long-term effectiveness of inservice training. This 2½-year research study involved pre- and postworkshop questionnaires completed by 235 regular classroom teachers who participated in 36 inservice projects. They found that teachers who cited content and skill inadequacies as a need for inservice were usually those who reported predicted, continued, and future use of the knowledge and skills gained. They reported statistically significant correlations ($p<.001$) between predicted use and continued use (.44), as well as with the amount of new knowledge acquired from the inservice (.60), knowledge used either during or immediately after an inservice (.55), and with indications of future use (.53). They concluded that "continued use of knowledge appears to hinge on two factors: early success in using the knowledge as well as current need and relevancy" (p. 23).

Evaluation of Inservice Effectiveness

The third essential component of effective inservice is evaluation. Evaluation is the process of determining whether or not inservice is meaningful, meets the needs of the participants, and has been successful. It provides a measure of accountability and helps to judge the effectiveness of inservice (Pochowski, 1988). However, inservices often lack systematic evaluation of their effectiveness (Knowlton, 1980). Rather than knowledge and/or skills gained or attitudes changed, inservice evaluations typically use a variety of "ill-conceived questionnaires and feedback forms" that attempt to assess how participants feel about the inservice program—whether the coffee was hot, if the seats were comfortable, the personal appearance of presenter, or the convenience of the lunch hour (Brinkerhoff, 1980; Knowlton, 1980; Wieck, 1979).

Nevertheless, guidelines for an efficient, functional workshop evaluation are available (Knowlton, 1980; Skrtic, Knowlton, & Clark, 1979). First of all, effective evaluation must permeate all program components, including the planning phases (Knowlton, 1980). Second, evaluation must be needs-based (Brinkerhoff, 1980). That is, it must discover and clarify the needed knowledge of inservice participants that can then be used to help design and implement strategies that address those needs. If these evaluative aspects were added, evaluation could become formative, that is, it could help inservice providers improve future endeavors (Brinkerhoff, 1980). Finally, evaluation should address whether the needed knowledge and/or strategies have been acquired. The rationale and guidelines provided by Knowlton (1980) and Brinkerhoff (1980) can be used to develop and implement inservice delivery and can serve to guide the methodology to evaluate an inservice.

Evaluation of Inservice in Music Education

In the music education literature, several studies report outcomes of inservice based on evaluative measures. Lehr (1977/1978) reported inservice outcomes using a survey completed by participants in a one-term course, Music for Slow Learners. After surveying former course members, Lehr utilized primarily qualitative data to draw positive conclusions regarding: (a) competencies needed by those who teach students with disabilities, and (b) types of music experiences most beneficial and most enjoyed by special needs students. A study by Gilles (1978/1979) involved inservice training via a special education music methods course. She was able to demonstrate significant results regarding knowledge gain ($p<.001$) and frequency of music usage ($p<.05$) during the course. She also reported a significant, positive increase ($p<.002$) in attitude toward teaching music to special needs students. Donley (1985) focused on outcomes of a summer workshop on music methods for mainstreaming settings. Evaluating teacher attitude before and after the workshop, Donley was able to demonstrate significant positive changes ($p<.01$) in attitude. Providing a workshop to preservice participants, Smith (1987) found statistically significant evidence that this training can influence improvements in knowledge and skills considered important to music educators working with special needs children.

Wilson and McCrary (1996) studied the pre- and postresponses to a questionnaire given to students before and after completing a graduate course about music and special students. Unlike other studies, the results of this study indicated that even though there was an increase in participants' perception of their capability to work with individuals with disabilities, pre-to-post scores revealed a decline in subjects' comfort level and a significant decrease ($p<.05$) in their willingness to work professionally with these individuals.

Music in Mainstreaming Survey

Research indicates the successful integration of students with disabilities depends not only on teachers' knowledge of the needs and management of special needs students, but also on teachers' attitudes toward mainstreaming. In turn, teacher attitudes are affected by their background, education and experience, and kinds of support, including educational inservice. One way to help teachers meet the needs and demands of mainstreamed music settings is the provision of well-planned inservice training programs. A survey by Heine (1996) has been developed to evaluate inservice effectiveness. Specifically, it can be used to determine: (a) attitude and background of prospective inservice participants, (b) what topics and issues are of most importance to elementary music educators responsible for the musical instruction of children with disabilities in music classes, and (c) appropriate content for inservice training.

The "Music in Mainstreaming Survey" (MMS) includes three main sections: a Background Survey, an Attitude Survey, and a Needs Assessment. The Background Survey requests information about the respondent's age, gender, educational background, years of teaching experience (including those with children who have disabilities), and availability of administrative and educational support services. The second section of the MMS is an Attitude Survey, which is designed to be used both as a pre- and posttest to identify any changes in attitude attributable to inservice training. The third section of the MMS, the Needs Assessment, can be used to identify specific needs and inservice topics perceived as important to elementary music teachers working with mainstreamed students. This information can be used to: (a) ascertain what areas of knowledge and skills are considered important to music educators participating in inservice, and (b) develop the content of inservice programs.

All sections of the MMS were developed in a step-by-step procedure to ensure that the final instrument was inclusive, reliable, and valid. This procedure included the assistance of three panels of experts, chosen to represent a cross-section of educators knowledgeable about instruction of children with disabilities. They were asked to perform specific tasks.

Prior to determining relevant items for this survey, Heine reviewed a variety of assessment instruments. Several were chosen to provide guidelines for the format of the MMS and items which could be adapted for use in the MMS. These selected assessments and inventories were given to the first panel of experts and these experts were asked to make suggestions and recommendations regarding items and topics specific to background information, needs assessment, and attitudes considered as relevant to music educators teaching in mainstreamed settings. Specifically, they were asked to: (a) assess the appropriateness of items relative to the development of inservice content based on the needs and attitudes of prospective inservice participants, (b) assess the clarity of meaning and relevance of each item, (c) identify redundancies in items, and (d) add any other "needs assessment" items. Upon receipt of critiques from panel members, specific items were selected, recommended word changes were incorporated, and items were categorized.

A second panel of experts was then asked to evaluate all three sections of the MMS regarding the appropriateness of items and the clarity and wording of each item. While the first two panels adequately addressed the concerns related to the background and attitude surveys, a third panel of experts was asked to evaluate the revised version of the Needs Assessment of the MMS in order to help establish content validity. Panel members were asked to determine the appropriateness of item placement in each category of the Needs Assessment. In addition, they were consulted to help determine whether or not a balance between positively and negatively stated items had been achieved. To do this, Heine grouped similar items, changed wording so that all items were paired and balanced, and renumbered items so that no similar items were in close proximity to one another. As a result of this extensive three-panel review, the MMS is believed to be a valid instrument that will provide the information needed to address the needs of both inservice providers and inservice participants.

In order to establish reliability, 10 students enrolled in graduate level music education courses at a major Midwestern university were administered the final form of the Mainstreaming in Music Survey. All 10 students had experience in teaching elementary school general music. Two administrations of the survey took place 1 week apart. A Pearson Product Moment Correlation coefficient of .74 showed the MMS to be adequately reliable.

In conclusion, the MMS consists of three distinct sections, including a section on background information, a survey on attitudes, and a needs assessment. All three sections underwent a systematic review by two panels of experts to assist in the formulation of a concise and inclusive survey which included appropriately placed and well-written items within categories that focused on the specific purposes of the survey. In addition, a third panel was engaged to provide an additional level of assistance. This panel was asked to assess the content validity of the Needs Assessment section of the MMS. Upon completion of the recommended changes by three panels of experts, the completed three-section MMS was submitted to a pilot trial to assess its reliability.

The three sections of the MMS can be employed for a number of purposes. The Background Survey can be used as a pretreatment procedure to provide data about inservice participants' background, education, and experience in teaching students with disabilities. The Attitude Survey section of the MMS can be used as a pre- and posttreatment assessment tool to measure the attitudes of the teachers participating in inservice programs. The Needs Assessment data can be used to determine topics of concern as identified by prospective inservice participants, specifically music educators working in mainstreamed music settings. In addition, the survey can be used to determine the content of inservice workshops.

With the establishment of both content validity and reliability, the Music in Mainstreaming Survey, including the Needs Assessment, is believed to be an inclusive instrument that not only can assist inservice providers to determine content based upon the assessed needs of music teachers working with special needs children, but also is designed to help inservice providers collect important pre- and posttreatment data regarding the effectiveness of the inservice training The final form of the MMS appears in the Appendix.

Inservice Delivery Models

Selecting inservice content that is recognized as necessary and applicable is an essential first step toward effective inservice (Hutson, 1981; Leyser & Cole, 1987; Powers, 1983; Spanier, 1987), but how such information is delivered to music teachers may be as important as the information itself. Prior research indicates that the mode of delivery, as well as content, is critical to inservice effectiveness (Blietz & Courtnage, 1980; Edelfelt, 1981; Hutson, 1981; Jamison, 1983; Korinek, Schmid, & McAdams, 1985; Leyser & Cole, 1987; Pochowski, 1988; Powers, 1983; Silver & Moyle, 1984). Yet, it is probably safe to say that even the best inservice programs fail unless there is a realistic and effective mode of delivery. In other words, inservice programs must be reasonable in terms of scheduling, location, and financial demands, and may differ from area to area.

The choice of inservice model may also be important. This is especially so when considering inservice in music education. For example, music educators have had access for many years to textbooks that give information about music education for special learners. However, textbook information requires teachers individually to derive applicability from this type of information delivery. Research studies in general education have indicated that interaction, collaboration, and, by implication, opportunity for discussion among teachers appear to make inservice more effective. In fact, deficit-oriented prescriptive models, in which teachers are viewed as "passive pawns to be remediated" (Hunt, 1978, p. 239), are generally not viewed as effective. Therefore, it appears that providing information alone, such as written material, may be ineffective in preparing teachers to work with students with disabilities. This seems especially true for a content area such as music education that includes many active and experiential types of learning experiences.

Inservice models come in all shapes and sizes. Some of these include short- and long-term workshops, statewide inservices, extension courses, graduate courses, or year-long, school-based inservice training programs. These inservice models may also incorporate consultation, training booklets, field observations and practice, and may utilize didactic, audiovisual, and experiential components.

In music education, research studies about the delivery of inservice training in music and mainstreaming are limited. Moreover, only descriptive information and limited empirical data exist to substantiate the relative benefits of delivery for music education inservice. However, several modes of inservice delivery have been attempted in providing inservice training for music educators. These include a variety of workshops, statewide inservices, and college-based or extension courses.

Inservice Workshops

The most typical and widely used mode of inservice delivery in education is the workshop format (Griffin, 1982; Stein, 1983). There are several positive aspects of a traditional inservice workshop. First of all, teachers seem to prefer workshop models over other types of inservice programming. For example, Blietz and Courtnage (1980) surveyed teachers and administrators (N=278) in a Midwestern state to determine attitudes and perceptions regarding mainstreaming. They found, among other things, that the majority of the respondents preferred inservices that were for shorter periods of time, that is, 1-day and/or ½-day sessions. Similarly, Beard (1989/1990) surveyed a random sample of 1,250 teachers across the United States regarding their preferences for 12 inservice delivery models and eight methods used to deliver inservice content. Comparing ratings percentages she found that one of the most frequently and highly rated delivery models was the short-term inservice planned to meet individual needs.

In addition, workshops offer qualities of flexibility, cost efficiency, and group dynamics. An inservice workshop model provides flexibility in terms of length of time, site, format, and target populations (Leyser & Cole, 1987). The length of workshops can vary from a 1-hour after school lecture, a 2-day weekend workshop, or a workshop during the summer lasting for 1 or more weeks. In addition to varied lengths, workshop sites may also vary from on-site, school-based programs to inservices offered on college campuses or a program offered at a centrally-located facility within the school district. Workshops provide a format that offers experiential opportunities, as well as theoretically-based lectures. In addition, the focus of a workshop may be on one or more topics that are based on specific needs, concerns, and interests of the teachers (Carberry, Waxman, & McKain, 1981; Healy, 1983). Furthermore, workshops, when content-specific, can provide meaningful training that may help to increase knowledge and skills, improve attitude, and in turn, can be cost effective (Jacobson, 1984).

In addition to the ability to meet specific needs of the participants, the workshop format also may provide a group dynamic believed to be important. In a study comparing differences between group workshops and individual consultation with instructional materials, Bernard (1988/1989) found that group workshops were the only ones in which collaborative planning and patterns of collegiality were observed and enhanced.

Not all studies support the workshop format as most effective. For example, Bass (1981) surveyed 243 teachers from 21 schools with diverse geographical locales. She found that teachers preferred impromptu help from school resource personnel in addition to 1-day workshops. Zigarmi, Betz, and Jensen (1977) surveyed a random sample of 1,239 teachers in South Dakota. In response to one part of their questionnaire, teachers were asked to identify and rate usefulness of various inservice models and activities. They found that summer workshops at local schools and "current trends" workshops were the preferred modes of delivery. They also found that, while short-term workshops were the most widely used, they were considered the least useful to teachers when compared to other types of inservice, and workshops held on college campuses were considered moderately to very useful.

In summary, there is considerable, though not conclusive evidence, that inservice workshops enhance teacher attitude and knowledge. They promote the exchange of ideas and offer opportunities to learn from other teachers by providing a venue that enables teachers to talk freely and discuss concerns (Carberry et al., 1981; Zigarmi et al., 1977). These key factors suggest that well planned, on-site inservice workshops can be especially helpful in providing a participant-friendly atmosphere for music educators.

Inservice Workshops and Short Courses in Music Education

Three studies by Smith (1987), Smith (1989), and Donley (1985) describe the use of short-term inservice workshops or instructional units with preservice or inservice music teachers as participants. Smith (1987) offered a 5-day workshop focusing on knowledge and skill adaptation in the education of children with disabilities. Results of this project revealed significant gains ($p<.01$) in instructional skills and indicated that a short-term workshop can be an effective mode of inservice delivery. In another study utilizing a short-term workshop delivery model, Smith (1989) was able to examine teachers' perceptions and attitudes toward mainstreaming. Results from his analysis supported current research findings regarding teacher needs and demonstrated the ability of a short-term workshop model to better prepare music educators to teach students with disabilities. Similarly, Donley (1985) reported that a short-term summer workshop focusing on teachers' attitude toward mainstreaming resulted in significant positive changes in attitude ($p<.01$).

Two studies focused on statewide inservice projects for special education teachers (Kearns, 1986/1987; Sheridan, 1979/1980). Sheridan (1979/1980) provided a series of statewide workshops for music educators to introduce her curriculum guide for music in mainstreaming.

Her workshops also provided special packets for each inservice participant containing ideas for mainstreaming. While she reported that, after participating in the workshops, teachers expressed increased confidence about teaching children with disabilities, Sheridan offered no detailed analysis of program effectiveness.

In Kearn's 1986/1987 post hoc evaluation of a statewide integrated arts inservice project, 96% of the survey respondents (N=254) reported that the inservice program (workshop format) had been valuable to them and 89% reported positive effects on teaching practices. The only problem cited by some of the respondents was that the inservice had not been as beneficial to them because: (a) they were already familiar with the information and materials covered in the inservice content, or (b) the inservice did not meet their specific needs. Once again, these outcomes indicate that, to have truly effective inservice training, it is important to provide needs-based inservice programs.

Graduate and Extension Courses

As in the workshop inservice model, college graduate and extension courses for teachers can be successful in changing teachers' perceptions and increasing knowledge about disabilities and mainstreaming (Hudson, Reisberg, & Wolf, 1983). Similar and often significant results have been reported in research studies that compare college-sponsored, on-site delivery models to other types of delivery models for general classroom teachers (Berrigan, 1979/1980; Brown, 1985; Hudson et al., 1983; Wang, Vaughan, & Dytman, 1985). This mode of inservice delivery may include university-sponsored inservice programs offered at a centrally located school within the school district (Cavallaro, Stowitschek, George, & Stowitschek, 1980; Hall, Benninga, & Clark, 1983; Waggoner, 1976/1977), as well as summer and extension courses.

College-Sponsored Courses in Music Education

Three studies in the music education literature demonstrate successful use of college-sponsored courses to help music educators working with special needs children (Gilles, 1978/1979; Lehr, 1977/1978; Wilson & McCrary, 1996). The primary emphasis of Lehr's course was on the musical development of regular classroom teachers to help them utilize music with special needs students in their classes. Gilles (1978/1979) offered a college course on the topic of music in special education to inservice teachers. Using a pre-post questionnaire, Gilles was able to show significant changes in knowledge gain, music usage, and teacher attitude. Wilson and McCrary (1996) offered a graduate course, Music for Special Learners. To determine participants' attitudes toward children with and without disabilities before and after the course, participants were given a questionnaire with responses based upon their comfort level and willingness to work with individuals with disabilities. The participants in this study indicated an increase in their capabilities to work with special needs children, but a decrease in their willingness to work with special needs students. Wilson and McCrary (1996) conclude that the lack of positive change in attitude "may be reflective of participants having developed a more realistic understanding of both the rewards and the challenges in providing music education services for students with disabilities" (p. 30).

Inservice Using a Self-Guided Study Format

Direct instruction using workshop, graduate, or extension course formats are commonly reported models of inservice delivery. Another model for disseminating information relevant to teachers is through self-guided inservice packets, manuals, or books with topics reflecting general needs and concerns based upon current research, pedagogical practice, or needs assessments. Wade (1984/1985) suggests that independent study and self-instruction are viable alternatives to the traditional workshop format. Similarly, Griffin (1982) asserts that self-study programs can play an important role because teachers have hands-on materials presented in a manual that is reality-based, situation specific, and written in a clear, concise manner.

According to some researchers, a self-guided delivery model may be preferred by some teachers (Bass, 1981; Beard, 1989/1990). Bass (1981), for example, found that, unlike their urban counterparts, rural teachers were willing to consider college courses but may have less access to conferences and formal university courses. As such, these teachers might welcome well-organized self-study programs for which little or no travel is required. In a study mentioned previously, Beard (1989/1990) surveyed a random sample of 1,250 teachers to find out their preferences regarding inservice models and method of delivering inservice content. She found that the two most highly rated, that is, preferred methods of content delivery were (a) varied formats and take-home packets, and (b) independent study.

While Beard (1989/1990) did not offer reasons for these preferences, one can predict several advantages to this mode of inservice delivery. Certain texts, books, and self-guided inservice manuals are self-contained and usually well-organized and are often available for class use (Griffin, Hughes, & Martin, 1982). In addition, they can be distributed easily and inexpensively to a large number of teachers. This may be important not only in large metropolitan areas, but also in sparsely populated, rural areas where access to a more formal or on-site inservice training workshop or extension course is not readily available. In addition, contrary to the workshop model, self-guided books and manuals provide flexibility and ease time constraints. They can address specific topics and can be practically-oriented, theoretically-based, or based on needs assessment. However, it is important to determine whether or not a self-study program, though it may be inexpensive and convenient, is actually an effective inservice mode, especially for a specialty area such as music education.

Music Education Inservice Through Self-Directed Study

To date, no studies in music education parallel those found in general education regarding self-directed inservice formats. A number of "how-to" books recommend techniques and instructional materials for use with special needs children (e.g., *Music for the Special Learner* by Sona Nocera [1979], *Music for Special Education* by Kay Hardesty [1979], *Music in Developmental Therapy* by Jennie Purvis and Shelly Samet [1976], or MENC's *In Tune with PL 94–142* [1980]). While these resources were popular among music educators and music therapists, most are out of print. Although many elementary music basal series now include some mention of music with special needs students, the success of incorporating ideas and suggestions for instructional adaptations included in these sources has yet to be investigated. In fact, no data or content analysis seems to exist regarding how effective any of these books, instructional materials or basal series are in preparing music educators to work with students who have disabilities.

Combination of Delivery Models

The literature in general education reports that a combination of delivery models, including both workshops and well-designed, self-guided inservice manuals, may contribute to successful inservice outcomes (Beard, 1989/1990; Bernard, 1988/1989; Fenton, 1974; Griffin, 1982; Stainback, Stainback, Strathe, & Dedrick, 1983). For example, Emmer, Sanford, Evertson, Clements, and Martin (1981) found that teachers who had access to a 3-hour workshop, plus a well-designed instructional manual, were more effective ($p<.05$) in demonstrating desired changes in classroom management behaviors than control group teachers who did not participate in the formal training program. While it was not clear whether the successful outcomes were a result of the short-term workshop alone or the combination of workshop and instructional manual, Griffin (1982) asserts that the manual played an important role in this experiment because it was well-written, was varied in format, and addressed teacher needs and concerns. On the other hand, the researchers (Emmer et al., 1981) suggest that perhaps the workshop was also important because it helped focus teachers' attention on content of the manual, and may have enhanced treatment participants' sense of accountability for following the manual.

There are very few studies that contrast the use of workshops and instructional books or manuals in terms of overall inservice outcome effectiveness; however, Fenton (1974) found that a variety of delivery systems, including the use of self-guided manuals, may be effective. Using the Rutgers-Gable Scale as a pre-post measure, he compared the effectiveness of four inservice programs on changing attitudes toward children with disabilities and knowledge of special education placement procedures. Each of four school districts took part in four different, state-funded inservice projects. The four models included: (a) a series of eight short-term workshops with a practicum after each workshop, consultation, and access to a demonstration center; (b) eight workshops plus a series of videos and access to a professional library; (c) 30 hours of instruction with self-guided training packets, observation of master teachers, access to 30 hours of support personnel services, and optional college course offerings; and (d) 30 hours of instruction including workshop, class visits, and a materials fair. Teachers in each of the four school districts volunteered to participate in the project. Fenton (1974) found that, in all but the third model (30 hours of instruction with training packet), posttreatment scores for teacher attitudes were significantly lower ($p<.05$). Although the participants in the third project showed no changes in attitude after inservice training, they were the only group to show any significant pre-to-post increase ($p<.05$) in knowledge gain. Interestingly enough, this is the only model of the four used in his study that combined the use of group interaction (workshop) with training packets.

A research project that is especially important to the discussion of modes of inservice delivery is a study by Kelly and Vanvactor (1983). Conducted with general classroom teachers, it is one of few that compared the effectiveness and cost efficiency of several modes of inservice delivery provided to regular classroom teachers in a sparsely populated state. The purpose of this study was to compare four inservice delivery models on the following dependent variables: knowledge gain, cost effectiveness, long-term knowledge retention, and the teacher's classroom effectiveness. The four types of models used in this study included: (a) on-site, school-based workshops provided by a master teacher who presented 40 hours of on-site instruction. Similar content, follow-up activities, and evaluations were provided to all workshop participants, with posttest on knowledge acquisition occurring at conclusion of the inservice week; (b) on-site, school-based workshop provided by university personnel who presented 40 hours of on-site instruction with similar content, follow-up and evaluation; (c) on-campus workshop offered by university personnel on the college campus with similar content, follow-up and evaluation; and (d) a self-guided, instructional packet, which was given to participants who received no formal instruction or assistance. The instructional packet, based on a needs assessment, included information about definitions and characteristics of various disabilities, mainstreaming materials, teaching strategies, and behavior management techniques. Assessment of knowledge gain and attitude change was conducted before and after the subjects' independent study of the instructional packet.

Results of the Kelly and Vanvactor study (1983) indicated that, compared to leader-directed workshop formats for inservice delivery, the least expensive delivery type was the instructional manual. However, while instructional manuals were less costly, they were not, in terms of long-term knowledge gain and overall effectiveness, the most cost effective. According to Kelly and Vanvactor, the most cost-effective model, in terms of learner outcomes, was the university personnel on-site model, followed by the master teacher on-site model, and then the university personnel on-campus model. The least cost-effective model was the instructional packet-alone format. In other words, the instructional packets were less costly, but, in terms of cost effectiveness (knowledge gain and learner outcomes), both on-site delivery models were the more cost effective.

Combined Inservice Models in Music Education

A new training program for music educators working with special needs children has recently been published by Silver Burdett Ginn. "Music for All Children" (Dark, Graham, Hughes, McCoy, & McKinney, 1996) offers an inservice training package including a facilitator manual, a participant handbook, and a video (either video cassette or videodisk). The training packet includes suggested materials, content, and activities for several sessions focusing on four topic-units. The topics include sessions on: (a) common educational goals designed to build positive attitudes and introduce the terminology and intent of mainstreaming; (b) music making with children with disabilities based on a broad overview of five major areas of educational concern; (c) planning for success with a focus on promotion of positive relationships among parents, administrators, special educators and music teachers; and (d) teaching in the mainstreamed music class with emphasis on cooperative learning, lesson planning, modeling, task analysis, and communication. A review of the materials revealed no descriptions of field testing or other evaluative efforts. Although the authors urge inservice facilitators to gather background information on participants, no needs assessment or evaluation instruments are provided.

Summary

In summary, if the transmission of information is the only goal for inservice, self-directed instructional packets or manuals may be sufficient (Korinek et al., 1985). However, when a self-guided instructional manual is the sole delivery format, group interaction is diminished, and it is precisely this group dynamic that, according to some, is essential for improvement of skill acquisition and behavioral change (Bernard, 1988/1989; Korinek et al., 1985). While Zigarmi et al. (1977) found that, in general, teachers do not like self-study formats, provision of such self-contained instructional materials may be a viable alternative for teachers in locations where distance and cost may interfere with the availability of on-site training.

Past research in general education indicates that the traditional workshop format is effective for helping teachers to improve attitudes and knowledge about mainstreaming. The workshop has the advantage of being flexible (it can be geared to specific content) and facilitating group interaction and participant involvement. In addition, on-site delivery makes it relatively convenient to teachers.

The workshop is not the only viable inservice format, however. Other research has noted the benefits of summer graduate and extension courses, statewide inservice training programs, self-guided, individualized study, and combinations of different inservice formats. The majority of evidence to date, however, is related to general education. Little data are available regarding the relative merits of inservice delivery in music education. Those extant studies reflect workshops that are as short as a few hours to as long as a multiweek extension or college course. The studies that include some evaluation suggest that such inservice models are effective in improving knowledge and attitude.

Music Educators Have Special Inservice Needs

It is possible that, for several reasons, music educators may differ in terms of their inservice needs and preferences for specific inservice delivery formats. Perhaps these differences have to do with the nature of the music education curriculum itself. Music education tends to include a substantial amount of experiential group activity such as playing instruments, singing, and movement. Can we then assume that the opportunity for group participation and discussion is essential to inservice in music education? In her study about music educators and their concerns and inservice needs regarding mainstreamed music settings, Stein (1983) found, among other things, that music teachers preferred workshops in which they could discuss problems and situations with other music educators. However, some music educators may work in small, remote school districts where regular inservice programming is unavailable. Is the self-guided information packet a viable alternative for improving knowledge and attitudes toward mainstreaming? Perhaps a combination of inservice formats would be beneficial. Would an inservice utilizing a workshop format that included a well-organized manual or packet of information (such as Silver Burdett Ginn's recently published training package, "Music For All Children") better meet the needs of music educators? Since no extant studies address these concerns, we can only speculate.

What is clear, however, is that whatever mode of delivery is used, we must examine and devise ways in which to provide meaningful and effective inservice training for music educators. We also know that research indicates that successful and meaningful inservice training must offer teachers information on current trends or ideas presented in a new way and designed in response to teacher needs (Zigarmi et al., 1977).

Best Practices for Inservice in Music Education

Positive teacher attitude is the key to the successful integration of special learners and is influenced by training. Teacher attitude is also an important key to successful inservice. The goal of inservice training is to help music teachers gain knowledge, skills, and positive attitudes about their jobs. In order to feel prepared and positive about mainstreamed music settings, teachers need adequate training and preparation. Inservice is a practical and positive way to achieve this goal. The following ideas will help inservice providers as they prepare inservices to meet the needs of their colleagues facing the challenges of music in the mainstream.

1. Inservice requires good planning, demanding attention to best practices in inservice training.
2. Inservice should be teacher-oriented, focusing on the development of additional skills rather than attempting to ameliorate teacher-deficits. It is important to recognize teachers as adult learners who bring to the inservice a host of ideas, experiences, needs, and strengths.
3. Inservice should focus on the development of knowledge, skills, and attitudes.
4. Inservice providers must be enthusiastic, interesting, well-prepared, interested in meeting the needs of the participants, and willing to utilize a variety of inservice delivery models and formats.
5. Inservices must be needs-based. A well-planned inservice program will incorporate at a needs assessment because: (a) it provides specific background information about inservice participants, (b) it provides information regarding the needs of inservice participants, and (c) it helps the inservice provider select meaningful content and a variety of formats to meet the needs of inservice participants. Needs assessments should provide a broad survey of possible information to identify specific needs of each inservice audience. A needs assessment may include questions about special needs children in mainstreamed music classroom settings, the components of PL 94–142, Individual Education Plan (IEP), Least Restrictive Environment (LRE), full inclusion, instructional needs and skills, classroom management, methods and materials, teaching strategies, resources, and teacher attitude. Not every inservice audience will need information on all these topics. Providing information that participants do not need is contrary to best practices in inservice. Teacher-participants prefer inservices that provide them with useful information.
6. Inservice delivery and content must be practical and directly applicable. It should translate theory into practice, focus on specific needs or differences in classroom as identified by inservice participants, and emphasize instructional activities.
7. Inservice content should be interesting and varied in format. Varying content delivery may add to learner interest and comprehension. Inservice providers may want to employ both didactic and experiential approaches and incorporate some of the following: lectures, demonstrations, simulations, group discussions, feedback sessions, and audio/visual components.
8. Inservices should incorporate an evaluation component. Evaluation is based on a needs assessment, is content-based, and must not only critique the inservice presentation, but also measure pre-to-post changes in participant behaviors such as: (a) positive (realistic) changes in teacher attitude; (b) increase in knowledge base; (c) increase in motivation to try newly learned skills and ideas (long-term, postcheck); and (d) improvement in skill level (long-term, postcheck).
9. Other factors that may influence the perceived success and usefulness of inservice programs are: (a) scheduling—where, when, and what time of day is the inservice

program being offered; (b) financial demands—cost of inservice; (c) incentives—free materials, CEUs and college credits, certificates, and (d) location—participants tend to prefer inservices that are on-site, centrally located, or as near to the work place as possible.

Chapter Conclusions

1. The music teacher is the key to success in the mainstreamed music setting.
2. Music educators need adequate educational preparation to meet the challenges and opportunities of mainstreaming.
3. Many music educators are willing to teach in mainstreamed settings despite lack of input into placement decisions, lack of information about special needs students, and lack of preparation and training.
4. Most research indicates that in the past 20 years, little has changed in terms of preparing teachers for mainstreamed music settings.
5. The need for inservice training has been identified as crucial to success of music in the mainstream.
6. For inservice to be successful, it must focus on content and formats designed to address the needs, concerns, strengths, and attitudes of the music teacher.
7. A needs assessment will provide inservice providers with ideas for content.
8. Inservice content that is practical and applicable to the music classroom will more readily engage the interests of the teacher-participants.
9. Music teachers are adult learners, and as such, they bring a wealth of ideas and insights to the inservice experience.
10. Inservices should include evaluation of training outcomes such as change in attitude, knowledge gain, skill development, and long-term effectiveness.
11. Inservice delivery models come in all shapes and sizes, including short- and long-term workshops; summer and extension courses; school-based, on-site programs; statewide inservices; and self-guided instruction.
12. Inservice in music education should include opportunities for group participation and discussion, experiential activities, and practical classroom strategies.
13. It is essential to provide well-organized, needs-based inservices to promote positive and successful music experiences for everyone (teacher and students alike) involved in the mainstreamed music setting.

Inclusion of special needs students in music education classes is a reality. However, in an article on mainstreaming, Graham (1988) warns that "music educators see themselves as unprepared to teach disabled students and are often reluctant to make curricular and program modifications for mainstreamed students" (p. 33). This statement is supported by research (Frisque et al., 1994; Gfeller & Hedden, 1987; Gfeller et al., 1990; Gilbert & Asmus, 1981; Stein, 1983) that suggests many music educators feel inadequately trained and unprepared to work with special needs children in their classes. This concern is probably related to limited preparation for instructing students with disabilities. In fact, several surveys suggest that if administrative support and opportunities for training are provided to music teachers, their attitudes toward mainstreaming improve (Gfeller & Hedden, 1987; Gfeller et al., 1990; Gilbert & Asmus, 1981).

While most teachers acknowledge a lack of preparation and opportunities for inservice training, there is some evidence to suggest that music teachers have positive attitudes toward mainstreaming (Jellison, 1992). In addition, some teachers have indicated a willingness to attend workshops that focus on teaching special needs students (Sideridis & Chandler, 1995). Nevertheless, it is clear that music teachers need and want training to meet the challenges and opportunities of the mainstreamed music class. Inservice education is an important key to the success of mainstreamed music education. Inservice programs provide opportunities for teachers to acquire additional knowledge, skills, and training essential to the successful integration of special needs students into the mainstreamed music class. Inservice experiences can uplift teacher attitude and provide the professional help needed to improve teachers' feelings of confidence as they plan musical experiences for the special needs children in their music classes.

For those who are called upon to provide inservice training to music educators so that they may work more effectively with students who have disabilities, the following components are deemed necessary for inservice to be effective: (a) the content should be based on the needs identified by the music teachers themselves, (b) the most effective mode of delivery for music education content should be utilized, and (c) the inservice training should include a systematic evaluation of inservice outcomes. Unless this occurs, we will, as in the past, be obliged to theorize on inservice effectiveness. Unless we provide well-planned, needs-based inservices to music educators, we will, as many current studies have concluded, continue to promote a cycle of inadequate teacher preparation and professional development that does nothing to serve the needs of the music educator nor change the status of music with special needs children within the general music classroom.

References

Atterbury, B. (1986a). A survey of present mainstreaming practices in the southern United States. *Journal of Music Therapy, 23*, 202–207.

Atterbury, B. W. (1986b). Success in the mainstream of general music. *Music Educators Journal, 72*(7), 34–36.

Atterbury, B. W. (1990). *Mainstreaming exceptional learners in music.* Englewood Cliffs, NJ: Prentice-Hall.

Bass, M. B. (1981). *Special education inservice priorities for regular educators* (Report No. EC 152 607). (ERIC Document Reproduction Service No. ED 231 162)

Beard, N. V. (1989/1990). Education reform time: Teacher preferences for inservice content types and methods. (Doctoral dissertation, University of South Carolina, 1989). *Dissertation Abstracts International, 51*(02), 351A.

Bernard, T. A. (1988/1989). Special education staff development and curriculum innovation. (Doctoral dissertation, Columbia University Teachers College, 1988). *Dissertation Abstracts International, 50*(01), 117A.

Berrigan, C. R. (1979/1980). Effects of an inservice education workshop on the attitudes of regular classroom teachers toward disabled students. (Doctoral dissertation, Syracuse University, 1979). *Dissertation Abstracts International, 40*(09), 5009A.

Blietz, J., & Courtnage, L. (1980). Inservice training for regular educators. *Teacher Education and Special Education, 3*(4), 10–18.

Brinkerhoff, R. O. (1980). Evaluation of inservice programs. *Teacher Education and Special Education, 3*(3), 27–38.

Broadwell, M. M. (1986). Five ways to keep supervisory training alive and well. *Training, 23*(9), 45–47.

Brown, K. R. (1985). Regular education teachers' attitudes and knowledge concerning the mainstreaming of handicapped students. (Doctoral dissertation, Texas Southern University, 1985). *Dissertation Abstracts International, 47*(03), 871A.

Carberry, H., Waxman, B., & McKain, D. (1981). An inservice workshop model for regular class teachers concerning mainstreaming of the learning disabled child. *Journal of Learning Disabilities, 14*(1), 26–28.

Cavallaro, C. C., Stowitschek, C. E., George, M., & Stowitschek, J. J. (1980). Intensive inservice education and concomitant changes in handicapped learners. *Teacher Education and Special Education, 3*(3), 49–58.

Damer, L. K. (1979/1980). A student of the attitudes of selected public school teachers toward the integration of handicapped students into music classes. (Doctoral dissertation, University of North Carolina, 1979). *Dissertation Abstracts International, 40*(07), 3862A.

Dark, I. D., Graham, R. M., Hughes, J., McCoy, M., & McKinney, D. D. (1996). *Music for all children.* Parsippany, NJ: Silver Burdett Ginn.

Darrow, A. A. (1990a). Beyond mainstreaming: Dealing with diversity. *Music Educators Journal, 76*(8), 36–39.

Darrow, A. A. (1990b). Research on mainstreaming in music education. *Update, 9*(1), 35–37.

Dillon-Peterson, B. (1981). Staff development—Overview. In B. Dillon-Peterson (Ed.), *Staff development/Organization development* (pp. 1–10). Alexandria, VA: Association for Supervision and Curriculum Development.

Donley, C. R. (1985). The effects of an inservice workshop for music teachers on teachers' attitudes toward teaching music to handicapped children. In R. R. Pratt (Ed.), *The third international symposium on music in medicine, education, and therapy for the handicapped* (pp. 101–111). New York: University Press of America.

Edelfelt, R. A. (1981). Six years of progress in inservice education. *Journal of Research and Development in Education, 14*(2), 112–119.

Elliott, C., & Sins, N. (1981/1982). Attitudes and opinions of middle school music students toward the presence of handicapped peers in music classes. *Contributions to Music Education, 9*(5), 48–59.

Emmer, E. T., Sanford, J. P., Evertson, C. M., Clements, B. S., & Martin, J. (1981). *Classroom management improvement student: An experiment in elementary school classrooms.* Research Report No. 6050. Austin, TX: Research and Development Center for Teacher Education, University of Texas at Austin.

Fenton, T. R. (1974). The effects of inservice training on elementary classroom teachers' attitudes toward and knowledge about handicapped children. (Doctoral dissertation, University of Northern Colorado, 1974). *Dissertation Abstracts International, 34*(09), 5966A.

Fresko, B., & Ben-Chaim, D. (1986). Assessing teacher needs and satisfaction of needs in inservice activities. *Studies in Educational Evaluation, 12*, 205–212.

Frisque, J., Niebur, L., & Humphreys, J. T. (1994). Music mainstreaming: Practices in Arizona. *Journal of Research in Music Education, 42*, 94–104.

Gavin, A. R. J. (1983/1984). Music educator practices and attitudes toward mainstreaming. (Doctoral dissertation, Washington University, 1983). *Dissertation Abstracts International, 45*(02), 446A.

Gfeller, K., Darrow, A. A., & Hedden, S. K. (1990). Perceived effectiveness of mainstreaming in Iowa and Kansas schools. *Journal of Research in Music Education, 58*, 90–101.

Gfeller, K., & Hedden, S. K. (1987). Mainstreaming in music education: The state of the state. *Iowa Music Educator, 40*(3), 24–27.

Gilbert, J. P., & Asmus, E. P. (1981). Mainstreaming: Music educators' participation and professional needs. *Journal of Research in Music Education, 29*, 31–37.

Gilles, D. K. C. (1978/1979). The development and evaluation of a special education music methods course for preservice and inservice teachers. (Doctoral dissertation, St. Louis University, 1978). *Dissertation Abstracts International, 40*(05), 2602A.

Goldsmith, G. K. (1984/1985). The effects of a university inservice program on the knowledge and attitudes of elementary school principals and teachers on the mainstreaming of handicapped children. (Doctoral dissertation, George Washington University, 1984). *Dissertation Abstracts International, 45*(11), 3327A.

Graham, R. M. (1988). Barrier-free music education: Methods to make mainstreaming work. *Music Educators' Journal, 74*(5), 29–33.

Griffin, G. A. (1982). *Staff development.* Washington, DC: National Institute of Education. (ERIC Document Reproduction Service No. ED 221 537)

Griffin, G. A., Hughes, R., & Martin, J. (1982). *Knowledge, training and classroom management.* (Report No. 6054). Austin, TX: Research and Development Center for Teacher Education, University of Texas at Austin. (ERIC Document Reproduction Service No. ED 251 445)

Haire, C. D. (1976). Effects of an inservice education model for supportive personnel on factors regarding exceptional children. (Doctoral dissertation, Texas Tech University, 1976). *Dissertation Abstracts International, 37*(05), 2796A.

Hall, J., Benninga, J., & Clark, C. (1983). A three-part model: A comprehensive approach to the inservice training of teachers. *NASSP Bulletin, 67*(61), 17–21.

Hardesty, K. W. (1979). *Music for special education.* Morristown, NJ: Silver Burdett.

Hawkins, G. D. (1991/1992). Attitudes toward mainstreaming students with disabilities among regular elementary music and physical educators. (Doctoral dissertation, University of Maryland, 1991). *Dissertation Abstracts International, 52*(09), 3245A.

Hayden, H. A. (1989/1990). A study of Maryland public school principals' perception of their special education inservice training needs. (Doctoral dissertation, University of Maryland, 1989). *Dissertation Abstracts International, 51* (03), 727A.

Healy, S. (1983). Planning inservice programs. *The Pointer, 28*(1),12–15.

Heine, C. C. (1996). *The music in mainstreaming survey.* Unpublished manuscript, Wartburg College, Waverly, IA.

Hesse, R. M. (1977/1978). A procedure for determining needs for inservice training of classroom teachers in a mainstreaming approach to the education of the mildly handicapped. (Doctoral dissertation, University of Oregon, 1977). *Dissertation Abstracts International, 38*(10), 6055A.

Hock, M., Hasazi, S. B., & Patten, A. (1990). Collaboration for learning: Strategies for program success. *Music Educators Journal, 76*(8), 44–48.

Hudson, F., Reisberg, L. E., & Wolf, R. (1983). Changing teachers' perceptions of mainstreaming. *Teacher Education and Special Education, 6,* 18–24.

Hunt, D. E. (1978). Inservice training as persons-in relation. *Theory into practice, 17*(3), 239–244.

Hutson, H. M. (1981). Inservice best practices: The learnings of general education. *Journal of Research and Development in Education, 14*(2), 1–10.

Jacobson, W. H. (1984). Teacher attitude toward mainstreamed blind children: The short term and long term effects of inservice training. (Doctoral dissertation, University of Arkansas, 1984). *Dissertation Abstracts International, 45*(08), 2483A.

Jamison, P. J. (1983). Systematic development and evaluation of quality practices for inservice education. *Teacher Education and Special Education, 6*(2), 151–158.

Jellison, J. A. (1992). *Music and students with disabilities: A preliminary study of Texas music educators' experiences, attitudes, and perceptions.* Austin, TX: Texas Music Education Association. Paper presented at the annual meeting of the Texas Music Education Association, San Antonio, TX.

Joyce, B., & Showers, B. (1980). Improving inservice training: The messages of research. *Educational Leadership, 37*(5), 379–385.

Kearns, L. H. (1986/1987). Outcomes of inservice programs on the arts in special education: The arts in special education project of Pennsylvania. (Doctoral dissertation, Pennsylvania State University, 1986). *Dissertation Abstracts International, 47*(11), 3950A.

Kelly, E. J., & Vanvactor, J. C. (1983). The relative cost effectiveness of inservice approaches in remote, sparsely populated schools. *Exceptional Children, 50*(2), 140–148.

Knowlton, H. E. (1980). A framework for evaluating inservice workshops. *Teacher Education and Special Education, 3*(3), 58–70.

Korinek, L., Schmid, R., & McAdams, M. (1985). Inservice types and best practices. *Journal of Research and Development in Education, 18*(2), 33–38.

Lehr, J. K. (1977/78). An investigation of music in the education of mentally and physically handicapped children in the United Kingdom, with particular reference to the course, Music for Slow Learners, at Dartington College of Arts. (Doctoral dissertation, Ohio State University, Columbus, Ohio, 1977). *Dissertation Abstracts International, 38*(11), 6594A.

Leyser, Y., & Cole, K. B. (1987). The reconceptualization and delivery of quality inservice education under Public Law 94–142. In J. Gottlieb & B. W. Gottlieb (Eds.), *Advances in special education* (Vol. 6, pp. 87–117). Greenwich, CT: JAI Press.

Miller, L., & Wolf, T. E. (1978). Staff development for school change: Theory and practice. *Teachers College Record, 80*(1), 140–156.

Music Educators National Conference. (1980). *In tune with PL 94–142: Guide for training teachers responsible for music education of handicapped learners.* Reston, VA: MENC.

Nevin, A. (1979). Special education administration competencies required of the general education administrator. *Exceptional Children, 45*(5), 363–365.

Nocera, S. D. (1979). *Reaching the special learner through music.* Morristown, NJ: Silver Burdett.

Nocera, S. D. (1981). A descriptive analysis of the attainment of selected musical learnings by normal children and by educable mentally retarded children mainstreamed in music classes at the second and fifth grade levels. (Doctoral dissertation, University of Wisconsin-Madison, 1981). *Dissertation Abstracts International, 42*(10), 4347A.

Parker, D. O. (1990/1991). Preparing vocational teachers to effectively serve special needs students: An inservice education model. (Doctoral dissertation, University North Carolina, 1990). *Dissertation Abstracts International, 51*(09), 3002A.

Pochowski, A. E. (1988). Compliance with educational legislation for handicapped children in relationship to the status of staff development in special education. (Doctoral dissertation, University of Wisconsin, 1988). *Dissertation Abstracts International, 49*(05), 1117A.

Powers, D. A. (1983). Mainstreaming and the inservice education of teachers. *Exceptional Children, 49*(5), 432–439.

Pratt, R. R. (1986). Music education of the handicapped: Some insights gained during the last decade. *MEH Bulletin, 1*(3), 24–34.

Purvis, S., & Samet, J. (1976). *Music in developmental therapy.* Baltimore: University Park.

Rappa, J. B., Genova, W. J., & Walberg, H. J. (1983). *Staff, school and workshop characteristics affecting continued use and adaptation of knowledge: A follow-up stud.* (Report No. SP 024 323). Boston: Massachusetts State Department of Education. (ERIC Document Reproduction Service No. ED 243 872)

Schultz, J. B., & Turnbull, A. P. (1984). *Mainstreaming handicapped students: A guide for classroom teachers* (2nd ed.). Boston: Allyn & Bacon.

Sheridan, W. F. (1979/1980). Public Law 94–142 and the development of the Oregon plan of mainstreaming in music. (Doctoral dissertation, University of Oregon, 1979). *Dissertation Abstracts International, 40*(09), 4878A.

Sideridis, G. D., & Chandler, J. P. (1995). Attitude and characteristics of general music teachers toward integrating children with developmental disabilities. *Update, 14*(1), 11–15

Silver, P. F., & Moyle, C. R. J. (1984). The impact of intensive inservice programs on educational leaders and their organization. *Planning and Changing, 13*(1), 18–33.

Sins, N. J. (1983). Mainstreaming the music class automatically brings about acceptance by the nonhandicapped. Right? (Wrong). *Update, 2*(1), 3–6.

Skrtic, T. M., Knowlton, H. E., & Clark, F. L. (1979). Action vs. reaction: A curriculum development approach to inservice education. *Focus on Exceptional Children, 2*(1), 1–16.

Smith, D. S. (1987). The effect of instruction on ability to adapt teaching situations for exceptional students. *MEH Bulletin, 2*(4), 3–18.

Smith, D. S. (1989). A content analysis of music educators' attitudes toward mainstreaming in middle school music classes. *Journal of the International Association for Music and the Handicapped, 4*(3), 3–20.

Spanier, L. D. (1987). Intensive in-school/inservice training of secondary special educators: An efficacy study. (Doctoral dissertation, George Washington University, 1987). *Dissertation Abstracts International, 48*(02), 264A.

Stainback, S., Stainback, W., Strathe, M., & Dedrick, C. (1983). Preparing regular classroom teachers for the integration of severely handicapped students: An experimental study. *Education and Training of the Mentally Retarded, 18,* 205–209.

Stein, A. R. (1983). The efficacy of the curriculum of special area teachers for servicing the needs of handicapped students and its implications for curriculum planning. (Doctoral dissertation, State University of New York-Buffalo, 1983). *Dissertation Abstracts International, 44*(09), 2672A.

Stuart, M., & Gilbert, J. P. (1977). Mainstreaming: Needs assessment through a videotape visual scale. *Journal of Research in Music Education, 25,* 283–289.

Thompson, K. P. (1986). The general music class as experienced by mainstreamed handicapped students. *MEH Bulletin, 1*(1), 16–23.

Thompson, K. P. (1990). Working toward solutions in mainstreaming. *Music Educators Journal, 76*(8), 30–35.

Tymitz-Wolf, B. L. (1982). Extending the scope of inservice training for mainstreaming effectiveness. *Teacher Education and Special Education, 5*(2), 17–23.

Wade, R. K. (1984/1985). What makes a difference in inservice teacher education? A meta-analysis of research. *Educational Leadership, 42*(4), 48–54.

Waggoner, L. G. (1976/1977). Effects of an inservice training model for mainstream teachers on factors regarding exceptional children. (Doctoral dissertation, Texas Tech University, 1976). *Dissertation Abstracts International, 38*(02), 714A.

Wang, M. C., Vaughan, E. D., & Dytman, J. A. (1985). Staff development: A key ingredient of effective mainstreaming. *Teaching Exceptional Children, 17*(2), 112–121.

White, L. D. (1981/1982). Study of the attitudes of selected public school music educators toward the integration of handicapped students into music class. *Contributions to Music Education, 9,* 36–47.

Wieck, C. (1979). Training and development of staff: Lessons from business and industry. *Education Unlimited, 1*(3), 6–13.

Williams, D. W. (1988). Regular classroom teachers' perceptions of their preparedness to work with mainstreamed students as a result of preservice coursework. (Doctoral dissertation, Indiana University, 1988). *Dissertation Abstracts International, 49*(09), 2622A.

Wilson, B., & McCrary, J. (1993). *A comparison of music education and music therapy students' attitude toward learners with disabilities.* Unpublished manuscript, Western Michigan University, Kalamazoo.

Wilson, B., & McCrary, J. (1996). The effect of training on inservice music educators' attitudes towards students with disabilities. *Journal of Research in Music Education, 44,* 26–33.

Zigarmi, P., Betz, L., & Jensen, D. (1977). Teachers preferences in and perceptions of inservice education. *Educational Leadership, 34*(7), 545, 547–551.

Appendix

MUSIC IN MAINSTREAMING SURVEY

<u>Please fill out the following background information</u>:   ___Female   ___ Male

Please check age category: ___20-29 ___30-39 ___40-49 ___50-59 ___60 and above

Number of years you have taught elementary music   ____
Number of years you have taught children with disabilities in music   ____
Total number of students seen in music each week   ____

Number of children with disabilities seen each week in **self-contained** music classes   ____
(classes comprised of children with disabilities only)
Number of children with disabilities seen each week in **mainstreamed** music classes   ____
(integrated classes containing both children with and without disabilities)

Highest level of academic preparation:

Bachelor's ____   Master's ____   Educational Specialist ____   Doctorate ____
Music Therapy Registration ____   Other _____

Number of college courses taken in music for special-needs children in last 15 years   ____
Number of college courses taken in special education in the last 15 years   ____

Number of workshops/inservices taken in music for special-needs children
in last 15 years   ____
Approximately how many total hours of workshop/inservice does this represent?   ____

Number of workshops/inservices taken in special education?   ____
Approximately how many total hours of workshop/inservice does this represent?   ____

I have had students in my **self-contained** music classes with the following disabilities. Please check (✓) all that apply:

___Mentally Disabled-Educable   ___Visually Impaired
___Mentally Disabled-Trainable   ___Hearing Impaired
___Mentally Disabled-Severe/Profound   ___Deaf-Blind
___Emotionally Disabled   ___Other Health Impaired
___Orthopedically Disabled   ___Multiply Handicapped
___Learning Disabled   ___Speech Impaired
___Behavior Disabled   ___Other (specify)_____

I have had students in my **mainstreamed** music classes with the following disabilities. Please check (✓) all that apply:

___Mentally Disabled-Educable   ___Visually Impaired
___Mentally Disabled-Trainable   ___Hearing Impaired
___Mentally Disabled-Severe/Profound   ___Deaf-Blind
___Emotionally Disabled   ___Other Health Impaired
___Orthopedically Disabled   ___Multiply Handicapped
___Learning Disabled   ___Speech Impaired
___Behavior Disabled   ___Other (specify)_____

Which of these special education support services are available to you? Check (√) all that apply.

____ School Psychologist   ____ Special Education Teacher   ____ Music Therapist
____ Special Education Consultant ____ Speech Therapist   ____ Physical Therapist
____ Behavior Specialist   ____ Occupational Therapist   ____ Social Worker
____ Other _____

From which of the following have you received services? Check (√) all that apply.

____ School Psychologist   ____ Special Education Teacher   ____ Music Therapist
____ Special Education Consultant ____ Speech Therapist   ____ Physical Therapist
____ Behavior Specialist   ____ Occupational Therapist   ____ Social Worker
____ Other _____

My administration supports the concept of mainstreaming.   ____ Strongly Agree
                                                                ____ Agree
                                                                ____ Disagree
                                                                ____ Strongly Disagree

If you agree or strongly agree, please check (√) ways in which you feel your administration
provides meaningful support of mainstreaming in music classes.

____budgetary support   ____ adaptive and supplementary equipment/materials
____time for professional development   ____ additional preparatory time/instructional time
____teacher aides   ____ personal encouragement
____other (specify)_____

Special education teachers in my school support mainstreaming in music.

                                                                ____ Strongly Agree
                                                                ____ Agree
                                                                ____ Disagree
                                                                ____ Strongly Disagree

If you agree or strongly agree, please check (√) ways in which you feel special educators in your
school provide meaningful support of mainstreaming in music classes.

____offers information regarding instruction   ____offers assistance in class
____asks questions about music program   ____encourages student musical involvement
____other (specify)_____

MUSIC EDUCATION IN MAINSTREAMING NEEDS ASSESSMENT

<u>Directions to Inservice Participants</u>:

Please indicate the extent to which you have a need for inservice education by drawing a circle around the appropriate letters (SA A D SD) in the column at the right. Please be as honest as possible. Your answers will be confidential, and your answers will provide valuable and meaningful information.

LEGEND:	Strongly Agree	=	SA
	Agree	=	A
	Disagree	=	D
	Strongly Disagree	=	SD

<u>I need information about</u>:

1. Handicapping conditions defined in PL 94-142. SA A D SD

2. Federal, state, and local guidelines for implementation of PL 94-142. SA A D SD

3. Special education terminology and definitions (e.g., "least restrictive environment"). SA A D SD

4. Requirements for Individualized Education Plan (IEP) development and implementation. SA A D SD

5. Legal requirements regarding child referral, evaluation, staffing, and annual review process. SA A D SD

<u>I need information about the basic characteristics and learning needs of students who are</u>:

6. Mentally Disabled-Educable. SA A D SD

7. Mentally Disabled-Trainable. SA A D SD

8. Mentally Disabled-Severe/profound. SA A D SD

9. Hearing Impaired. SA A D SD

10. Visually Impaired. SA A D SD

11. Deaf-Blind. SA A D SD

12. Emotionally Disabled. SA A D SD

13. Orthopedically Disabled. SA A D SD

14. Multiply Handicapped. SA A D SD

15. Other Health Impaired. SA A D SD

16.   Learning Disabled.   SA A D SD

17.   Speech Impaired.   SA A D SD

18.   Behaviorally Disabled.   SA A D SD

I need information about:

19.   Preparation of the music classroom and students for the entry   SA A D SD
       of special students.

20.   Developing lesson plans which include options for students with   SA A D SD
       disabilities.

21.   Selecting and adapting songs and instruments appropriate for use by   SA A D SD
       students with disabilities.

22.   Adapting teaching methods to meet each student's level of functioning. SA A D SD

23.   Structuring music activities that will facilitate interaction between SA A D SD
       and among regular and special education students.

24.   Identifying optimum level of achievement of various disabling conditions. SA A D SD

I need information about:

25.   Establishing a realistic evaluation system for the school and the   SA A D SD
       students with disabilities.

26.   Methods to assess the present level of functioning on musical tasks   SA A D SD
       for each student with disabilities.

27.   Formulating appropriate instructional objectives for various levels   SA A D SD
       of functioning.

28.   Organizing a system to collect and record data by which to evaluate   SA A D SD
       student progress toward goal achievement.

29.   Understanding educational disabilities (i.e., physical or cognitive   SA A D SD
       conditions) which will impact on music learning.

30.   Evaluating non-musical correlates (i.e., behavior and socialization) SA A D SD
       which are desirable goals for mainstreamed students.

<u>I need information about</u>:

31. Principles of reinforcement (i.e., selection, presentation, timing, type.)   SA A D SD

32. Steps in behavioral management (target behavior, implementation, intervention).   SA A D SD

33. Methods to increase desirable and decrease undesirable behaviors (i.e., prompting, token economy, time-out).   SA A D SD

34. Surface management techniques (i.e., planned ignoring, signal interference, proximity control).   SA A D SD

35. Role of structured lesson plans in behavior management.   SA A D SD

36. Generalizing behavioral management programs from the special education classroom to the music classroom.   SA A D SD

MUSIC IN MAINSTREAMING ATTITUDE SURVEY

<u>Directions to Inservice Participants</u>:

Please indicate the extent to which you agree with the following statements by drawing a circle around the appropriate letter (SA A D SD) in the column at the right. Please be as honest as possible. Your answers will be confidential, and your answers will provide valuable and meaningful information.

LEGEND:	Strongly Agree	=	SA
	Agree	=	A
	Disagree	=	D
	Strongly Disagree	=	SD

1. Those who favor integration of students with disabilities into regular music classes are not concerned with quality music education.   SA   A   D   SD

2. Attendance of students with disabilities in integrated music classes is similar to that of non-disabled students.   SA   A   D   SD

3. Musical enjoyment is generally more difficult for students with disabilities than for non-disabled students.   SA   A   D   SD

4. Students with disabilities are as compliant in music classes as are non-disabled students.   SA   A   D   SD

5. Non-disabled students often resent having to work with students who are disabled.   SA   A   D   SD

6. Students with disabilities participate in music education as successfully as non-disabled students.   SA   A   D   SD

7. Mainstreaming regulations provide little real help to music teachers.   SA   A   D   SD

8. Because students with disabilities tend to interact inappropriately with non-disabled peers, placement in self-contained music classes seems more appropriate.   SA   A   D   SD

9. Students with disabilities participate in music education as easily as non-disabled students.   SA   A   D   SD

10. Placement of students with disabilities in regular music class is often inappropriate.   SA   A   D   SD

11. Students with disabilities usually interact appropriately in class with non-disabled peers.   SA   A   D   SD

12. Musical creativity is a realistic educational goal for students with disabilities in mainstream music classes. SA A D SD

13. Students with disabilities have a hard time adjusting in regular music classes. SA A D SD

14. Having students with disabilities in a classroom tends to hamper the musical progress of non-disabled students. SA A D SD

15. Students are placed in music class in order to provide an appropriate and complete education. SA A D SD

16. Attendance of disabled students in music class tends to be erratic and irregular. SA A D SD

17. In general students with disabilities can be easily accommodated in mainstream music classes. SA A D SD

18. School participation in music class is more difficult for students with disabilities than for non-disabled students. SA A D SD

19. Students with disabilities in self-contained classes have little opportunity to interact with their non-disabled peers. SA A D SD

20. Students with disabilities generally have lower achievement levels in music than do their non-disabled peers. SA A D SD

21. Students with disabilities generally are accepted socially by their peers in music classes. SA A D SD

22. The special needs of students with disabilities are adequately met in mainstreamed music classes. SA A D SD

23. The musical progress of non-disabled students in mainstream classes is not affected by the presence of students with disabilities. SA A D SD

24. A self-contained class allows teachers to provide more adequate instruction for students with disabilities. SA A D SD

25. Students with disabilities in self-contained classes are seldom accepted socially by non-disabled peers. SA A D SD

26. Students with disabilities can be participants in most music activities. SA A D SD

27. Students with disabilities generally are less creative than non-disabled students. SA A D SD

28. Music classes often contain too many mainstreamed students. SA A D SD

Code #____ Page 8

29. Music teachers are usually asked for their input concerning individual placement of students with disabilities into music classes.   SA   A   D   SD

30. Mainstreaming students with disabilities generally results in discipline problems in music classes.   SA   A   D   SD

31. Students with disabilities enjoy music as much as non-disabled. students.   SA   A   D   SD

32. Having children with disabilities in regular music classes does not inhibit the quality of instruction provided for non-disabled students.   SA   A   D   SD

33. I am satisfied with current mainstreaming processes.   SA   A   D   SD

34. Students with disabilities can be best served in self-contained music classes.   SA   A   D   SD

Section Two:
Models of Music Therapy Interventions
in School/Educational Environments

MUSIC THERAPY FOR LEARNERS WITH SEVERE DISABILITIES IN A RESIDENTIAL SETTING

Laurie A. Farnan

Overview

RESIDENTIAL placement and education of children with mental retardation has a long history. This history, like that of many longstanding traditions and institutions in our society, reflects the beliefs of the society at the time. For example, the *primary role* of a residential treatment setting in the 1850s and early 1860s was *to provide educational programs* to mentally retarded youngsters and adolescents chronological age (CA) 6–16 or 18 (Scheerenberger, 1983, pp. 123, 125). Facilities were reported to be small (5–10 students) and begun as experiments in private homes or wings of existing facilities such as the Perkins School for the Blind in 1848 in South Boston (Crissey & Rosen, 1986, p. 5). Between 1848 and 1898, the number of residential schools increased to 24 and the resident census to approximately 8,000 (Crissey & Rosen, 1986, p. 6). Until the turn of the century, public schools had little role in educating students with mental retardation. Formal education was available only in residential settings and few public school programs were available before 1940 (Crissey & Rosen, 1986, p. 65). There were some authorities who believed that after an appropriate education in a residential facility, students would be able to return to their home and community (Seguin, as cited in Scheerenberger, 1983, p. 70). It appears that the notion of least restrictive educational environment is deeply rooted.

As the years evolved, so did the role of residential care and placement. Facilities grew larger, some would suggest too large. By 1950, 125,375 people with mental retardation resided in residential facilities across the United States. The height of population was reached in 1970 with a resident census increase to 189,549 (Scheerenberger, 1983, p. 252). Various models of treatment and education developed ranging from Edouard Seguin's physiological method, to behavior modification, developmental models, normalization, mainstreaming, and deinstitutionalization philosophies. Historically, these models effected both residential education and public school education programs. But it was with the passage of PL 94–142 in 1975 that the most sweeping changes in education for persons with mental retardation occurred. Public schools began to assume a much more active role in development of individualized education programs for students with special needs. Subsequently, the role of education in residential settings changed as well.

Many of those involved in providing education in the early institutions (circa mid to late 1800s) believed that "music" should be part of the training experience. Scheerenberger (1983) cited five programs which mentioned music as a scheduled part of the educational day (Bucknill, 1873; Fernald, 1892; Ireland, 1877; Maennel 1909; Seguin, 1843). Along with standard curriculum areas (i.e., arithmetic, reading, writing, and gymnastics), these early programs viewed child development and sensory stimulation/development as important components of an appropriate education for students with mental retardation. We can see that there is a historical precedent for involvement in music activities as part of education and program delivery.

It is within current residential educational programs that the medical and education models converge. In the residential setting, a physician and/or nurse is available 24 hours every day since the medical needs of the residents can be quite complex. Students are sustained by tube feedings, dependent on others for care, and may experience seizures, often severe, and in some cases, life threatening. Yet, these same residents do attend school as their health status allows. The music therapist practicing in this type of setting must have knowledge of models of infection control practices, emergency procedures, child development, education, and rehabilitation. The purpose of this chapter is to describe the role of music therapy service delivery within the educational program of a residential setting for persons with developmental disabilities who have pervasive and intense needs.

Population

Central Wisconsin Center for the Developmentally Disabled in Madison, Wisconsin is one of three Intermediate Care Facilities for the Mentally Retarded (ICF–MR) residential facilities in the State of Wisconsin maintained by the Division of Care and Treatment Facilities in the Department of Health and Social Services. It is designated to provide services for less than 500 children and adults with developmental disabilities. Central Center provides 24-hour daily care including access to medical, dental, nursing, psychological, religious, and social services plus music, occupational, physical, recreation, respiratory, and speech therapies. In addition, there is an on-grounds education program, which serves school age students (ages 3–21), plus an early childhood program for very young children (ages birth–3). Adult education programs and vocational services are also available. Of the 477 people currently residing at Central Center, only 18% (88) are under the age of 21 or classified as school age. Of that number 6% (30) are educated off grounds by the Madison Metropolitan School District (MMSD), while 12% (58) are educated in Cardinal School, the on-grounds education program at Central Center. With the onset of the philosophy of deinstitutionalization (circa 1970), the population of residential treatment centers, including Central Center, has been decreasing. It is projected that residential populations will continue to decrease in the future.

Decreasing the population in residential centers was and is an important element of deinstitutionalization. Additional elements include preventing initial admission, increasing the independence of persons residing in facilities, preparing them for community placement, and developing community services necessary to maintain placement (Scheerenberger, 1983, 1987). Not only were residents being placed elsewhere thus decreasing residential populations, but long-term admissions were also decreasing. Where in the past, a person with mild cerebral palsy, spina bifida, mild to moderate retardation, ambulation abilities, and no severe medical problems may have been admitted to a residential facility, only the person with the most profoundly medically fragile conditions (nonambulatory, profound retardation, failure to thrive, severe osteoporosis, and severe respiratory conditions including tracheotomies, etc.) will now be admitted. Subsequently, the demographics of the school age population have changed as well. Figure 1 shows the changes in enrollment statistics over years 1984–1996 for Cardinal School and MMSD (Central Wisconsin Center Annual Reports, 1984–1996).

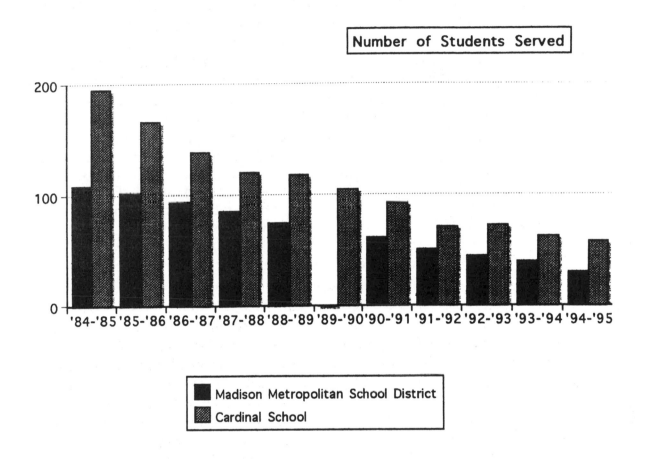

Figure 1. Enrollment Statistics for Madison Metropolitan
School District and Cardinal School, 1984–1986

It is important to note that even though an educational program may be physically located within a residential treatment setting, the laws and regulations which govern delivery of services to students in the public schools also apply to students who live in a residential setting. Students with identified exceptional educational needs receive educational services as outlined and identified on their Individual Education Plan (IEP). These services include but are not limited to classroom instruction, adaptive physical education, occupational, physical, and speech therapy, community outings, all school programs, and in some situations, music therapy.

Although those individuals under the age of 22 years are *residents* of the facility, when they go to school they are *students* of Cardinal School. They attend school Monday through Friday and follow the same school calendar year as the local school district. Each of these students has a diagnosis of profound mental retardation. Based on the 1992 terminology of the American Association for Mental Retardation (AAMR) these students would be described as persons with mental retardation with pervasive support needed in the areas of at least two adaptive skill areas. The 1992 AAMR definition states:

> Mental retardation refers to substantial limitation in present functioning. It is characterized by significantly subaverage intellectual functioning (IQ 70–75 and below), existing concurrently with related limitations in two or more of the following applicable adaptive skill areas: communication, self-care, home living, social skills, community use, self-direction, health and safety, functional academics, leisure, and work. Mental retardation manifests before age 18. (p. 5)

Note that changing terminology has been an ongoing process. AAMR has published six revised definitions of mental retardation since the first definition issued in 1877. Gone are the 1877 terms such as imbecile, idiot, and moron. Also, the four classifications of mildly, moderately, severely, and profoundly retarded are no longer used by AAMR. (These classifications however, are mentioned in PL 94–142.) The new (1992) definition, classification, and system of supports seeks to describe a person as either having or not having mental retardation and then identify the support necessary in adaptive skill areas necessary for this person to function as independently as possible in free society.

The identified adaptive skill area, as well as the intensity and type of support needed varies from individual to individual. The four possible intensities of needed support are defined as intermittent, limited, extensive, and pervasive (American Association for Mental Retardation, 1992, p. 26). Using the current 1992 AAMR diagnosis criteria, a typical student at Cardinal School "is a person with mental retardation with pervasive support needed in the areas of self-care, health and safety, self-direction, leisure, communication, and functional academics." AAMR suggests this terminology to be "more functional, relevant, and oriented to service delivery . . ." (1992, p. 34). All of the Cardinal School students are nonambulatory and use assistive devices for mobility. They are also nonverbal although they may use assistive devices or technology for communication. Table 1 illustrates the chronological age, functional behavioral age as assessed by the Wisconsin Behavior Rating Scale (WBRS), and the diagnosis of six students. The composite picture of these six students reveals chronological ages ranging from 9 to 17, with functional behavioral ages assessed at 2.7 to 5.7 months.

Service Delivery Model

All Cardinal School students are served by the music therapy department at Central Center. The students attend music therapy sessions once or twice a week with their special education teacher and teacher assistant. Students attend with their class (class size is generally 3 or 4 students) and in some situations two classes are combined for group music therapy. Students must get out of their wheelchairs every two hours while they are in school to relieve any possible pressure points and maintain skin integrity. Classrooms have mat tables to provide the students with out-of-chair accommodations. Music therapy sessions must either be planned for in-chair or out-of-chair times. When their out-of-chair time coincides with their scheduled music therapy session, the emphasis in music therapy is out-of-chair sensory stimulation activities, range of

Table 1

Composite Student Profiles

Student Profiles

Chronological age / Assessment of functional age / Diagnosis

CA AGE	WBRS SCORE	DIAGNOSIS
17	5.2 months	Profound MR due to microcephaly, CP spastic quadriplegia, cortical blindness and seizure disorder.
15	2.8 months	Profound MR due to hydrocephalus spastic quadriplegia and an uncontrolled seizure disorder.
15	5.7 months	Profound MR due to unknown prenatal influence seizure disorder of unknown etiology.
12	2.7 months	Profound MR due to other endocrine disorder, visually impaired.
9	4.7 months	Profound MR – microcephaly, impaired vision.
19	3.5 months	Profound MR due to unknown prenatal influence, perceptual blindness.

motion, gross motor activities, and activities that can be performed while in supine, prone, sidelying, or supported sitting positions. Sessions are held in the school classroom or students are transported to one of the three rooms used for group music therapy. Changing location allows the students opportunities to socialize with others and to move freely within their environment. Two larger music therapy rooms allow for in-chair motor and music activities. In a smaller room designed for out-of-chair activities, students are lifted from their wheelchairs and positioned following physical therapy recommendations on a specially designed wooden sound floor used to provide an opportunity to feel tactile vibrations of live music supplied by the music therapist through the use of subcontra bass tone bars, guitar, electronic instruments, drums, or piano.

IEP or IPP or Both?

Interesting situations can occur when multiple regulations coexist simultaneously in a person's life. PL 94–142 mandates a free and appropriate education be provided through implementation of the Individual Education Plan (IEP). The 1971 amendments to the Federal Title XIX (Medicaid) of the Social Security Act mandate that certain standards be followed in providing care and treatment to persons in ICF–MR facilities. The following two standards directly influence the music therapist working in such a setting:

> STANDARD: Each client must have an individual program plan developed by an interdisciplinary team that represents the professions, disciplines,or service areas that are relevant to: (i) Identifying the client's needs, as described by the comprehensive functional assessments required in paragraph (c)(3) of this section; (ii) Designing programs that meet the client's needs; (iii) Identifying the client's need for services without regard to the actual availability of the services needed; and (iv) Including physical development and health, nutritional status, sensorimotor development, affective development, speech and language development and auditory functioning, cognitive development, social development, adaptive behaviors or independent living skills necessary for the client to be able to function in the community, and, as applicable, vocational skills. These objectives must: be stated separately, in terms of a single behavioral outcome; be assigned projected completion dates; be expressed in behavioral terms that provide measurable indices of performance; be organized to reflect a developmental progression appropriate to the individual; and be assigned priorities.

(a) STANDARD: Active Treatment

Active treatment: (1) Each client must receive a continuous active treatment program, which includes aggressive, consistent implementation of a program of specialized and generic training, treatment, health services and related services described in this subpart, that is directed toward: (i) the acquisition of the behaviors necessary for the client to function with as much self-determination and independence as possible; and (ii) the prevention or deceleration of regression or loss of current optimal functional status (State of Wisconsin, 1989).

The Individual Program Plan (IPP) dictates the overall plan of care through the delivery of the concept of active treatment. It is, therefore, possible for one person to have two major individual plans (IPP *and* IEP) guiding the delivery of care, treatment, and education. The system of checks and balances is vast.

To illustrate this situation consider the example of two individual students, "Sarah" and "Kellie" (both age 6), who are residing at Central Center. Both youngsters have been diagnosed as profoundly mentally retarded and assessed to be functioning at the 3.6-month level of development. Both girls receive a full gamut of services (see above) including attending special education classes in Cardinal School. They each receive music therapy five times a week. Two of those music therapy sessions occur during school time, while the other three occur after school, on the living unit in coordination with the girls' therapeutic recreation program. Does their music therapist follow the goals and objectives on the IEP or the IPP or both?

The answer is both. According to the Standards of Clinical Practice for Music Therapists (American Music Therapy Association, 1998) the music therapist is to deliver an integrated individualized plan of care and treatment once assessment procedures are completed. Therefore, if a music therapist is working with a client in more than one setting, and under more than one set of regulations, it is the responsibility of the music therapist to integrate *all* plans of care. Such integration might include designing music therapy goals and objectives which reflect the emphasis of both the IEP and IPP for school age children and adolescents. In that way, the music therapist can report relevant data back to both systems: reporting progress to the special educator for IEP reviews and team meetings; *and* writing Annual Review Progress Reports for the transdisciplinary team and the Qualified Mental Retardation Professional (QMRP). In other words, the music therapist reports on the IEP to the teacher and on the IPP to the QMRP! More importantly, the music therapist must be able to report progress on integrated objectives for the individual person. This is not an impossible situation. The music therapist can, through careful analysis of goals and objectives, implement specifically designed music activities which address either the educational objectives and/or the adaptive skill areas of need.

In the case of Sarah, the *IPP* developed by her transdisciplinary team includes a long-term goal area (LTG) to use her tactile senses as a priority need and the short-term objective (STO) for Sarah is to maintain contact with a textured object using an open hand for 10 seconds, 60% of all trials by the stated ending date. Her *IEP* suggests an annual goal area of working toward increasing her appropriate head and arm movements in response to sensory materials. One of her short-term objectives is to move one or both arms with a relaxed, controlled pattern to initiate contact with toys near her, six times per classroom period, 80% of all trials (see Table 2).

The music therapist would then combine approaches and focus on development of an objective that would provide opportunities for Sarah to develop these skills in all of her music therapy sessions. Two sample objectives for Sarah in music therapy may read: Sarah will reach to touch an instrument presented to her in midline once per session, 60% of all trials by a specified ending date. Further, using an open hand, Sarah will maintain contact with the vibrating surface of an instrument as it is played with her, once per session, for 10 seconds, 60% of all trials by a specified ending date (see Table 3).

For Kellie, the transdisciplinary team identified responding to auditory stimuli as a priority need area. Her IPP short-term objective suggests localizing a sound source by turning her head toward the sound 80% of all trials by a specific end date. Her *IEP* suggests a short-term objective of after localization of a sensory target demonstrated by a head turn, Kellie will reach out to touch the object (see Table 4).

Table 2

Sample IEP and IPP Objectives

IEP	**IPP**
LTG: S will increase her appropriate head and arm movements in response to sensory materials.	LTG: S will use her tactile senses.
STO: 1. S will raise her head up in a variety of positions for one minute, 60% of recorded trials.	STO: Following relaxation procedures, S will maintain contact with textured objects using an open hand for 10 seconds 60% of all trials by 7/19/96.
STO: 2. S will move one or both arms with a relaxed, controlled pattern to initiate contact with toys near her, 6 times per class period, 80% of recorded trials.	
STO: 3. S will purposefully grasp a small object placed in either hand for 30 seconds, 80% of recorded trials.	

Table 3

Sample Music Therapy Objectives

Music Therapy Integrated Objectives

LTG: S will use her tactile senses.

STO: S will reach to touch an instrument (drums, maracas, bells, tambourines, guitar, etc.) presented to her in midline, once per session 60% of recorded trials by 7/19/96.

STO: S will maintain contact with the vibrating surface of an instrument (drums, maracas, bells, tambourines, guitar, etc) as it is played with her once per session for 10 seconds, 60% of recorded trials by 7/19/96.

Table 4

Sample IEP and IPP Objectives

IEP	**IPP**
LTG: K will reach out to touch objects or people.	LTG: K will respond to auditory stimuli.
STO: Following a head turn towards a sensory target, K will reach out to touch the object two times per class period, 75% of recorded trials by 6/6/96.	STO: K will localize a sound source to either side (turning head towards auditory presentation) 80% of recorded trials, by 7/17/96.

The music therapist can integrate both systems in service delivery through implementation of objectives that will use musical sounds and instruments as motivation for Kellie to develop these life skills and responses (see Table 5).

Table 5

Sample Music Therapy Objectives

Music Therapy Integrated Objectives

LTG: K will respond to auditory and tactile stimulation.

STO: When presented with a musical sound source (drums, maracas, bells, tambourines, guitar, etc), K will localize the sound source by turning her head toward the sound, twice per session, 80% of recorded trials by 7/17/96.

STO: After localizing a musical sound source (drums, maracas, bells, tambourines, guitar, etc) , K will reach to touch the sound source once per session, 75% of recorded trials by 7/17/96.

Assessment

All students are assessed annually in the fall using the CWC Music Therapy Assessment Form. The Music Therapy Assessment includes the following skill areas: cognitive, communication, psychosocial, and motor skill development, plus the music skill areas of vocal, instrumental, and specific music preferences. IEP objectives are reviewed with teachers and IPP goals and objectives are reviewed. Specific objectives are adapted from both the IEP and the IPP to provide for a coordination of both systems. Data are taken each time the student (client) is seen, whatever the setting—during school time or during other programs.

Task Analysis

What are the "best practice" music activities for this population? How does a music therapist design appropriate interventions for use in this setting? The answer is no different than in any other setting. The therapist looks to the needs and abilities of the student (client) and manipulates the materials of music—rhythm, melody, and harmony—to enhance the student's achievement of a particular experience, task, or understanding. Figure 2 illustrates an activity development loop based on assessment and objectives. Once an objective has been identified, the music therapist can design an appropriate activity to meet the client needs based upon the components of the objective. For example, if a student is to look toward sound, the activity design would include the particular cuing phrase necessary paired with an instrument sound within an specifically composed song. Data from the activity would help the therapist decide whether to rewrite the objective or redesign the activity to provide the greatest success for the client.

Refer back to Sarah and Kellie. Their assessments included phrases such as "looks toward sound source," "reaches to touch objects," "smiles when name is heard," "takes deep inhalations when relaxed," "notices the presence of others," etc. The music therapist can develop specific objectives based upon such information and other existing documentation to create or adapt appropriate music materials and activities. If activity development begins with student assessment then the data back from the activity will indicate whether the objective needs to be rewritten or the activity has to be redesigned. It is a student/client engendered model of activity development.

Role of Music Therapy

The mission of the Music Therapy Department at Central Wisconsin Center is "to provide professional program planning and implement goal oriented, quality, music therapy services specifically designed to develop and enhance functional life skills for individuals with developmental disabilities" (Farnan, 1993). The three music therapists at Central Center are responsible primarily for delivery of active treatment through music therapy services. Since 60% of the music therapist position description calls for direct service, the IPP is of utmost importance in program design. At present, the school age population represents only 17% of the total population at Central Center, with 11.6% served at Cardinal School. The school age population, therefore, is only 17% of the caseload served by CWC music therapists. The remaining 83% of the population is adults and is served in conjunction with other programs (vocational services, occupational therapy, speech therapy, therapeutic recreation, adult education), not with school.

As students age and graduate, the school age population will continue to decrease, while the adult population will increase.

In addition, the music therapists are expected to function within the *transdisciplinary* team format. In this format, all staff are expected to *learn, teach,* and *work* together (Schmiedlin, 1982) (see Figure 3).

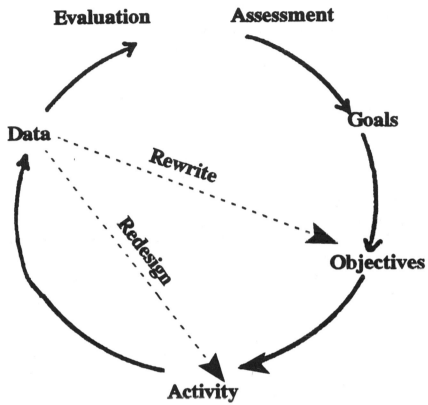

Figure 2. Objective-based Activity Development

Traditional professional boundaries are to be transcended and authoritative disciplines are expected to role release when possible. For the music therapist, this may mean setting the tempo for a particular activity, but the special education teacher would be playing the two-note pattern on the tone bar while the music therapist works directly with the students. The music therapists may offer introductory piano or guitar lessons to education staff so they can better use instruments with the students. Providing suggestions and guidance on the use of electronic instruments in the classroom is also important. In that regard, the music therapist in this setting also provides consultation regarding music materials and equipment. Farnan (1989) identified the role of a music therapist in the transdisciplinary setting as that of composer, consultant, and session leader (see Figure 4). The music therapist as composer must *learn* about the needs and abilities of the student in order to write appropriate music for sessions. The music therapist as consultant must *teach* other staff about the role of music and music materials in achieving goals and objectives. The music therapist as session leader *works* side by side other staff in modeling delivery of direct service using the medium of music in a therapeutic way.

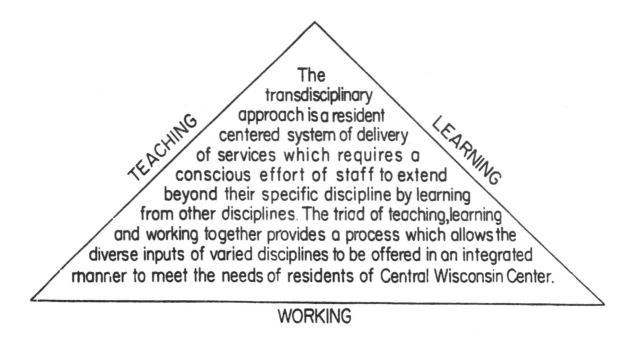

The
transdisciplinary
approach is a resident
centered system of delivery
of services which requires a
conscious effort of staff to extend
beyond their specific discipline by learning
from other disciplines. The triad of teaching, learning
and working together provides a process which allows the
diverse inputs of varied disciplines to be offered in an integrated
manner to meet the needs of residents of Central Wisconsin Center.

Figure 3. Transdisciplinary Team Approach

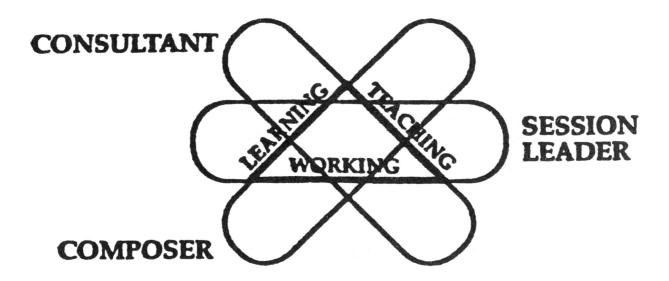

Figure 4. Music Therapist Roles in the Transdisciplinary Setting

Strategies

The delivery of music therapy in a self-contained classroom in a residential setting can at first glance appear complicated. The children and adolescents have profound mental retardation and may have complex medical needs. Despite the fact that there are two systems of documentation, and the convergence of the medical and educational models, the center of the delivery of service must always be the student. The student deserves quality music and effective therapy designed to assist him or her to attain functional life skills by fully participating in musical activities. Sensory stimulation and usage are important developmental activities for individuals with severe disabilities and have been so documented since 1843. Practitioners should remember to use more than one sensory channel for stimulation and to allow sufficient time for the student to process the information and make a response. Such multisensorial stimulation is critical with students whose sensory systems can be so profoundly impaired. Response time may be longer and responses more subtle than with other populations. Responses to live musical stimuli through auditory and tactile stimulation can be achieved by assisting students to touch the instrument sound source. Such assistance may include facilitation to touch the vibrating front surface of a guitar during an opening or closing song, or placing an open hand on a tone bar or tambourine as it is played with a steady predictable rhythm, creating both auditory and tactile stimulation. Responses may be as subtle as a change in facial expression, a change in pupil dilation, a change in respiration rate, a vocalization, or reaching or turning toward the sound source. These responses indicate an awareness and basic processing of stimuli—a necessary life skill.

The Future

Fewer people are living their entire lives in residential settings. Intermediate care is no longer considered a lifelong living arrangement. As the role of residential facilities continues to evolve, the need for specialized intermediate residential care, treatment, and education for people with profound mental retardation and intense needs still exists. Nevertheless, a music therapist in such a setting must design services with future transitions and placements in mind. Programming must assist the client in acquiring the functional skills necessary to lead a more independent life. Expression of choices, development of preferences, acquiring life experiences, and personal interests all contribute to building an independent quality of life. If transitions are in the future, music may provide a familiar link to bridge one situation to another. For example, if school-age children participate in music therapy in a self-contained classroom in a residential setting, care must be taken to provide those children with music activities commensurate with their school-age peers. Besides offering a variety of specifically composed and goal-oriented programmatic songs, a diverse musical diet of culturally based children's songs should also be provided. Checking local curriculums and adapting commonly used songs may build a familiar repertoire for a child. If such children are to be eventually included in the public school setting, these songs may provide a familiar link in transition to that new setting. For the children who may not be appropriately accommodated in public school but rather will make their transition to adult programming within the facility, the program activities may provide the familiar link in their transition.

Conclusion

What will the picture of education in a residential setting be in the future? The beliefs of current society embrace inclusion, downsizing, and deinstitutionalization. History illustrates that the populations served in residential settings change as the values and politics of a society change. Progressive and sophisticated medical interventions have given life and sustained life with children who previously would probably not survived birth (L. Leggett, MSW, Admission Social Worker, personal communication, May 17, 1995). Community-based services are in place for many children with identified special needs but not for the children who are the most medically complex, fragile, and profoundly impaired with intense needs. These students are currently identified as best being served in residential settings. Facility interventions and programs, including music therapy, will continue to be provided to these students as long as such interventions are deemed appropriate and necessary.

Inclusion in music-based programs as a component of the education of persons with mental retardation has been documented since 1843. We now must shift with societal changes to develop techniques and procedures for the future of these students, however, and wherever that future may continue to grow. Residential facilities are downsizing and their populations are decreasing. Students are being served elsewhere. The direct service model of music therapy intervention may evolve to be increasingly more consultative to public schools in order to provide resource models and effective techniques for direct service delivery.

References

American Association for Mental Retardation. (1992). *Mental retardation 9th edition: Definition, classification, and systems of support.* Washington, DC: Author.

American Music Therapy Association. (1998). *Standards of clinical practice.* Silver Spring, MD.

Central Wisconsin Center Annual Reports. (1984–1996). *Education/Cardinal School report.*

Crissey, M. S., & Rosen, M. (1986). *Institutions for the mentally retarded: A changing role in changing times.* Austin, TX: PRO–ED, Inc.

Farnan, L. A. (1989). Music therapy service delivery within a transdisciplinary model. *Journal of Practical Approaches to Developmental Handicap. 13*(2), 14–17.

Farnan, L. A. (1993). *Strategic information technology planning statement.* Music Therapy Department, Central Wisconsin Center for the Developmentally Disabled. Madison, WI.

Federal regulations document: Interpretive guidelines—Intermediate care facilities for the mentally retarded. (1989). State of Wisconsin Department of Health and Social Services, Division of Health, Bureau of Quality Compliance. Madison, WI.

Scheerenberger, R. C. (1983). *A history of mental retardation.* Baltimore, MD: Brooks Publishing.

Scheerenberger, R. C. (1987). *A history of mental retardation: A quarter century of promise.* Baltimore, MD: Brooks Publishing.

Schmiedlin, J. (1982). *Transdisciplinary concepts.* Staff training handout. Central Wisconsin Center for the Developmentally Disabled. Madison, WI.

MUSIC THERAPY FOR JUVENILE OFFENDERS IN A RESIDENTIAL TREATMENT SETTING

Susan C. Gardstrom

Introduction

SOME researchers indicate that the rate of serious and violent juvenile crime in this country is escalating (National Coalition of State Juvenile Justice Advisory Groups, 1993). Other organizations report a decline in violent offenses by youngsters, citing statistics of the Federal Bureau of Investigation (FBI) as one source which may exaggerate the problem of youth violence (Jones & Krisberg, 1994). Despite conflicting data and resulting confusion, one thing is for certain: More than ever, this country is keenly aware of the issue of violent crime among juveniles. Increasingly, youths are being committed for rehabilitation and education in secure, residential settings. Music therapists are joining the ranks of professionals who share the challenging task of facilitating the academic, physical, social, and emotional growth of the young offender in residential treatment. In 1993, the National Association for Music Therapy (NAMT) reported that 14 of its members worked in adult and juvenile correctional facilities (National Association for Music Therapy, 1993). As of 1994, that number had increased to 26 (National Association for Music Therapy, 1994). It is this author's belief that many more music therapists are servicing an "unidentified" delinquent population, that is, adolescents found in public schools, psychiatric treatment facilities, and community centers, who exhibit delinquent behaviors but who have not yet been formally involved in the juvenile adjudication process.

Offender Defined

Various terms are used to describe young people who have been in trouble with the law. "Juvenile offender," "youthful offender," and "delinquent" are used interchangeably to denote a child or adolescent who has committed a status, misdemeanor, or felony offense. *Status* offenses (such as curfew violations, incorrigibility, and truancy from home and school) are behaviors that, if committed by adults, would not be considered a crime. The terms "misdemeanor" and "felony" are borrowed from the adult correctional system. *Misdemeanor* offenses include such behaviors as simple traffic violations and trespassing. *Felonies* are the most severe offenses and include both nonviolent crimes such as manufacture of a controlled substance and car theft, and violent crimes like rape, armed robbery, and murder.

Juvenile Court

Before a child has contact with the juvenile justice system, he or she has typically established a pattern of anti-social behavior, often manifested first in the classroom. Teachers are quick to recognize "problem kids," those youths who constantly miss assignments, cheat, act in a hostile or withdrawn manner, or behave disrespectfully toward adults. Trips to the principal's office and discussions with parents may or may not be effective in modifying such behaviors. More severe acts of delinquency (e.g., fighting, stealing, carrying a weapon, and substance use) are most often met with detention, suspension, or expulsion. Depending upon the frequency, intensity, and duration of his or her delinquent behaviors, the child may be referred to the courts for legal action.

The juvenile justice process differs from state to state and a youth who is charged with having committed an offense is subject to that individualized process. In general, an alleged offender is required to participate in a preliminary hearing during which the facts of the case are reviewed by a judge or appointed court representative. A teen who is charged with a serious felony offense may be transferred to adult criminal court for trial by means of a legislative, prosecutorial, or judicial waiver; lesser offenses are usually tried in juvenile or family court. (Public opinion polls indicate that the majority of all voting age adults want juveniles who commit felonies tried in the adult criminal courts rather than in juvenile courts [Schwartz, 1992] even though the evidence suggests that such transfers do not result in harsher penalties [Jones & Krisberg, 1994]). Before a formal court appearance, a child is often removed from the home and school and placed in a county youth home or detention center. These centers are not designed for long-term treatment of adjudicated delinquents, but, rather, for the short-term, pretrial holding of alleged offenders who are deemed a high risk to commit additional offenses or flee before their trial (Barton, 1994). However, in this author's experience, some youths may spend up to 12 months in crowded, chaotic youth homes awaiting trial or placement in a treatment/education facility.

If found guilty, the child is sentenced. This process is also affected by statutory schemes, as well as by individual factors like age, record of prior offenses, severity of the current offense, and resources and attitudes of the youth and his or her family. Eisenman (1991) found that the severity of sentences for juvenile felons seemed to depend on jurisdiction with some judges routinely sentencing while others almost never exercising this right. Sentencing may result in relatively lenient solutions such as probation, community service, or acts of restitution. In these cases, the child would continue to attend his or her regular school. More restrictive sanctions include mandated therapy, placement in day treatment, or incarceration in a public or private residential institution. In 1989, it was estimated that approximately 80,000 youths occupied beds in adult and juvenile correctional facilities in this country (United States Department of Justice, 1991).

Demographics

Delinquent behavior is not restricted to youths of a particular race, socioeconomic status, gender, or intelligence; it appears in all groups of youths. However, it surfaces three times more frequently in males than females (Schwartz, 1992) and more often in youths exhibiting the following characteristics: (a) a delinquency adjudication prior to age 13, (b) low family income, (c) being rated troublesome by teachers and peers between the ages of 8 and 10, (d) poor school performance by age 10, (e) psychomotor clumsiness, (f) poor nonverbal IQ, and (g) having a sibling convicted of a crime (Blumstein, Farrington, & Moitra, 1985; Greenwood, 1986; Mahoney, 1991). Further, studies of serious juvenile offenders typically show disproportionate rates of mental health problems, including chemical dependency (Baird, 1987; Elliot, Huizinga, & Morse, 1988; Krisberg, 1987). A history of physical or sexual abuse and an unusually high incidence of head injuries has been linked to violent offenders as well (Lewis et al., 1985; Lewis et al., 1988).

Needs

Emotional/Social Needs

By definition, a delinquent youth manifests a constellation of anti-social behaviors, of which aggression is perhaps the most problematic. Aggressive behaviors in youths have been linked to genetics, acquired biological factors, such as birth trauma or head injury, and psychosocial factors. Antisocial behavior among parents and punitive or inconsistent disciplinary parenting styles seem to contribute to a child's aggressive patterns. Exposure to violence in the media is also correlated with increased violent behavior (American Psychological Association, 1993).

Interpersonal problems are common among those who demonstrate delinquent behaviors. Brendtro and Ness (1983) write, "It is assumed that many problems of children, both those that are situational and those that are chronic, exist because children lack the skills to build relationships, handle interpersonal conflicts, and manage their own emotions in constructive ways" (p. 163). With lifelong histories of turbulent family relationships, these children generalize deep-seated fear and mistrust to relationships outside the family system. At first meeting, they may appear hostile, indifferent, resistive, aloof, guarded, or superficial. They may do everything in their power to project themselves as "tough" so as not to risk ridicule, rejection, or harm from what they perceive to be yet one more intervening adult or aggravating peer.

In both rural and urban areas, opportunities for safe, legal, and productive socialization may be limited. "Cruising" or "hanging out" on the streets may be the most attractive recreational options for adolescents who come from overcrowded or poverty-stricken communities in which leadership is scarce and few positive role models exist. All too often, the unmet need for bonding among males from single-parent, female-headed households is met through socialization into a gang, with its "attendant delinquent/criminal system" (Schwartz, 1992, p. 21).

Physical Needs

Physical needs within this population are varied. Medical and dental care may have been neglected due to financial strain and a lack of health insurance. The importance of proper nutrition and personal hygiene may not have been emphasized in the home and the use and abuse of alcohol and other drugs may have caused or contributed to specific illnesses. Some youths may have chemical imbalances that contribute to emotional problems. Many females designated as delinquent have experienced one or more pregnancies which were unplanned and problematic.

The physical symptoms of stress may be tempered by the stability and structure of a residential treatment program in that a consistent, predictable schedule may reduce anxiety. While sleeping in a locked room may be unnerving for some teens, others could find relief in the physical security it provides, taking comfort in the knowledge that no one will physically or sexually abuse them during the night.

The importance of providing these youths with basic physical needs of food, clothing, and shelter cannot be overstated. The three nutritious meals received each day in residential care may be one or two more than they have ever known.

Academic Needs/Educational Services

Many of the youths classified as juvenile offenders are believed to have learning disabilities, mental or emotional impairments, or substance abuse problems that interfere with learning. Others may have experienced repeated failure in a school system which is ill-equipped to deal with the student's needs and the family's resources. Still others come from families in which education is not valued or, if valued, falls by the wayside in the face of more pressing emotional or economic concerns. Some students have lagged behind academically while in detention awaiting placement in a treatment facility. Still others have little consistency in their lives. Attendance in school may be interrupted when the family uproots and relocates.

The scope and delivery of educational services in juvenile corrections are influenced by federal and state policies as well as related issues such as institutional security, students' prior school experiences, and fiscal constraints. Unfortunately, the juvenile justice system is ". . . largely segregated from other systems such as medical care, mental health services, and schools that serve children and families" (Jones & Krisberg, 1994, p. 7). Residential facilities for juvenile offenders frequently offer on-campus remedial reading, spelling, writing, and mathematics instruction as well as core academics such as history, social studies, health education, science, and English. Depending upon its financial and human resources, a facility may also offer vocational training or specialty classes, e.g., home economics, computer literacy, parenting skills, art, music, etc. Incarcerated students are educated most often in small, self-contained classrooms for several reasons. First, these individuals' behaviors can be unpredictable and unmanageable, even violent, posing a threat to the community and an undue challenge to the regular education system. Second, due to resistance to treatment and education, some students are a truancy risk. Finally, because these students' needs are so complex and disparate, individualized instruction in a highly monitored setting is often crucial to academic success.

Educational programs do exist within public school systems for students whose delinquent behaviors are manageable in these settings. *Alternative education* programs, for example, may serve at-risk or mildly delinquent students for some or all of the school day. These programs, usually staffed by special educators, are tailored to non-traditional styles of learning and tend to embrace experiential teaching techniques and emphasize the development of social and interpersonal skills. In rare cases, incarcerated students are mainstreamed into regular education programs.

Special Education Services

The provisions of the Individuals With Disabilities Education Act (IDEA) apply to all states receiving federal financial assistance. However, states may be slow to extend these rights to eligible *incarcerated* students (Leone, 1994). Ideally, within 30 days of arrival at a residential facility, a student must undergo academic and psychological testing to determine strengths, deficits, and educational needs. Based on this information, a committee will develop the student's Individual Education Plan (IEP). Committee members usually include a teacher or educational consultant from the facility, the student's case worker, and parents or legal guardians. Leone (1994) cites that, although the IEP is required under federal law, IEP committees are typically slow to convene, parents or legal guardians rarely attend planning meetings, and educational programs may not be implemented when the student is sent to disciplinary segregation. In this writer's experience, music therapy is very rarely included as a required service on the IEP of incarcerated youths.

Students who do not carry a special education label when they arrive may be reassessed for special education services. It is crucial to complete accurate and timely educational assessments on each student so that designated funds can be accessed for those needing specialized services. When a student leaves residential treatment, the receiving school may accept the recommendations of the treatment facility with respect to that student's specific educational needs.

Music Therapy Services

Introduction

Where, with whom, how frequently, how long, and in what way music therapists work with juvenile offenders is impacted by a variety of factors including work setting, state law, regulation and policy, internal organizational structure and treatment philosophy, and financial resources, all of which are constantly changing. Youth homes, typically overcrowded and understaffed, do not usually have the financial resources to employ nonmandated professionals. Some music therapy services, however, may be funded by governmental, community, or private foundation grants. Most music therapists in juvenile corrections work in long-term public or private rehabilitation/education facilities.

The Work Setting

Despite extensive reform spawned in the 1970s by growing public dissatisfaction with governmental programs, large state-run institutions (a.k.a. training schools) still operate in many states. In 1991, the Office of Juvenile Justice and Delinquency Prevention estimated that 28,535 youths resided in public training schools (as cited in Barton, 1994). A music therapist in this type of school is usually a state employee with the civil service administration, bearing one of a number of professional titles such as Music Therapist, Activity Therapist, or Recreation Specialist. Typically, in this setting, caseloads are large, money is limited and tedious to access, and working conditions are less than ideal; yet jobs are relatively secure. The complexion of music therapy services varies depending upon the agency's overall philosophy and specific treatment program.

Private programs service a significant proportion of total delinquent admissions in the United States. The number of youths confined to private juvenile facilities increased from 100 per 100,000 in 1979 to 150 per 100,000 in 1991 (Jones & Krisberg, 1994). Programs in the private sector enjoy freedoms and benefits not possible in state institutions. Private agencies: (a) can easily circumvent the burdensome bureaucracy of the state system, (b) are more receptive to innovative treatment philosophies and "cutting edge" techniques, (c) tend to be housed in newer and well maintained facilities, and (d) acquire instruments and equipment of higher quality. The music therapist in this setting is more likely to gain access to "state of the art" training and education opportunities.

The number of adjudicated youths educated in public schools is on the rise in this country (Jones & Krisberg, 1994). Music therapists may be hired by the public schools or the residential facilities from which the students are referred. One state training school for young felony offenders in Michigan places many of its students in their regular junior high or high school, depending upon the youths' safety within the community, the level of risk they pose to the community, and their educational needs. In this particular situation, music therapy is provided after school, in the evenings, and on weekends at the residential facility and is viewed as a rehabilitative/supportive service, along with therapeutic recreation, individual counseling, and academic tutoring.

Despite blatant differences between most public and private facilities, a successful music therapy program can be launched and maintained in either setting. In this writer's opinion, more important than the environment is the therapist's competence, dedication to the students, enthusiasm for the work, resourcefulness, and creativity.

Music Therapy and the Interdisciplinary Treatment Team

The complex nature of delinquency requires treatment that is highly coordinated. Ideally, this coordination is overseen by an interdisciplinary treatment team comprised of professionals who represent all facets of the therapeutic program. Teachers, educational aides, youth workers, group leaders/counselors, family therapists, psychologists, social workers, and adjunct staff (i.e., music, art, recreational, and occupational therapists; healthcare workers; volunteers; religious/spiritual counselors; and community liaisons) all have a role in assessing and treating the young people to whom they have been assigned. Unlike some professionals who serve on only one treatment team representing a finite group of youth, the music therapist in juvenile corrections may serve the entire student population of a residential facility. In this case, she or he is an active member of several interdisciplinary teams. This position can be an awesome responsibility, for it requires not only becoming acquainted with all staff but also understanding and respecting the unique personality of each team. Rules and "norms" may differ from team to team even though each operates as part of the same facility. Likewise, each team may respond differently toward the music therapist. Ideally, the music therapist's input is welcomed and his or her services are solicited. In the worst case scenario, however, the music therapist is viewed as an outsider who competes for time with other "more necessary" educational or therapeutic services. Therefore, in-service training on the foundations and benefits of music therapy in this field is often needed.

Referrals

Since music therapy is not ordinarily mandated by the IEP committee, referrals for treatment may come from a variety of sources, especially if a facility espouses *team primacy* (i.e., each member of the interdisciplinary team has equal power and equal responsibility in the adolescents' treatment). Referrals may be informal (e.g., a phone call from the group leader requesting treatment), or formal (e.g., a written referral form specific to the facility and signed by all members of the team). It is the music therapist's task to educate his or her colleagues as to which students might be indicated for involvement in therapy. General referral criteria are specific to each facility, but may include: treatment needs/goals (e.g., develop interpersonal relationships, express feelings related to criminal behavior, boost sense of individuality, etc.), interest in music, musical talent, and prior involvement in music activities or music therapy.

Goals and Interventions

The goals of music therapy treatment for young offenders can be classified within four behavioral domains: emotional, social, physical, and cognitive (academic). Table 1 outlines long-term goals and short-term objectives in each of these domains and provides music therapy interventions that can be used to accomplish these aims.

Emotional Domain

Music experiences can assist teenagers in exploring and expressing their feelings, values, ideas, opinions—even secrets. For example, music with powerful lyrics can be used therapeutically to stimulate group discussion about themes such as drug use, crime, sexuality, interpersonal relationships, current social events, or family dynamics. Group songwriting encourages the expression of thoughts and feelings. Freed (1987) reports that writing songs can provide opportunities for validation of feelings, self-awareness, socialization, listening, establishing rapport, building empathy, and solving problems within a group. Self-esteem can also be positively altered through the use of music. Successful singing and playing experiences can lead to increased confidence and a sense of mastery and control of one's world.

Social Domain

Music therapy programs in residential care can address adolescents' valid needs for peer interaction, appropriate competition, relaxation, and leisure. Brooks (1989) suggests that, ". . . music therapy is the preferred treatment method in helping adolescents improve their interaction skills with peers" (p. 38). A performance group, such as a band or handbell choir, assists in the development of many social skills. Besides learning care, maintenance, and basic playing technique on a particular instrument, a sense of responsibility and cooperation is fostered. Youths learn to give and accept constructive feedback about their playing from their peers. A successful performance in the community may help the young offender and the citizens of that community feel more positively toward one another. Finally, music is a viable leisure pursuit for students who have few nondelinquent interests.

Physical Domain

Regular exercise is a vital component of a rehabilitation program for any age group, particularly adolescents. This may be offered through traditional physical education and recreation programs as well as through creative arts such as music, dance, and drama. Motor activity can not only help to increase strength, endurance, and flexibility, but can also provide an outlet for excess energy, anger, or frustration. Exercise to music may promote muscle toning and weight loss, thereby improving self-image. Body image is particularly negative among youthful offenders, a high percentage of whom have been physically and/or sexually abused (Lewis et al., 1988).

Table 1

Goals/Objectives/Interventions

DOMAIN: EMOTIONAL

Goal: To enhance the identification and healthy expression of feelings

Objective: To stimulate feeling responses
   Interventions: guided music listening*, creative movement

Objective: To increase the verbal and nonverbal expression of feelings
   Interventions: instrumental improvisation, song-writing, singing,
            creative movement, singing and sign language

Goal: To build self-esteem

Objective: To improve body image
   Interventions: creative movement, dance, music and exercise

Objective: To reduce shame for past behaviors and experiences
   Interventions: guided music listening, song-writing

Objective: To build confidence through skill mastery
   Interventions: performance ensembles, vocal and instrumental instruction

DOMAIN: SOCIAL

Goal: To promote the development of positive relationships

Objective: To decrease isolation
   Interventions: performance ensembles, dance, recreational music

Objective: To increase verbal interaction
   Interventions: singing, musical games, guided music listening

Objective: To increase self-disclosure
   Interventions: song-writing, guided music listening

Objective: To develop leadership skills
   Interventions: musical games, performance ensembles

Objective: To provide opportunities for healthy competition
   Interventions: musical games

DOMAIN: PHYSICAL

Goal: To improve physical health (i.e., strength, mobility, endurance, coordination, and balance)

Objective: To develop gross motor skills
Interventions: creative movement, dance, singing and sign language, music and exercise

Objective: To develop fine motor skills
Interventions: creative movement, singing and sign language, instrumental instruction

Objective: To reduce physical stress
Interventions: guided music listening, dance, creative movement

DOMAIN: COGNITIVE (ACADEMIC)

Goal: To increase ability to receive, process, and express information

Objective: To increase attending and following directions
Interventions: performance ensembles, musical games, instrumental instruction

Objective: To improve short- and long-term memory
Interventions: performance ensembles, singing, instrumental instruction, dance, musical games

Objective: To support specific educational goals (e.g. reading, history, etc.)
Interventions: guided music listening, song-writing, musical games

---

Adapted by this writer with permission from R. Unkefer (Ed.). (1990). *Music Therapy in the Treatment of Adults With Mental Disorders.*

* "Guided Music Listening" is defined as music and relaxation, Guided Imagery and Music (GIM), and music listening and discussion activities.

Educating youths about their bodies is also essential. Using music activities to generate open talk about topics such as anatomy, sexuality, and pregnancy, for example, can help alleviate some of the anxiety teens commonly feel about their rapidly changing bodies and labile emotions. Through music and movement techniques, adolescents can learn to appreciate their bodies, their space, and the space of others (Brooks, 1989).

Cognitive (Academic) Domain

Music can serve as a reinforcer for the development of academic skills. It may be used as a contingency (e.g., the students who have completed their mathematics assignments are allowed to sing with the chorus which meets immediately after school). Music therapy interventions can also teach academic concepts. Songwriting, lyric analysis and musical games can promote spelling, reading, and writing skills. Learning about current and historical events can be fun when music is interjected into the learning process. Students who have difficulty learning via traditional methods may especially benefit from the multisensory nature of the musical experience.

Goals typically associated with music education may be addressed, depending upon the needs and interests of the students, the educational requirements of the state, and the educational philosophy of the facility in which the therapist works. Often, basic rhythmic and melodic concepts are taught as a prerequisite to other activities (e.g., songwriting and performance ensembles).

Music Therapy Service Delivery

Documentation

In both public and private residential settings, documentation is of utmost importance. Students' behaviors are closely monitored and recorded. As with other aspects of service in this setting, documentation requirements will vary from site to site. Once a student has been referred for treatment, a written *assessment* form may be required before a *program plan* (i.e., treatment plan outlining educational and therapeutic goals) is developed. Both of these records may be placed in the student's permanent file. Ongoing *progress notes* inform other members of the interdisciplinary treatment team as to the student's progress toward goals and objectives. Finally, an *after-care plan* detailing future goals and interventions may be required.

Direct Service

Music therapists in residential settings for juvenile offenders are most often hired to provide direct client service to both groups and individuals. Recognizing that young offenders are typically resistant to adult authority, many rehabilitation programs embrace a group-oriented treatment modality such as Positive Peer Culture (PPC), in which the peer group is viewed as the principal agent of change (Brendtro & Ness, 1983). In this environment, the music therapist may be limited to group activities. In many instances, a student may attend a music therapy session because it has been mandated by his group's professional treatment team, not because he wants to be involved. Some students may feel afraid, apprehensive, or resentful about participating. Thus, initial music therapy activities should be low risk, requiring minimal musical skill level and little individual self-disclosure from the youths in the group. The therapist's goal is to equalize the group so that each individual member feels she or he has made a competent contribution to the musical experience (Gardstrom, 1987). Group drumming, chanting, and singing are interventions suitable for a "fledgling" group in which participation, trust, and cohesiveness are minimal. As a group matures, "riskier" interventions such as improvisation and songwriting are indicated.

Several therapeutic aims can be accomplished through individual music therapy. Individual sessions can provide students the opportunity to: (a) develop a positive relationship with an adult/ authority figure, (b) express thoughts and feelings in a personal way, (c) develop an interest or skill needing concentrated attention, (d) gain confidence and learn how to maintain it within the context of the peer group, and (e) experience unconditional care and concern from an adult/parent figure. Consider the following case example:

> Paula, age 15, was sent to the state training school after having assaulted two peers at her junior high school with a baseball bat. Although the assault was Paula's first felony offense, she had exhibited problem behaviors at home and in the classroom since age 10.
>
> Paula had a moderate hearing loss in one ear and a mild loss in the other due to physical abuse by her father when she was a toddler. Although she had an IQ within normal range (95), Paula was labeled a "slow learner" by teachers in elementary school and "isolative" by the school social worker. Her slight speech impairment was thought to be the result of her problematic home life. In fourth grade, her hearing was tested and the impairment discovered. She was fitted for hearing aids which she wore sporadically prior to her arrival at the school.
>
> Paula was transported to the training school in hand and foot restraints due to her assaultive behavior. She spit and cursed at the other students and attempted to bite anyone who touched her. Paula was separated from her peer group until she no longer proved a physical threat to herself and others, about 1 week. When she rejoined the group, she was withdrawn and sullen. She rarely spoke, although she appeared to listen and occasionally wept when the other students talked in group meeting about problems in their families.
>
> When Paula was first introduced to the music therapist at the school, she was shy but polite. She told the music therapist that she had taken 1 year of piano lessons when she was 8 or 9 years old and had "really liked it." The therapist informed her that students could "earn" individual music therapy sessions and then referred her to her peer group for more information.
>
> During group music therapy, Paula vacillated between isolating herself and acting in a belligerent manner. Several times during the first 3 months of treatment, Paula was physically restrained during music therapy after threatening to hurt her peers.
>
> One day in the fourth month, the music therapist asked Paula's group to participate in a special activity involving a musical timeline. Students were allowed to browse through a collection of tapes and CD's and were directed to choose four musical selections which represented significant years or periods in their lives. Paula refused to participate in the activity and sat quietly while the others shared their findings. As one

group member played "Luca" and spoke about the sexual abuse she had endured from both her father and her uncle, Paula began to sob. The group supported her efforts to talk about her own secret—that she, too, had been sexually abused as a child. This admission was a turning point in Paula's treatment. She became gentler, less hostile, and more cooperative. She also began taking responsibility for her own behavior.

After Paula had been at the school for 6 months, she requested individual music therapy sessions. This first request was denied by her treatment team because she had been refusing to wear her hearing aids to school on campus and had fallen behind in her work. Three weeks later, Paula asked for music therapy again. The request was approved as she had worn her hearing aids every day without fail and had completed all homework assignments.

Paula came to her first Tuesday session without either of her hearing aids. The therapist explained that it was imperative Paula wear the aids so that teaching and learning could be successful. Paula was then escorted back to her living unit to retrieve the aids but she refused to put them on. She sat in the corner of the room, seemingly embarrassed. The therapist noted Paula's behavior in the staff log book and restated the expectation that Paula wear her hearing aids to each and every session. On the following Tuesday and every Tuesday henceforth, Paula met the expectation.

Based on observations of Paula in her group, discussions with the interdisciplinary treatment team, and a brief interview with Paula, the music therapist determined the following objectives for treatment: To increase the verbal and nonverbal expression of feelings; to build confidence through skill mastery; to decrease isolation; and to develop fine motor skills. Initially, Paula's reason for wanting the sessions was to "learn to play the piano again." During the first three sessions, the music therapist reviewed rhythmic and melodic concepts. Musical notation was introduced and homework was assigned.

The course of treatment changed as the therapeutic relationship blossomed and Paula's skills improved. She began to disclose information about her physical and sexual abuse and her resulting feelings. The focus of the sessions turned to listening and discussion and songwriting activities. One original song, which Paula entitled, "Devil in My Dreams," talked about the intense fear she felt each evening and her rage toward her mother for "letting the devil come in." At the music therapist's suggestion, Paula played a tape of the song in her family meeting in order to help her convey these feelings to her mother.

After 11 months at the training school, Paula earned her release from the treatment program. A few weeks before Paula left, the music therapist conducted an "exit interview" during which Paula had a chance to communicate her impressions of the therapy sessions and to set some musical goals for her return to regular public education. Before she left, Paula indicated a desire to play percussion in the marching band at her school. The therapist gave Paula a "crash course" in marching band instrumentation and mallet techniques. She then placed a phone call to the band director and offered support for Paula's future involvement.

A follow-up call 6 months after her release indicated that Paula was living with her mother and had not been re-arrested. She was enrolled in school and was maintaining average to above-average grades. She was working in a supermarket and was described by her boss as a "friendly, hardworking girl." Although the band teacher at Paula's school determined that her musical skill level did not allow her to play in the marching band, he invited her to serve as the band librarian, assist in fundraising events, and travel with the band to all social and athletic activities.

The Future of Juvenile Justice

Juvenile justice experts are voicing concern about the increase in juvenile admissions to detention centers and the overcrowding and fiscal strain which results. Research suggests that the numbers of youths confined in these facilities can be substantially reduced without unduly jeopardizing the community (Schwartz, Barton, & Orlando, 1991). Small, intensive programs for serious and violent offenders can succeed with most youths when coupled with integrated community-based systems (Jones & Krisberg, 1994). Such alternatives to long-term residential treatment have been successfully implemented in Massachusetts, Utah, and Missouri (Barton, 1994). One can only speculate as to the impact this type of reform may have on the profession of music therapy. Will jobs be lost with the downsizing and closing of large residential institutions? Or will jobs be gained in community programs? Jones and Krisberg (1994) write:

> Existing research strongly supports the need for a comprehensive violence reduction strategy. This strategy should include prevention programs, intermediate sanctions, well-structured community based programs, small secure facilities for the most serious offenders and sound re-entry and aftercare services. (p. 7)

They continue:

> . . . prevention programs must emphasize opportunities for healthy social, physical, and mental development. Such programs must involve all components of the community, including schools, healthcare professionals, families, neighborhood groups, law enforcement, and community-based organizations. (p. 41)

Will more prevention-based programs be established thereby opening the door to a whole new form of preventative school music therapy?

Privatization of state correctional systems may also affect the status of music therapy with the delinquent population. Barton (1994) writes:

> Maryland and Colorado have already turned over their training schools to private providers, and other states may follow suit. The merits of private institutions have not yet been determined. Proponents claim that private programs offer greater administrative flexibility, more treatment integrity, and greater cost-effectiveness. Critics note the lack of standards and monitoring and the potential for cost cutting at the expense of the youths in care. (p. 1572)

Will private music therapy practitioners find their niche in this new system?

Summary

Youths are being confined in detention centers, state training schools and private correctional facilities at an alarming rate. Many of these youths respond to and benefit from the unique power of music. With the support and guidance of an interdisciplinary treatment team, the music therapist uses prescribed interventions to promote the emotional, social, physical, and cognitive (academic) growth of young offenders.

References

American Psychological Association (1993). *Violence and youth: Psychology's response.* Washington, DC: Author.

Baird, S. C. (1987). *The development of risk prediction scales for the California Youthful Offender Parole Board.* San Francisco. National Council on Crime and Delinquency.

Barton, W. H. (1994). Juvenile corrections. In National Association of Social Workers (Ed.), *Encyclopedia of Social Work* (19th edition). Washington, DC: NASW Press.

Blumstein, A., Farrington, D. P., & Moitra, S. (1985). Delinquency careers: Innocents, desisters, and persisters. In M. Tonry & N. Morris, (Eds.), *Crime and Justice, 6,* 187.

Brendtro, L., & Ness, A. (1983). *Re-educating troubled youth.* New York: Aldine Publishing Company.

Brooks, D. M. (1989). Music therapy enhances treatment with adolescents. *Music Therapy Perspectives, 6,* 37–39.

Eisenman, R. (1991). Is justice equal: A look at restitution, probation or incarceration in six states. *Louisiana Journal of Counseling and Development, 11* (2), 47–50.

Elliot, D., Huizinga, D., & Morse, B. (1988). A career analysis of serious violent offenders. In *Violent juvenile crime: What do we know about it and what can we do about it?* Ann Arbor: University of Michigan Press.

Freed, B. (1987). Songwriting with the chemically dependent. *Music Therapy Perspectives, 4,* 13–18.

Gardstrom, S. (1987). Positive peer culture: A working definition for the music therapist. *Music Therapy Perspectives, 4,* 19–23.

Greenwood, P. (1986). Differences in criminal behavior and court responses among juvenile and young adult defendants. In M. Tonry & N. Morris, (Eds.), *Crime and Justice, 7,* 151.

Jones, M. A., & Krisberg, B. (1994). *Images and reality: Juvenile crime, youth violence, and public policy.* San Fransisco: National Council on Crime and Delinquency.

Krisberg, B. (1987). Preventing and controlling violent street crime: The state of the art. In *Violent juvenile crime: What do we know about it and what can we do about it?* Minneapolis: Center for the Study of Youth Policy.

Leone, P. E. (1994). Education services for youth with disabilities in a state-operated juvenile correctional system: Case study and analysis. *Journal of Special Education, 28,* 43–58.

Lewis, D. O., Moy, E., Jackson, L. D., Aaronson, R., Restifo, N., Serra, S., & Simos, A. (1985). Biopsychosocial characteristics of children who later murder: A prospective study. *American Journal of Psychiatry, 142,* 1161.

Lewis, D. O., Pincus, J. H., Bard, B., Richardson, E., Prichep, L. S., Feldman, M., & Yeager, C. (1988). Neuropsychiatric, psychoeducational, and family characteristics of 14 juveniles condemned to death in the United States. *American Journal of Psychiatry, 145,* 584.

Mahoney, A. R. (1991). Man, I'm already dead: Serious juvenile offenders in context. *Notre Dame Journal of Law, Ethics & Public Policy, 5,* 443.

National Association for Music Therapy, Inc. (1993). *Sourcebook.* Silver Spring, MD: Author.

National Association for Music Therapy, Inc. (1994). *Sourcebook.* Silver Spring, MD: Author.

National Coalition of State Juvenile Justice Advisory Groups. (1993). Myths and realities: Meeting the challenge of serious, violent, and chronic juvenile offenders. *1992 Annual Report.* Washington, DC: Author.

Schwartz, I. M. (1992). *Juvenile justice and public policy: Toward a national agenda.* New York: Lexington Press.

Schwartz, I. M., Barton, W. H., & Orlando, F. (1991). Keeping kids out of secure detention. *Public Welfare, Spring 20–26,* 46.

United States Department of Justice (1991). *Juveniles taken into custody: Fiscal year 1990 report.* Washington, DC: Office of Juvenile Justice and Delinquency Prevention.

Unkefer, R. F. (Ed.). (1990). *Music therapy in the treatment of adults with mental disorders.* New York: Schirmer Books.

MUSIC THERAPY FOR LEARNERS WITH SEVERE DISABILITIES IN A PUBLIC SCHOOL SETTING

Kathleen A. Coleman

IN the public school setting, students with the label "severely/profoundly handicapped" or "SPH" are generally the most impaired and lowest functioning students served by the district. Typically, their functioning tends to be under a 2-year developmental level and reflects a diagnosis of mental retardation, autism, cerebral palsy, and/or sensory impairments. It is also common in this setting to find students who have more than one handicapping condition.

Despite the diversity of their disabilities, these students usually have similar educational needs. Since academic goals in the traditional areas of reading, writing, and mathematics have little relevance for this population, educational programming for these students primarily focuses on the acquisition of the most functional life skills in the areas of communication, socialization, and self-help (activities of daily living). The music therapist who works with this group of students will need to focus his/her energies on developing strategies that reinforce these very basic skills.

According to IDEA, the educational placement for each student with special needs is to be made on an individual basis; thus placements even for students with similar disabilities can vary widely. Across the state of Texas, students with severe/profound disabilities may be found in segregated special schools, self-contained special education classrooms on age appropriate campuses, or in fully inclusive placements in their home schools. Placements for students with severe disabilities can also vary within the *same* school district, as a result of different opinions among families as to the needs of their child. The music therapist will need creativity and flexibility in order to provide meaningful services to students within their particular type of educational placement.

Service Delivery Models and Choices

With the help of the special education administrator, the first step for the music therapist is to determine the types of service delivery models that can potentially be utilized when a student is designated as needing music therapy to benefit from his or her education. The final choice of service delivery for a student, though, can only be made once the assessment is completed. It is illegal to predetermine (without parental input) exactly the services and type of service delivery a student will receive. The potential choices of models that can be utilized are shown in Table 1.

Table 1

Music Therapy Service Delivery Model

Direct: Student	Consult: Student	Consult: Teacher & Program
Must be referred by ARD Committee for assessment	Must be referred by ARD Committee for assessment	No official ARD Committee referral
Formal assessment required	Formal assessment required	No formal assessment required
Observation/Record review required	Observation/Record review required	Observation/Record review required
Teacher interview required	Teacher interview required	Teacher interview required
Parent input required	Parent input required	Parent input may be solicited
Separate music therapy goals and objectives OR initialing of IEP goals and objectives required.	Separate music therapy goals OR initialing of IEP goals and objectives required	No separate music therapy goals and objectives
Therapist designs and implements hands-on music therapy program for student	Therapist designs, demonstrates and monitors carry through of music therapy program for a special education student by designated special education personnel	Therapist designs and demonstrates music therapy program appropriate for the whole classroom and/or designated students
Therapist sees students individually OR in small groups (size of group depends on the type of disability experienced by the students)	Therapy is carried out individually or in small groups initially by the therapist, then continued by designated special education personnel AND monitored by the therapist.	Therapy is carried out with the class as a whole or designated students by the therapist or teacher on a regular basis as specified

Direct Service

In this model, the student receives weekly or biweekly individual or group sessions directly from the music therapist. The related service of music therapy is identified on the student's IEP as a needed service that will assist the student in benefiting from his/her special education program. An individual music therapy assessment is required under this model of service. The music therapist will either write a separate page of goals and objectives, or will initial specific objectives on the master IEP that can be addressed appropriately through music therapy. With students who have severe/profound disabilities, initialing the IEP objectives is often the most effective route to take since the skills being worked on by the teacher and other therapists will be very similar in nature, due to the low functioning level of the students. Writing separate goals and objectives is generally seen as repetitious. Delivery of service through this model can be effective whether the student is in a self-contained setting or an inclusive setting.

Consult Service

In this model, the student initially receives weekly or biweekly individual or group sessions directly from the music therapist for a period of 6 to 8 weeks. During this period, the teacher is observing the sessions and being trained by the music therapist to carry out a specifically designed program for a student or group of students. Once the teacher begins implementing the program, the music therapist then monitors the program on a consistent basis, usually once or twice a month. This ongoing monitoring of the music therapy program is necessary for the model of service to be designated "consult to student." The related service of music therapy is still identified on the student's IEP as a needed related service that will assist the student in benefiting from his/her special education program. An individual music therapy assessment is also required under this model of service. Goals and objectives are developed in the same manner as described above for the direct service model. Consult service to the student can be effective, provided the teacher is willing to carry out the program designed by the music therapist and is also responsive to ongoing supervision and consultation. Delivery of service through this model can be effective with students in a self-contained setting. If the student is in an inclusive setting, consult service to the student will be successful only if there is personnel available to regularly implement the program designed by the music therapist.

Consult Service—Program Based

In this model, the services of the music therapist are designed to support the overall programming for self-contained classrooms such as early childhood, autism classes, and life skill classes. The music therapist works with the teacher in designing a group based music therapy program that can be implemented with the entire class. Under this service delivery model, each student's IEP states that a music therapist will be serving as a consultant to the classroom as a whole. An individual music therapy assessment is not required under this model. However, each student's IEP is reviewed by the music therapist to extract a list of skills which will then be a part of the group program designed by the therapist. In this model of service delivery, the music therapist provides weekly demonstration sessions with teacher and aide participation mandatory. The focus is on familiarizing the teacher and aide with the session materials, so that the music therapy session can be repeated throughout the week. This model is often the most effective with students with severe/profound disabilities. The weekly presence of the therapist combined with the follow-through by the teacher tends to generate the most effective results. Paperwork is minimized under this model, allowing the music therapist more time to design strategies and materials for use in the sessions.

Assessment

The music therapist cannot begin a music therapy assessment until a student has been referred for such an assessment by the Admission, Referral, and Dismissal (ARD) committee. The assessment of a student with severe/profound disabilities should be done in both a formal and informal manner. Since these students are very low functioning, it is critical to observe them in several settings, in addition to conducting the actual music therapy assessment. Students can respond very differently, depending on the personnel with whom they are interacting, their current state of health, effects of medications, as well as many other factors. In order to make an accurate decision as to whether or not music therapy is a needed related service, the music therapy clinician has to determine whether, in fact, music provides the student with significant motivation and/or a significant assist in the learning process.

A music therapy assessment includes a study of each student's unique problems and needs. It compares the student's skill performance with and *without* music strategies. The basic steps of an assessment are as follows:

- review reports and evaluations contained in the student's cumulative file
- interview the student's teacher
- interview other related service personnel working with the student
- interview the student's parents
- observe the student functioning in his/her classroom
- review the student's current IEP (Individual Education Plan)
- administer an appropriate music therapy assessment (i.e., one assessment that has worked well is the Westplate Auditory Perceptual Tool; Prelude Music Therapy Products—see Resource section)
- write up the final comprehensive report, which includes: determination of the need for service of music therapy if needed, how often the service should be provided and the length of each session, title of the person who will provide the service (RMT–BC), identification of the service delivery model–direct, consult, or consult to program.

Since the ARD committee members will most likely not have observed the assessment session, the only input they will consider at the ARD meeting is the written report. Therefore, it is critical that the report be professional and thorough and include the following information:

- the purpose of the assessment
- an outline of the assessment procedure
- relevant information from the files reviewed
- information from the interviews (be sure to indicate who made each statement)
- summary of your classroom observation
- description of the setting and general student behavior on the day of testing
- results of the assessment (indicate which one was given)

- suggestions
- recommendations

It is important to remember that the standard for therapeutic intervention in a school district is different from one that would be used in a residential center, state school or hospital (see Table 2). In order to recommend music therapy, the music therapist *must* describe how the music therapy intervention would significantly assist the student in benefiting from his or her educational program. The therapist may see potential or abilities that could be nurtured, but the special education administration only wants to know whether music therapy will provide a necessary and effective way for the student to meet IEP goals and objectives. If the music therapist is new to working in the school system, it is important to talk with other experienced therapists to make the language in the report consistent with that used by other education professionals.

Comparing the student's demonstrated abilities with and without music therapy intervention is a primary objective of the assessment process. If the student performs as well or better in the classroom without music, then music therapy is not a necessary service. With an individual who has severe/profound disabilities, the response to music is usually very definite—he/she may be much more alert or may not react at all.

When writing a report for an ARD committee, it is necessary to make a clear distinction between suggestions and recommendations. Recommendations indicate your professional opinion regarding the school district's responsibility to the student. Because these recommendations can be used as future evidence in legal proceedings, statements made in this section need to be substantiated. Another section titled "suggestions" is appropriate for comments on the role music could play in the home, or the availability of programming outside the school district. This is helpful information, but does not designate services the school district is obligated to provide.

The IEP Process

Once the assessment has been completed, including the recommendations as to whether or not service should be provided, a meeting of the ARD committee is scheduled. During this meeting, the music therapy assessment, along with any other assessments of the student will be reviewed. The results of the reports will be discussed, and the committee will attempt to arrive at a consensus of opinion as to which recommendations will be implemented. Remember, the recommendation might be for *or* against the provision of music therapy. The therapist may be called upon to defend the recommendation and answer questions but will *not* (because music therapy is a related service) be part of the group (administration representative, teacher, and parents) that makes the final consensus.

If it is determined that music therapy service will be provided, a discussion and development of IEP objectives will follow. While the music therapist may bring a draft of suggested objectives to the meeting, it is *only* considered a draft. Developing an IEP is a group process completed at the meeting and must include the parents of the student. As discussed earlier in the chapter, the music therapist may develop a separate page of objectives for the IEP or initial objectives on the main IEP draft that would be appropriate for music therapy intervention. Choosing which approach to use is determined by the school district.

Table 2

Music Therapy Models

School Based Model	Medical Model	Private Therapy
Goal: To assist a student with handicaps in attaining educational goals. To train educational staff in the use of music therapy strategies to assist students in attaining.	**Goal:** To treat the student's continuum of needs (from acute through rehabilitated status)	**Goal:** To assist the student with handicaps in attaining educational goals. To provide enrichment and quality of life. To provide more intensive help towards meeting educational goals than is possible in the school setting.
Frequency of sessions: Based on educational need as specified in the Individual Education Plan for a student	**Frequency of sessions:** As prescribed	**Frequency of sessions:** As decided upon by the parent and the therapist. May also be prescribed
Caseload of therapist: Larger, students usually seen in small groups ranging from two to eight students	**Caseload of therapist:** Smaller, students usually seen individually	**Caseload of therapist:** Smaller, students usually seen individually or in very small groups
Implementer of Services: Therapist, school personnel, parent, student	**Implementer of Services:** Therapist, parent	**Implementer of Services:** Therapist, parent
Duration of Therapy: Ranges from one time consult to weekly or bi-weekly services for one or more years	**Duration of Therapy:** Determined by medical needs of student. May be short or long term	**Duration of Therapy:** Weekly or bi-weekly services for as long as parent and therapist indicates need
Decisions on Therapy: Made by the ARD committee	**Decisions on Therapy:** Made by doctor, therapist and parent	**Decisions on Therapy:** Made by parent and therapist
Service Delivery: Direct therapy; and/or with the following; consult with student and/or teacher; program equipment consultation; individual and classroom modifications; inservice training	**Service Delivery:** Direct service with some parent consultation; recommendations and suggestions for equipment	**Service Delivery:** Direct service with some parent consultation; recommendations and suggestions for equipment

A music therapist can be a helpful part of the IEP process, particularly in assisting the committee to write clearly worded, functional objectives. The acronym "SMART" is a valuable tool when writing objectives:

>S   specific
>M   measurable
>A   attainable
>R   realistic
>T   time frame

With students who have severe/profound disabilities, it is important to look at the long term value of a skill. Because the learning process will be very slow with these students, it is critical that the skills chosen by the committee reflect functional, age appropriate skills that will have potential for assisting the student later in life. When an IEP has been drafted and approved by the core committee members (parent, teacher, administration), the document can be signed and the meeting is over.

If you are not able to attend the ARD meeting where the music therapy assessment is to be reviewed, have your report reviewed by a committee member prior to the meeting. It is also strongly recommended that a parent conference be scheduled to review the music therapy assessment. Otherwise, the parents have the right to request the rescheduling of the ARD meeting.

Session Planning and Task Analysis

Music therapy sessions for students with severe/profound disabilities will tend to focus on very basic skills. Some of the most common skills addressed in sessions include:

- holding and grasping objects
- manipulating objects
- eye contact
- focus of attention
- indicating by gesture or movement these words: finished, hello, good-bye, more, yes/no
- following simple one step directions
- accessing and operating a pressure switch
- imitating gestures
- reaching and touching objects
- recognizing voices and faces
- showing awareness of self
- localizing sound
- making choices between several items
- matching
- sorting

For students with severe/profound disabilities, skills need to be task analyzed into the smallest and simplest of steps. Conferring with the special education teacher and other therapists can be a helpful way to insure that all tasks have been broken down sufficiently. Progress is often measured in tiny increments with these students.

Sessions need to balance frequent repetition with some variety. A significant advantage of music therapy for this population is that the student can work on the same learning task for a long time since music strategies can be varied in order to maintain his/her interest. A group session for students with severe/profound disabilities is typically more like a series of one to one interactions since each student frequently lacks the requisite skills to respond as a group. For example, rather than give a group direction such as "clap your hands" and expect everyone to respond appropriately, the therapist would most likely need to provide individual attention to each student to accomplish this task. Even when the students are not able to respond as a group, they can still benefit from watching their peers respond. In some cases, the students will learn important concepts such as waiting and taking turns by watching others.

Age appropriateness is also an issue to carefully consider when providing music therapy intervention for these students. Even though they will learn very slowly and function at a low developmental level, it is important whenever possible to use music and materials that are consistent with chronological age. This definitely demands creativity on the part of the therapist!

One way to plan effective sessions for students with severe/profound disabilities is to work from a general session outline—choosing songs and strategies using the materials listed below and matching the materials and strategies to an overall list of skills from each student's IEP. The following outlines suggest a plan for elementary school students and a plan for middle school/high school students.

Elementary School Outline

1. **Hello song**: Select a song to consistently open the session. It is helpful if the song offers an opportunity for the group to attempt to perform a simple action such as patting knees or clapping.
   Possible Objectives: eye contact, name recognition, hand shaking

2. **Puppets**: Select a song or two that feature colorful puppets with interesting textures. Songs that feature the puppets making silly sounds or performing silly actions may provoke responses from the students.
   Possible Objectives: vocalizing, holding and grasping items, focus of attention, reaching and touching objects

3. **Percussion instruments**: Select percussion instruments that have an unusual sound or appearance, such as the rainstick, cabasa, or the clatterpillar. These types of instruments are often more motivating to low functioning students and encourage attention and interaction. Choose songs that match the sound quality of the instrument. Adapt mallets (see end of chapter) for students who can not hold them.
   Possible Objectives: focus of attention, cause and effect, localizing sound, making a choice between several items, manipulating objects

4. **Vocal imitation with or without a pressure switch**: Select a song with a repeated line ("Train Is a-Coming,"which has "oh, yes" as a repeated line). Record this line on a tape

recorder connected to a switch or a voice activated device. Prompt the students to depress the switch at the correct time and "sing" along.
Possible Objectives: vocal imitation, accessing and operating a pressure switch, following simple one step directions

5. **Motor imitation**: Select a song with one or two actions. Prompt the students (physically if necessary) to complete the actions. Selected songs will need to be repeated many, many times with these students.
Possible Objectives: imitating gestures, following one step directions

6. **Tagboard books**: Make a simple illustrated version of a song familiar to the student into a book with tagboard pages. Pictures from magazines or coloring books can be used to develop patterns if the music therapist is not skilled at drawing. Commercially developed songbook patterns also can be utilized to develop materials. (See Resource section.) Attach small pieces of sponge between the pages to make the pages thicker and easier to turn. Prompt students to turn pages as the song is sung.
Possible Objectives: holding and grasping objects, manipulating objects, focus of attention

7. **Song file folders**: Make or locate pictures to illustrate key words in a song. It is best to choose a song with concrete vocabulary words. Attach black and white pictures illustrating these words to the file folder and have students match the colored version of the picture to the folder as the song is sung. Severely physically involved students may indicate the correct picture for matching via eye gaze, or other communication method.
Possible Objectives: matching, following simple one step directions

8. **Large tone bars**: High quality wooden tone bars (such as those made by Sonor—see Resource section) produce vibrations and sounds which can be appealing to low functioning students. Use the tone bars to accompany simple, familiar songs. Place students between tone bars or sitting on tone bars for additional stimulation.
Possible Objectives: localizing sound, showing awareness of self, eye contact, focus of attention

9. **Manipulatives**: Use items such as bean bags or yarn balls and encourage students to pick up and place these items according to directions in a song.
Possible Objectives: following simple one step directions, holding and grasping objects, manipulating objects

10. **Good-bye**: Select a song to close the session that encourages eye contact, name recognition and waving good-bye.
Possible Objectives: imitating gestures, eye contact, focus of attention, handshaking

Middle School/High School Outline

1. **Hello**: Select a song to regularly begin the session. Aim to be age appropriate by using adapted versions of popular songs, or songs that stylistically approach popular or folk types of music. (i.e., "Hello, How Are You" recorded by The Doors)
    Possible Objectives: eye contact, handshaking, self-awareness, name recognition

2. **Omnichord**: Have available a selection of song choice cards which contain a picture illustrating the song on the front and words and chords printed on the back. Allow the student to choose a song from a choice of two cards. Program the Omnichord with the chords to the selected song and prompt the student to depress the pressure switch at the correct time.
    Possible Objectives: making choices between several items, accessing and operating a pressure switch

3. **Percussion instruments**: Use a variety of percussion instruments, including those with unusual sounds or appearances. Encourage the students to play the instrument for the duration of a song. Utilize popular music when possible (such as "La Bamba," recorded by Richie Valens). Adapt mallets (see end of chapter) for students who can not hold them.
    Possible Objectives: holding and grasping objects, manipulating objects, making choices between several items

4. **Singing with or without a pressure switch**: Select a song with a repeated line or repeated words (such as "I Get By With A Little Help from My Friends," recorded by the Beatles, which frequently repeats the word "friends"). Record this word on a tape recorder connected to a switch or a voice activated device. Prompt the students to depress the switch at the correct time and "sing" along.
    Possible Objectives: vocalizing, accessing and operating a pressure switch, recognizing voices

5. **Motor imitation**: Select an age appropriate song with one or two actions. Folk or camp songs are good sources. Prompt the students (physically if necessary) to complete the actions. Selected songs will need to be repeated numerous times with these students.
    Possible Objectives: imitating gestures, following simple one step directions

6. **Tagboard books**: Make a simple illustrated version of a song familiar to the student into a book with tagboard pages. Pictures from magazines or coloring books can be used to develop patterns by the music therapist who does not draw. Commercially developed songbook patterns also can be utilized to develop materials. (See equipment resource list at the end of the book.) Attach small pieces of sponge between the pages to make the pages easier to turn. Prompt students to turn pages as the song is sung.
    Possible Objectives: holding and grasping objects, manipulating objects, following simple one step directions

7. **Song file folders**: Make or locate pictures to illustrate key words in a song. It is best to choose a song with concrete vocabulary words. Attach black and white pictures to the file folder and have students match the colored version of the picture to the folder as the song is sung. Severely physically involved students may indicate picture via eye gaze, or other communication method.
    Possible Objectives: matching, manipulating objects

8. **Choir chimes**: Use choir chimes to have students (if they can grasp) play a simple repeated ostinato to accompany a song. For students who can not grasp, the therapist can play the ostinato and encourage them to focus and turn towards the sound.
    Possible Objectives: localizing sound, recognizing voices and faces

9. **Good-bye**: Select a song to close the session that encourages eye contact, name recognition and waving good-bye. For age appropriateness, try to select a song that is an adaptation of a popular or folk song.
    Possible Objectives: imitating gestures, focusing attention, eye contact, handshaking

Consulting With Special Educators and Other Therapists

Regardless of which service delivery model is utilized (direct, consult, or consult to program), the music therapist's ability to consult and communicate effectively with the special educator and other therapists is the key to positive outcomes for the students. It is a rare school district that provides music therapy more than twice a week; therefore, follow through by the teacher (or other therapists) on the days between music therapy sessions is essential to the student's ability to benefit fully from music therapy.

Consulting with school district personnel is not just a matter of issuing orders and commands for others to follow. Skilled communication, demonstration of techniques and preparation of quality materials and tapes is essential. If the teacher feels that he or she is being treated in a demeaning manner by the music therapist, there will be no follow through. Since teachers and other personnel are often apprehensive about their ability to sing or perform musical tasks, it is the job of the music therapist to task analyze this situation so that the teacher can easily carry through with the programming.

One helpful method is to create a notebook for the teacher that contains the following:

* general information about music therapy
* charts or data forms showing the relationship of learning objectives to the musical tasks
* copies of songs to be utilized in the sessions (only original songs or those in the public domain)
* a cassette tape containing a completely recorded session
* a schedule, showing where and how the music therapist can be located during the week
* a section where the teacher can jot down questions and student responses for discussion during the next scheduled consultation

A notebook system can clearly show the teacher what to do and how to do it. Since special educators are busy, with many demands on their time, developing a clearly organized program increases the likelihood of regular, weekly follow-through with the students.

Inclusion in Music Education Classes

Students with severe/profound disabilities may or may not be included in a music education class. This is an individually based decision that should be made at the student's IEP meeting. It is helpful at the meeting to discuss the following questions before a decision is made to send a student to a music education class.

- Can the student remain seated for the duration of the class?
    Independently?
    With a few verbal reminders from teacher or peers?
    With the presence of an adult support staff member?

- Can the student remain quiet at appropriate times during the class?
    Independently?
    With a few verbal reminders from teachers or peers?
    With the presence of an adult support staff member?

- Can the student keep his/her hands to himself and avoid hitting, pinching, or otherwise distracting the other students from learning?
    Independently?
    With a few verbal reminders from teachers or peers?
    With the presence of an adult support staff member?

- Can the student use materials in the classroom in a reasonably appropriate manner? (i.e., refrain from tearing up books, or mouthing or throwing instruments?)
    Independently?
    With a few verbal reminders from teachers or peers?
    With the presence of an adult support staff member?

- Would attending the class have some degree of meaning for the student?

- Can the student participate in at least one of the activities presented in the lesson plan with or without modifications?

- If an adult support staff member is required, will there be an available person to attend the class with the child at the scheduled time?

When discussing this issue, there may be some confusion among school personnel as to why the student would be considered for a music education class if he/she is already receiving music therapy. It is important at this time to review with the school personnel the difference between a public school class (music education) and a related service (music therapy). Traditionally, music education teaches music literacy and aesthetic appreciation to a group, while music therapy focuses on *individual* learning skills selected from the IEP and presented through the medium of music.

Although there is no easy answer as to which student with severe/profound disabilities should be included in music education, careful discussion of the above questions can enhance the chances for a successful placement for the student.

Basic Instrument Adaptations

Many students with severe/profound disabilities have physical or cognitive problems that require adaptation of materials. It is important to have quick and easy methods to adapt common materials used by the music therapist, particularly adaptations for simple percussion instruments. The following adaptations are inexpensive and easy to use.

One Wrap Velcro Straps: One wrap Velcro is Velcro that comes in one long strip with the rough texture on one side and the fuzzy texture on the other side. To assist a student in keeping grasp on an instrument (such as bells or a shaker), try the following:
- Cut two pieces of one wrap Velcro long enough to wrap around the student's hand.
- Place the instrument in the student's hand and wrap the two pieces of one wrap Velcro snugly around the student's hand, with the FUZZY side against the student's hand.

Mini Mallet: This adaptation will give you a "handle" in which to place the mallet securely and will attach to the student's hand with one wrap Velcro. This adaptation is best for students with small hands. The "mini mallet" is made as follows:
- Materials:
  — One piece of built up foam for spoon handles, cut to equal slightly more than the width of the student's palm
  — Two pieces of one wrap Velcro cut so that the pieces will wrap easily around the student's hand
  — One mallet, appropriate for use with that particular student
- Put the mallet inside the built up foam. Place mallet and foam combination in the student's hand so that the end of the mallet sticks out between the index and middle fingers. Wrap the two pieces of one wrap Velcro snugly against the student's hand with the fuzzy side against the hand.

Super Mallet: This adaptation will give you a "handle" in which to place the mallet securely and will attach to the student's hand with one wrap Velcro. This adaptation is best for students with larger hands. The "super mallet" is made as follows:
- Materials:
  — eight inch piece of one wrap Velcro
  — one large rubber triangle pencil grip
  — one bicycle handlebar grip
  — one mallet
- Thread the piece of Velcro through the pencil grip, keeping the ends unattached.

- Thread the Velcro and the pencil grip through one end of the bicycle handlebar grip. Sometimes one end of the bicycle handlebar is larger than the other. In that case, thread it through the larger end.
- Pull the Velcro through the hole at the other end of the bicycle grip. You may need tweezers to do this if the grip has a smaller hole at the other end.
- Place a mallet in the pencil grip which is now inside of the bicycle grip. It will hold the mallet securely. The adapted mallet can now be placed in the student's hand and attached snugly with the ends of the Velcro.

Tips

- Be patient, and remember that creative repetition is the key with this population.
- Be as age appropriate as possible!
- Think long term and functional; these students take a long time to learn skills; spend time on what is truly valuable.
- Use pressure switches and voice output devices; give students a voice to "talk" and "sing."
- Encourage teachers and parents by pointing out the positive improvements; when you are the one with the student every day you may not notice these small increments of progress.
- Purchase and utilize quality, durable, and drool-proof equipment!

Music Therapy for Learners With Autism
in a Public School Setting

Angela M. Snell

> People treating autistic children should avoid falling into the trap of using
> just one type of treatment. A variety of methods used together would
> probably be the most successful. . . . A good program should also have
> flexible nonaversive behavior modification, sensory treatment, speech
> therapy, exercise, and music therapy.
>
> (Grandin & Scariano, 1986)

The Monroe County Intermediate School District (MCISD), in Monroe, Michigan, serves as a link between the local school districts of Monroe County and the Michigan Department of Education. Programs are designed to meet the educational needs of Monroe County individuals with disabilities from birth through age 25. Because MCISD recognizes that the needs of each student are individual, varied, and unique, a continuum of services and educational settings are coordinated with the families, local school districts and the community in order to provide the best opportunity for full realization of each student's educational potential. MCISD's Monroe County Educational Center (MCEC) provides center-based programming for students with severe mental impairment (SMI), severe multiple impairment (SXI), trainable mental impairment (TMI), and Autism (AI). Music therapy is one of the related services MCISD provides at the MCEC.

Background

History

Monroe County residents approved a ½ mill for nonmandated special education in 1956. A county board of education administered programs until 1963 when Michigan legislation required formation of Intermediate School Districts (ISDs) in each county. Throughout the 1960s, students who were considered slow learners or educable mentally impaired were placed in self-contained classrooms in local schools that served special education students of varying ages and functioning levels. In addition, there were separate classrooms for students with hearing impairment and for students who were physically or otherwise health impaired (POHI). Although they had been receiving some services through the mental health agency, in 1971 the state mandated that ISDs run programs for students diagnosed as trainably or severely mentally impaired. That same year, Monroe County passed a bond issue to build the Monroe County

Educational Center (MCEC). The MCEC was officially opened in 1973 to house center-based categorical programs for students, age 25 and younger, who were labeled as SMI, SXI, and TMI.

With the passage of PL 94–142 and subsequent changes in the state special education code regarding autism, the MCEC opened its first Autistically Impaired (AI) categorical classroom in the early 1980s. Since 1987, the center has maintained two AI classrooms in accordance with state and federal laws. Due to the unique educational needs of the child with autism, a maximum of five students are allowed per one special education teacher and one classroom aide. The special education teacher must have an AI endorsed teaching certificate and the AI program must include (a) language and communication development, (b) personal adjustment training, and (c) prevocational education (Michigan State Board of Education, 1994a).

Today, the MCEC serves approximately 140 students from all nine local school districts in Monroe County, who are between the ages of 2½ and 25. In addition to the two self-contained AI classrooms, there are six TMI classrooms and five SMI/SXI classrooms. A range of services, including speech therapy, physical therapy, music therapy, occupational therapy, adaptive physical education, and community-based education, among others, are made available according to individual and group needs. Based on changing educational needs, new research, and state and federal laws, the center's approach to special education continues to evolve, as does MCISD's entire delivery system.

Autism Defined

The Autism Society of America (ASA) (1995) describes autism as a lifelong developmental disability which appears during the first 3 years of life. It is a neurological disorder that affects functioning of the brain and is manifested in a variety of behaviors including deficiencies in communication and social interaction, repeated body movements, unusual responses to people or objects, and resistance to any changes in routine.

The *Diagnostic and Statistical Manual* (4th ed.) (*DSM–IV*), published by the American Psychiatric Association (1994), identifies autism as one of the "pervasive developmental disorders" and lists the following conditions as indicative of the Autistic Disorder:

1. Qualitative impairment in social interaction, such as the inability to decode nonverbal behaviors (i.e., facial expression, gestures), develop interpersonal relationships, and/or respond to other people socially or emotionally.

2. Qualitative impairments in verbal and nonverbal communication, such as a lack of or delay in verbal language, impaired ability to initiate or sustain a conversation with others (when speech is present), repetitive use of unrelated phrases, abnormal voice quality (i.e., monotone or questionlike), inability to understand questions or directions, and/or the absence of imaginative play.

3. Limited, repetitive, and stereotypical patterns of behavior, interests, and activities, such as stereotyped body movements (i.e., clapping, finger flicking, rocking), odd body postures, preoccupation with parts of objects, restricted range of interests (i.e., electricity, traffic signs), unusual play rituals, insistence on sameness (i.e., even minor details like the layout of the dinner table), fascination with moving objects (i.e., spinning blades of a fan) and/or attachment to an inanimate object (i.e., a piece of string or a chain).

4. Associated characteristics emerge as unusual responses to sensory stimuli, abnormal posture and motor behavior, uneven development of cognitive skills, self-injurious behavior, peculiar eating and sleeping habits, or abnormal mood swings.

The initial description of children with early infantile autism (Kanner, 1943) has been debated and modified over the past 50 years (Center for Quality Special Education [CQSE], 1993). Kanner's definition and the various definitions existing today include a predominant amount of problems associated with communication development (American Psychiatric Association, 1987, 1994; Autism Society of America, 1995). The behavioral criteria, rather than medical tests, used to diagnose autism continue to change. Grandin (1995) reports that the criteria listed in an earlier version of the American Psychiatric Association's *Diagnostic and Statistical Manual* (3rd ed., revised) (*DSM–III–R*) (1987) would result in 91% of children displaying autistic symptoms being labeled as autistic. Based on criteria published in the latest edition of this manual (*DSM–IV*) (American Psychiatric Association, 1994), only 59% of the same children would be labeled as having autism. In addition to autism, *DSM–IV* lists several autism-related disorders under the general heading "Pervasive Developmental Disorder" (PDD) that includes Autistic Disorder, Rett's Syndrome, Childhood Disintegrative Disorder, Asperger's Syndrome, and Pervasive Developmental Disorder Not Otherwise Specified (PDD–NOS). While some believe that these categories reflect distinctly separate conditions, others feel they lie on a continuum of autism, from mild to severe. This "Autistic Continuum" (Grandin, 1995, p. 52) places children with Kanner's or Asperger's syndrome at the highest functioning level, children with childhood disintegrative disorder at the lowest functioning level with a wide range of combinations throughout the middle. Grandin (1995) also describes this as a "sensory processing continuum"; those with high-functioning autism have mild sensory oversensitivity problems and the low-functioning person receives severely distorted information visually and aurally (p. 52).

Based on each professional's training, jargon, and experience with autism, there can be a multitude of labels used to describe a person with autistic traits. The applied labels include autistic-like, learning disabled with autistic tendencies, high functioning or low functioning autism, typical or a-typical autism, severe, moderate or mild autism, Kanner's autism, and Asperger's syndrome. Professionals working with individuals with autism, and/or persons with a range of developmental delays, should review the literature and become familiar with the extensive list of behavioral traits associated with autism and related disorders.

Unique Educational Needs

Since there is a wide range of ability levels manifested in individuals with autism, individualized programming is essential (Schopler & Mesibov, 1988). For example, although approximately 75% of the people diagnosed with autism have functional abilities in a mentally retarded range, many have uneven cognitive abilities, such as an advanced reading level (i.e., hyperlexia) or mathematical knowledge simultaneously present with the inability to engage in meaningful verbal conversations (American Psychiatric Association, 1994). In addition to severe deficiencies in communication and social skills, unusual behaviors, such as stereotyped body movements (i.e., flapping, clapping, rocking), odd responses to sensory stimuli (i.e., over- or undersensitivity to tactile, visual, auditory, stimuli) (Ayres, 1979; Grandin, 1988, 1995; Ornitz, cited in Thaut, 1984), self-stimulation, and resistance to change present challenges when implementing the Individual Education Plan in the recommended social setting (CQSE, 1993).

Highly structured treatment models using various combinations of therapies, including music therapy, are recommended for individuals with autism (Clarizio & McCoy, 1983; Grandin, 1995; Olley, 1987). Early intervention designed to address the development of functional language and communication skills is crucial when one considers that the degree of language development in the child with autism by age 5 is directly related to the child's degree of success later in life (Bagley & McGeein, 1989; Kurita, 1985; Schopler & Mesibov, 1985). Special education programming should also include opportunities to expand functional skills (Alper, 1981), learn social and interpersonal skills (i.e., imitation, interactive play, sensitivity toward others) (Schopler & Mesibov, 1983), and develop control over stereotypical behaviors (CQSE, 1993). The educational team should plan lessons that teach the student how to decode nondirect verbal or nonverbal communication (Hermelin, 1978; Volkman 1987). Special emphasis should be placed on helping the student generalize learned behaviors in as many situations as possible (Paul, 1987; Schopler & Mesibov, 1988).

Placement Options

In a center-based program such as the one at MCEC, the students' chronological age and special education label typically determine the classroom placement. However, with the Reauthorization of IDEA (PL 101–476, formerly PL 94–142) and the push for inclusion and the Least Restrictive Environment (LRE), the Individual Education Planning Committee (IEPC) is now advocating that the students be placed according to their educational needs rather than their special education label. This reflects current trends that consider it important to place the student with age-appropriate peers according to chronological age. In fact, placement in the regular education setting with age-appropriate peers must be considered each time the IEPC convenes. If it has been determined that the inclusion setting is not considered least restrictive, an alternative setting can be recommended, from a continuum of placement options (see Figure 1). Each one of these placements can be supported by law if it is deemed "least restrictive" for the student by the IEPC.

Placement settings are indicated on the top row of the chart (see Figure 1). Placement in a setting located to the left of the chart (such as "Homebound/Residential") is considered "most dependent," reflecting the belief that the severity of the student's disability, typically medical in nature, requires that the educational programming be done in a residential setting. As one moves across the diagram to the right, the settings are considered more independent. Inclusion (i.e., full-time placement in the special education student's home district regular education system with chronological age grade placement) would then be considered "most independent" for the special education student. In some cases, however, inclusion may not be considered as either "most independent" or "least restrictive." Since the methods necessary for each student to attain his or her educational goals are uniquely individual, there are cases in which the inclusion setting may be viewed as inadequate by the IEPC. For example, support systems necessary for inclusion (i.e., a full-time aide, an adapted curriculum, and a battery of special services) of a particular student may foster dependency rather than function as a stepping stone to increased independence in the achievement of educational goals (academic and/or social). Having the availability for a

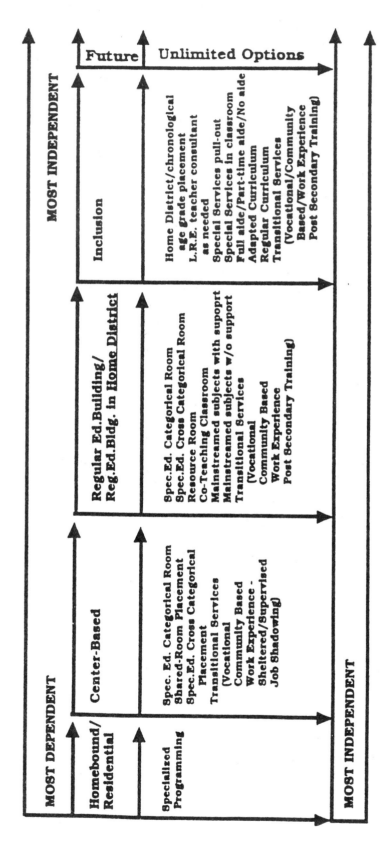

MONROE COUNTY INTERMEDIATE SCHOOL DISTRICT
Continuum of Placements

MOST DEPENDENT

Homebound/Residential

Specialized Programming

Spec. Ed. Categorical Room
Shared-Room Placement
Spec. Ed. Cross Categorical
Placement
Transitional Services
(Vocational
Community Based
Work Experience -
Sheltered/Supervised
Job Shadowing)

Center-Based

Regular Ed.Building/ Reg.Ed.Bldg. in Home District

Spec.Ed. Categorical Room
Spec.Ed. Cross Categorical Room
Resource Room
Co-Teaching Classroom
Mainstreamed subjects with supoprt
Mainstreamed subjects w/o support
Transitional Services
(Vocational
Community Based
Work Experience
Post Secondary Training)

Inclusion

MOST INDEPENDENT

Home District/chronological
age grade placement
L.R.E. teacher consultant
as needed
Special Services pull-out
Special Services in classroom
Full aide/Part-time aide/No aide
Adapted Curriculum
Regular Curriculum
Transitional Services
(Vocational/Community
Based/Work Experience
Post Secondary Training)

Future   Unlimited Options

MOST INDEPENDENT

The Continuum of Placements chart briefly outlines placement settings available to MCISD students. It seeks only to address placement settings and does not outline specific program designs. The settings listed are not exhaustive but placed in an approximate sequential order from "most dependent" to "most independent." Recognize that each student's needs and conditions are uniquely varied, so placement in the "most independent" setting may not be age-appropriate or "least restrictive," thus the need for a continuum. Movements down and to the right are considered progress toward increased independence. Conversely, if a student is placed too far ahead on the continuum, there is a safety net of options the individual can access by reconvening the IEPC.

Figure 1. Monroe County Intermediate School District Continuum of Placements

continuum of placements then becomes very important since some individuals may realize more success in a center-based program like the MCEC.

Placement options within each placement setting are listed in approximate sequential order with items shown at the top of the chart being "more dependent" and the bottom being "more independent." For instance, in the center-based school, the most dependent setting for a student with autism would be the special education AI categorical room, and the most independent setting would be a cross-categorical placement (i.e., student with autism placed in a TMI classroom) with community based and work experience transitional services.

The AI categorical room is designed to help the student more severely afflicted with autism develop skills and strategies to interact effectively with people and objects. But as time passes, the self-contained classroom could become restrictive and exclusionary if the educational team does not guide the student toward more independence in other settings. For example, consider that the AI categorical room is located close to the "most dependent" corner of the chart. On the one hand, a self-contained classroom with a 5 (students) to 2 (adults) ratio could be viewed as a positive teaching situation. But, if the student is 10 years old and has severely impaired functional use of skills due to autism, he could remain in an AI classroom for another 15 to 16 years (Michigan provides services through age 25). Since there are only 2 MCEC AI classrooms, the student could encounter only two different teachers over 15 years, or even longer if he entered the AI program at age 2½ as provided by the law. To prevent this, the MCEC multidisciplinary team designs experiences demanding generalization of skills and interaction with peers from other classrooms. As the student becomes successful in these situations, the IEPC may consider a shared-room (i.e., placement divided between an AI classroom and a TMI classroom) or a cross-categorical placement for the student.

The student is not restricted to the center-based program if the IEPC determines an even more independent setting is needed. For example, programming for the MCEC teenaged students who are trainable mentally impaired involves work experiences and activities of daily living such as cooking. The 8-year-old MCEC student with autism whose functional skills match those of the teenagers would not be placed in an older TMI classroom because the activities and peers would not be age-appropriate. Instead, this student could be placed in a more independent setting, like a regular education building cross-categorical room (a self-contained special education classroom with a maximum of 15 students of various ages and disabilities) or fully included in regular classes. The student with autism, or any other disabling condition, can be placed in any setting along the continuum despite the label or diagnosis if the IEPC determines it to be the "least restrictive environment."

Framework of Music Therapy Services

Background

Music therapy has been available to the students placed in the MCEC AI categorical classrooms since 1985, when a part-time music therapy position was created. Due to individual and group needs, each student in the AI classroom received 1:1 and small group music therapy weekly. Additionally, the music therapist provided weekly group therapy for the students in the preprimary impaired classrooms. As music therapy became increasingly valued to both the AI and PPI programs, the MCISD administrators looked for ways to provide those services to other students with special needs. In 1987, a full-time music therapy position was established to serve the MCISD Preschool Program and the MCISD Monroe County Educational Center program (which included the trainable, severely/multiply impaired, and autistic impaired programs). Additionally, the new position served the small center-based Day Treatment Program for students with emotional impairment (EI) and one self-contained classroom for those who were physically or otherwise health impaired (POHI).

By the following year, the music therapy program evolved to include written goals on the IEP for all the MCEC students. The therapist attended the IEPCs for each of the students from the AI classrooms and participated in their 3-year Multidisciplinary Evaluation Team (MET) assessments. The classroom teachers for the other MCEC students submitted the recommended music therapy goals to the IEPC, as time restraints prevented the music therapist's attendance. Eventually, a music therapy curriculum (Snell, 1990) was developed and included in the *Curriculum Guide For Trainable Mentally Impaired Students: A Sequence of Annual Goals, Short Term Instructional Objectives, and Performance Objectives* (Monroe County Intermediate School District, 1990). This music therapy curriculum was subsequently used for the students in the AI and SMI/SXI programs as well.

The decentralization trend of the late 1980s and early 1990s resulted in the restructuring of categorical programs. A number of students and categorical classrooms from self-contained programs shifted to regular education buildings. Eventually the Day Treatment Program was closed, the POHI classroom was eliminated, and the MCEC and Preschool programs were restructured. Some positions were eliminated, while others were created. Educational approaches were re-evaluated and the music therapy program changed accordingly.

Today, MCISD music therapy services include (a) direct music therapy, (b) music therapy consultation, and (c) music therapy workshops. Students in the AI categorical classrooms receive 1:1, small group, and larger group music therapy, as do a few individuals in other classrooms who demonstrate educational needs for more intensive music therapy programming. Direct group music therapy is also provided for all other students in the center-based MCEC program and the preschool program. While music therapy consultation is made available for teachers, support staff, and aides as needed, the primary focus of the consultative services is on three cross-categorical classrooms and several preprimary impaired classrooms that are located in regular education buildings. For 6 or more weeks, the music therapist conducts weekly therapy groups with these classrooms and provides information and support for the teacher to incorporate music into the curriculum and behavior management. Several music therapy workshops are also scheduled each year for parents, professionals, and the community.

As a member of the multidisciplinary team, the music therapist participates in all team meetings, the IEPC (including Transition Planning, which outlines lifetime goals and compares them with annual goals) and 3-year MET evaluations for each of the students who receive individual music therapy. The music therapist is welcome, but not required, to attend these meetings for the remaining students unless music therapy observations/assessments could impact IEPC/MET decisions. The teachers for those students submit the music therapy goals to the IEPC as directed by the music therapist.

The Role of Music Therapy

When a student is placed in an AI classroom at the center, he or she usually has low functional skills, poor adaptive abilities, and/or unusual or severe stereotypical behavior which interfere with learning. The team of professionals (i.e., AI teacher, speech pathologist, music therapist, and occupational therapist) servicing these individuals are trained to assess and develop educational programming for people with autism and related disorders. Other staff (i.e., social worker, community-based educator, adapted physical educator, or physical therapist) are included as necessary. The parents and the student also have vital roles on the team by defining the student's needs at home, outlining immediate and long-range student expectations, sharing information, and sharing responsibility in program outcomes. The administrator is present and kept abreast of programming successes or concerns. The team's unified goal is to help the student achieve his or her educational potential with a maximal amount of independence.

The music therapist collaborates and consults with the other team members to help facilitate generalization of skills in different settings. For example, the music therapist must be familiar and comfortable with the communication system (e.g., combination of signs, gestures, pictures, and verbalizations) established by the speech pathologist. Information regarding sensory integration needs is provided by the occupational therapist. The teacher and classroom aide, central players in the student's programming, often function as a clearinghouse of information among team members. In turn, the music therapist needs to make sure that these individuals know and understand the value of music therapy treatment techniques, particularly how the process relates to nonmusical skills and where applications outside the music therapy session are appropriate. For instance, a student whose music related behaviors include abilities to match/anticipate changes in tempo and dynamics may be able to use song, chanting, or rhythmic patterns to engage in give-and-take interactions, to tolerate change, and to functionally apply academic knowledge. When abilities emerge within a musical context, the music therapist first helps support and strengthen these skills musically, then guides the student in applying the skills without a musical accompaniment. Examples might include:

1. A simple good-bye song to help the student maintain control during activity transitions. The teacher may only need to chant and/or gesture the final words of the familiar song to be effective during activity changes in a nonmusical situation.

2. The teacher can encourage the student to initiate interaction with peers by chanting the first and last lines to the "Shake Their Hand" (Snell, 1991) song during social time with other classrooms, such as:

    "Find a friend and shake their hand, . . .
    Give 'em a smile and say 'Hello'."

    Or use an alternate version (after it has been experienced or effectively explained), such as:

    "Find a friend and tap them on the shoulder, . . .
    Find a friend and ask them,
    'Would you like to listen to the radio?'"

The music therapy component of the AI program provides an important link to age-appropriate peers and the community outside the classroom and school walls. The music therapist often facilitates initial exposure and interaction with people in more demanding social settings, such as those listed on the Continuum of Placements (Snell, 1995) (see Figure 1), for the student from the AI classroom. By servicing more than one program, the music therapist: (a) knows the dynamics of each classroom/program and is able to make creative programming suggestions on behalf of the student to other professionals and to the IEPC; (b) can bring unlikely groups successfully together despite wide ranging ability levels; (c) is able to bridge the gap for students moving across settings by providing immediate success and generalization of skills via music interventions, being perhaps the only familiar person to a student in a new situation, and carrying valuable information about the student to the new receiving teacher/staff.

The skills gained in the 1:1 setting can be musically supported by the therapist in the group setting where it is most difficult for the person with autism to generalize abilities. For instance, in the 1:1 setting the student can develop functional use of music skills, develop tolerance for the sound and feel of different instruments, lengthen time of self-control, and develop social skills such as in-seat behavior and turn-taking. The music therapist can then encourage functional use of these abilities in more demanding social situations. This can be done initially by adapting the student's 1:1 music experiences for his or her group music therapy session involving classmates and staff from the AI room. Over time, the student can become a regular visitor and/or active member of a larger group of peers independent of his classroom teacher and classmates. These experiences may lay the groundwork for future involvement with other peer groups or for a cross-categorical placement.

Many times the music therapist, teacher, or other professional will make a formal or informal request for a student to "visit" another classroom's music therapy session. Observations during the visit(s) often are helpful to the IEPC when considering a program or placement change. For example, the preschool-aged student placed in the AI classroom has access to participate in music therapy with a MCISD preschool classroom designed for children with preprimary impairment (PPI) (90% end up in regular education programs), a preschool classroom for those with trainable mental impairment (TMI), or a preschool classroom for individuals who are severely mentally/multiply impaired (SMI/SXI). The students age 7 through preteen can join TMI or SMI/SXI classrooms of students the same age. Students in these classrooms often enjoy exposure and interaction with regular education age-appropriate peers through companion classrooms (reverse mainstreaming). The teenaged student from the AI classroom can be integrated into a music therapy group with an SMI young adult classroom or into the MCEC music therapy "specialty groups," such as Vocal Choir, Rhythm Band, Chimes Choir, and Creative Expressions (a music therapy movement group). The specialty groups are made up of primarily young adult students with trainable mental impairment. They perform for various school functions and for the community at least twice yearly. The Chimes Choir is frequently performing for such community events as banquets, meetings, and ceremonies. Performances are viewed as normalized school activities. The music therapist will allow performances only in settings appropriate to the skill level. Most members participate in all performances unless it is not consistent with individual therapeutic goals.

Case Example

"Sarah," a teenage student with autism, had severe deficits in communication and social skills. Verbalizations were echolalic in nature and she would often utter unrelated phrases repeatedly. She did not initiate interactions with peers. There were significant inconsistencies in her reactions to sensory input, in that sounds or tactile textures would result in distressful crying one moment and indifference the next moment. In addition, Sarah had many disruptive behaviors which included continuous giggling, self-stimulation, crying, getting out of her seat, and hitting other people. Although this student had an abundance of melodic and rhythmic abilities, she was unable to apply them functionally in a social setting. Melodic singing was frequently observed, but she became silent when others joined in to sing. She could create or imitate complex rhythm patterns, but when performed with other people, the tempo of the patterns would speed out of control. Sarah's music therapy IEP goals and objectives were:

Goal 1:   The student will improve personal skills.
  Objective 1.1: Maintains self-control under stress
  Objective 1.2: Identifies opinions/likes/dislikes/ of self/others
  Objective 1.3: Attempts new activities/adapts to change

Goal 2:   The student will improve interpersonal skills.
  Objective 2.1: Participates in group discussions/activities
  Objective 2.2: Works appropriately with peers and adults

The music therapy approaches included 1:1 and small group therapy, structured and improvisational music to encourage sustained application of musical skills, use of new and familiar music, and musical interaction with peers through chanting and rhythmic movement. In addition, picture communication cards, such as "yes/no," "shh," and "happy/sad," were used to establish opinions, feelings, or basic commands.

When her spontaneous melodic singing diminished, Sarah was placed in the music therapy vocal choir made up of teenage students with trainable mental impairment. Her participation in choir supplemented her individual and small group music therapy sessions. Prior to her arrival, the choir was given an explanation for Sarah's erratic behavior. The group voted to allow her conditional entrance into the choir. Since the initial sessions were distressful to Sarah, early release from the "practices" were used as a reward for good behavior. Choir members cheered Sarah when she was able to exercise self-control during two songs, three songs, and finally an entire practice. Soon afterwards, removal from the practices became an effective punishment rather than a reward. Typically, Sarah's affect appeared flat or unrelated to the situation; however, during choir she could appropriately express displeasure when removed from practice. She also began to smile when praised and appear surprised when peers asked her to be quiet during a song.

One year later, Sarah was able to perform outside the Monroe County Educational Center with the choir at a local high school. She remained in line on stage unassisted by staff and was able to successfully imitate choreographed movements and chanting. Two years later, the objectives during choir included rhythmic synchronization with peers, simultaneous melodic singing with peers, maintaining self control, and increased peer interaction. In a recent performance with the choir at a community auditorium, Sarah melodically sang in sporadic fashion with the group and melodically sang two short vocal solos. She continues to receive music therapy individually, in a small group, and in vocal choir. Outside the music therapy setting, she is now able to work at a sheltered workshop once a week. Soon, according to the latest IEPC, Sarah will soon be in a cross-categorical placement (i.e., a classroom for students with trainable mental impairment, which has a maximum of 15 students with one teacher and one aide) and attend workshop 3 days a week with her peers from the classroom and choir.

Assessment

The Revised Index of Autistic Behavior (Holovka & Domsic, 1976), the Childhood Autism Rating Scale (CARS) (Schopler, Reichler, & Renner, 1986), and the Autistic Behavior Composite Checklist and Profile (Krug, Arick, & Almond, 1984) are frequently used by the AI teacher and/or the school psychologist at the MCEC to determine support or nonsupport of a diagnosis of autism. The Autism Checklist (Autism Society of America, 1995) is a shorter observational guide than those listed above. Persons with autism usually exhibit at least half of the following characteristics from that checklist:

- Difficulty in mixing with other children
- Insistence on sameness; resists changes in routine
- Inappropriate laughing and giggling
- No real fear of dangers
- Little or no eye contact
- Unresponsive to normal teaching methods
- Sustained odd play
- Apparent insensitivity to pain
- Echolalia
- Prefers to be alone; aloof manner
- May not want cuddling or act cuddly
- Spins objects
- Noticeable physical overactivity or extreme underactivity
- Tantrums—displays extreme distress for no apparent reason
- Not responsive to verbal cues; acts as if deaf
- Inappropriate attachment to objects
- Uneven gross/fine motor skills (may not want to kick ball but can stack blocks)
- Difficulty in expressing needs; uses gestures or pointing instead of words

Individuals who display several of the aforementioned behaviors should be referred for a more thorough assessment in order to confirm the diagnosis of autism.

The unique conditions associated with autism (e.g., complex sensory problems, severe communication deficits, inability to understand social cues, limited ability to generalize skills, and unusual behavior patterns that limit interaction) sometimes make it difficult to assess the child's inner potential. The music therapist assesses immediate physical and emotional concerns and can properly adapt the music not only to support and encourage the child, but also to ensure a positive experience. This builds trust and keeps the individual engaged in music making which may yield valuable assessment information.

The music therapist keeps informal monthly progress notes and performs an annual assessment just before the IEPC. Progress is also noted on the IEP as goals and objectives are updated. Specific achievements are mentioned on the student's copy of MCISD Music Therapy Curriculum (Snell, 1990) located in each individual's curriculum guide binder (Monroe County Intermediate School District, 1990) (see Figure 2 and Appendix). The Music Therapy Curriculum is used successfully with all the students at the MCEC. It was written in the same format as other sections of the curriculum; each section has one annual goal with a number of instructional objectives and specific performance objectives. For example, the music therapy curriculum's annual goal is to develop/improve expression in the music setting, while the instructional objectives are to (a) increase responses to music, (b) improve music vocalization skills, (c) improve musical movement skills, (d) improve instrument manipulation, (e) improve social/ emotional skills in group music, and (f) generalize isolated skills in different settings. Performance objectives are detailed under each instructional objective (see Figure 2 and refer to the Appendix for the entire curriculum).

The MCISD Music Therapy Curriculum was written in musical terms with the nonmusical goal: To develop/improve expressive language skills. Each MCEC student has a Curriculum Guide (Monroe County Intermediate School District, 1990) binder which dates their achievements. The guide follows the student through graduation. The main objective areas begin with basic performance objectives (e.g., "quiets when music stimuli is presented") and ends with a performance objective which requires more independence, choice, and expression (e.g., "expresses feelings musically by choosing a song, improvisation, dance, creative movement, or song writing"). While following the curriculum to help develop skills, such as "start and stop a musical response" and "matches changes in duration, tempo, or dynamics of music," the music therapist can also design experiences which support the music therapy IEP goals (e.g., "expresses feelings appropriately" or "attempts new activities/adapts to change"). Furthermore, the same skill areas can be addressed with any student or groups of students, regardless of functioning level, by individualizing success criteria and assistance levels (i.e., 100% accuracy with physical assistance or 75% accuracy with verbal prompts) (see Figure 3).

Multidisciplinary Evaluation Team (MET) Evaluation

When a 3-year MET evaluation is required or requested, a meeting date is scheduled. Each member of the team conducts an assessment before the posted date and brings his or her findings, conclusions, and recommendations to the MET meeting. The purpose is to re-evaluate special education eligibility status and to thoroughly review progress, as well as program effectiveness and placement. For the student with autism or AI traits, the teacher and/or the psychologist will administer the autism behavioral assessments. Other tests, such as the Leiter International

Performance Scale, the Developmental Test of Visual-Motor Integration, Test of Nonverbal Intelligence, Vineland Adaptive Behavior Scales, and Draw a Person Test may be administered by the psychologist.

MONROE COUNTY INTERMEDIATE SCHOOL DISTRICT
ANNUAL GOALS AND SHORT-TERM INSTRUCTIONAL OBJECTIVES
APPLIED IN MUSIC THERAPY

STUDENT_____PLACEMENT_____DATE_____

MUSIC THERAPIST_____

ANNUAL GOAL: *THE STUDENT WILL DEVELOP/IMPROVE EXPRESSION IN THE MUSIC SETTING*

A. *EVALUATION PROCEDURES*	B. *SUCCESS CRITERIA*	C. *ASSISTANCE LEVEL*
1. Observation	1. With 100% Accuracy	1. Passively cooperating
2. Standardized Test	2. With 75% Accuracy	2. With physical assistance
3. Teacher Made Test	3. With 50% Accuracy	3. With physical prompts
4. Developmental Profile	4. With 25% Accuracy	4. With imitation
5. Skill Inventory	5. With_____% Accuracy	5. With verbal and/or
6. Curriculum	6. Maintain present	gestural prompt
7. Other_____	level of functioning	6. With repeated requests,
	7. Standard Score of_____	no prompts
		7. Independently w/wo
		adaptive device
		8. Maintain Skill

A.   B.   C.   A) *INCREASE RESPONSES TO MUSIC*   A.   B.   C.

___ ___ ___   1. Quiets when music stimuli is present   ___ ___ ___   10. Start and stops a musical response

___ ___ ___   2. Exhibits movements related to music   ___ ___ ___   11. Matches/anticipates changes
            stimuli (i.e., startle, eye contact, etc.)   duration, tempo, or dynamics of

___ ___ ___   3. Moves rhythmically in response to pulse   music (i.e., stop/go, loud/soft)
            of music (i.e., tap, rock, clap, etc.)   ___ ___ ___   12. Indicates likes/dislikes of musical

___ ___ ___   4. Exhibits spontaneous singing or humming   stimuli (i.e., smile, frown,

___ ___ ___   5. Accepts sound of various instruments   verbalize opinion)
            representative of each instrumental family   ___ ___ ___   13. Names/indicates 3 or more favorite

___ ___ ___   6. Touches/holds instruments from each   songs
            instrumental family   ___ ___ ___   14. Identifies at least 3 musical styles

___ ___ ___   7. Accepts by touch sound vibrations from   (i.e., Pop/Rock, Country, Classical)
            musical/nonmusical sources (i.e., drum   ___ ___ ___   15. Identifies tonal/mood changes in live
            head, strings, amplifier, wood, etc.)   or recorded music

___ ___ ___   8. Locates hidden sound   ___ ___ ___   16. Labels at least 2 musical passages

___ ___ ___   9. Matches individual rhythm instruments by   with a feeling (i.e., happy, sad, etc.)
            sound: a. drum   ___ ___ ___   17. Expresses feelings musically by
                  b. sticks   engaging in improvisation, dance,
                  c. bell   creative movement, song writing, or
                  d. maraca   by choosing a song.
                  e. other

Figure 2. Monroe County Intermediate School District Music Therapy Curriculum

The psychologist and the social worker will report their observations of the student during a school activity. In addition, the social worker will also interview the parents, the speech pathologist will evaluate language and communication functioning, the occupational therapist evaluates sensory and motor functions, the teacher will summarize ability levels as related to the educational curriculum, the nurse will report medical history, and the music therapist evaluates behavior related to music. The reports list and interpret test results which usually are in the form of IQ levels, developmental ages, rating scales, and observations. Recommendations are made regarding classification/diagnosis, programming, and therapy services. If the MET is establishing or re-establishing the AI classification, a form is completed to list documented behaviors associated with autism found in the assessments (see Figure 3).

SE1014-AI
Rev. 8/91

MONROE COUNTY INTERMEDIATE SCHOOL DISTRICT
MULTIDISCIPLINARY EVALUATION TEAM REPORT
AUTISM

Student Name: _Sarah T._____ MET Report Date: _3-15-93_

The following items are deemed correct if a check mark is recorded.

✓ 1. Evidence of disturbances in the rates and sequences of cognitive, affective, psychomotor, language and speech development. See attached reports: ☑ Psychological ☐ Social Work ☑ Speech ☑ Teacher/TC ☑ Other _Music Therapist_

✓ 2. Disturbance in the capacity to relate appropriately to people, events and objects. See attached reports: ☐ Psychological ☐ Social Work ☑ Speech ☑ Teacher/TC ☑ Other _Music Therapist_

✓ 3. Absence, disorder or delay of language, speech, or meaningful communication. See attached reports: ☐ Psychological ☐ Social Work ☑ Speech ☑ Teacher/TC ☑ Other _Music Therapist_

✓ 4. Unusual, or inconsistent response to sensory stimuli in 1 or more of the following:
  ✓ sight   ✓ touch   ___ balance   ✓ taste
  ✓ hearing   ___ pain   ✓ smell
  ✓ the way a child holds his or her body
  See attached reports: ☑ Psychological ☑ Social Work ☑ Speech ☑ Teacher/TC
  ☑ Other _Music Therapist_

✓ 5. Insistence on sameness as shown by stereotyped play patterns, repetitive movements, abnormal preoccupation or resistance to change. See attached reports: ☐ Psychological ☐ Social Work ☑ Speech ☑ Teacher/TC ☑ Other _Music Therapist_

✓ 6. An absence of the characteristics associated with schizophrenia, such as delusions, hallucinations, loosening of associations and incoherence. See attached reports: ☑ Psychological ☐ Social Work ☐ Speech ☐ Teacher/TC ☐ Other_____

✓ 7. Impairment of adaptive behavior is documented in the following attached reports: ☑ Psychological ☑ Social Work ☑ Teacher/TC ☑ Speech ☑ Other _Music Therapist_

✓ 8. Parent input to this evaluation, which includes name of staff who provided parent opportunity for input and date, along with a description of input (summarize or specify report): ☐ Psychological ☑ Social Work ☐ Teacher/TC ☐ Speech ☐ Other _____

✓ 9. Determination that the student requires special education and/or related services to profit from education.

✓ 10. The impairment is not based solely on behaviors relating to environmental, cultural or economic differences.

Figure 3. Monroe County Intermediate School District
Multidisciplinary Team Report: Autism

When there are several professionals testing a student, the education team looks for support and nonsupport of individual evaluation results. Because reactions and interactions to music are not dependent on verbal or visual communication, a music therapy assessment may help provide a glimpse at hidden potentials. At the MCEC, music therapy assessment information strives to complement the other professionals' evaluations, rather than stand alone. The music therapy evaluation documents the observed music related behavior and interprets their relationship to nonmusical skills, such as social skills or cognitive abilities.

The MCEC music therapist often uses the Suggested Areas of Behavioral Observation from the Diagnostic Assessment of Music Related Expression and Behavior (DAMREB) (Boone, 1980) as an observational guide when assessing a student for a MET evaluation. The specific behavioral areas (i.e., Oral Expression, Instrumental Expression, Motoric Expression, Emotional Expression, Imitation, and Interaction) are useful in determining modes of strength and preference for emotional expression, social interaction, and meaningful use of skills. Other music therapy assessments used in totality or in combination at MCEC include the MCISD Music Therapy Curriculum (Snell, 1990), Boxill Music Therapy Assessment (1985), and the Scale I. Child-Therapists Relationship in Musical Activity and Scale II. Musical Communicativeness (Nordoff & Robbins, 1977).

At the MCISD and MCEC, recommended student placements are based more on assessed needs and displayed behavior than on a label, which may have little meaning. This approach is especially helpful when there is a lack of agreement on the diagnosis between the multidisciplinary team members and the parents or physicians. While the continuing problem of accurately diagnosing autism remains, special education in Michigan is moving to de-emphasize, or eliminate, the use of labels (Baldwin, 1994; Biklin, 1992; Center for Quality Special Education, 1993; Michigan State Board of Education, 1994b). In the Special Education Delivery System Task Force Report, published by the Michigan State Board of Education (1994b), the recommendation on use of labels states, "Educational support services shall be available to all students within the educational system based on documented need rather than on labels" (p. 51). It further suggests that other agencies also eliminate the use of labels and base services on documented need. This is usually not a difficulty for the professionals who are developing goals and objectives, but problems can arise when funds are attached to access of treatment and subsidies. Specifically, the lack of a label or an improper diagnosis may result in poor or inadequate programming, gross misunderstanding of behaviors as related to sensory input and communication, and frustrated caregivers and professionals who lack appropriate training or information (Ackerly, 1988; DeMyer, 1979; Tsai & Scott-Miller, 1988).

IEPC

The MCISD has one standard IEP form with preprinted goals/objectives. Each professional presents his or her student goals and objectives and places them on the proper pages. Approaches and strategies are shared with the parents. All of the following are noted on the form: (a) present level of performance, (b) annual review status, (c) performance criteria, (d) schedule for evaluation, and (e) evaluation procedures. The goals/objectives are listed under Instructional Competencies, Speech and Language, Social/Emotional Skills, Psychomotor/Orientation and Mobility Skills, and Functional Living/Vocational Skills.

The music therapy goals/objectives may fall under any of the areas listed. Typically the social/ emotional subheadings of Personal Skills and Interpersonal Skills will be a primary music therapy focus, particularly for the student with autism (see Figure 4, Sample IEP/Curriculum Goals and Objectives). Specific performance objectives are noted in the therapist's student files and/or in the student's Curriculum Guide (Monroe County Intermediate School District, 1990). For instance, the IEP goals and objectives for a low functioning nonverbal 6-year-old may be marked as shown in Figure 4.

Page 3 of the IEP addresses the Least Restrictive Environment and student placement. Music therapy services are specified at the bottom under Ancillary and Other Related Services (see Figure 5).

Transition Planning

Through the IEP and its planning processes, the school is bound by law to include a statement of needed transition services for each student with a disability who is 16 years of age and older (or younger when appropriate) (IDEA, PL 101–476). This coordinated plan between the school, parents, student, and community agencies lays out annual goals and long-range goals for postschool services that provide opportunities to realize successful adult living. This is due to the disproportionate number of unemployed persons with disabilities who have unused skills. It may also be a means to hold schools, families, and communities accountable for obligations regarding services for individuals with disabilities.

"Transition" is simply "the process of planning and preparing your child for the completion of school and movement into adult life" (Monroe County Intermediate School District, 1993a, p. 2). Planning, review, and assessment regarding lifetime goals are required in the Individuals with Disabilities Education Act. Since PL 101–476 mandates transition services, identification of and planning for postschool transition services for all students with disabilities must begin by the time they reach age 16. The transition process is defined as:

> A coordinated set of activities for a student, designed within an outcome-oriented process, which promotes movement from school to post-school activities, including: Post-secondary Education, Vocational Training, Integrated Employment (including supported employment), Continuing and Adult Education, Adult Services, Independent Living, and Community Participation. (U.S. Congress, 1990)

More simply put, transition planning is a written plan which sets long-term goals to be realized upon completion of school and is coordinated with the IEP annual goals and objectives.

Transition is also addressed in the Rehabilitation Act of 1973 as amended in 1992, the Carl D. Perkins Vocational and Applied Technology Education Act, and the Americans with Disabilities Act (ADA) (Michigan Department of Education & Michigan Jobs Commission, 1995). Transition services are identified on the IEP and re-evaluated yearly. The school must collaborate with the student and his family, other responsible agencies, postsecondary institutions, and the community to ensure successful transition to the following areas: Employment, Post-School Adult Living, Community Participation and Post-Secondary Educational Training (Michigan Department of Education & Michigan Jobs Commission, 1995). The State of Michigan awarded MCISD a Transition Grant to develop a comprehensive site-based transition model to

ANNUAL GOALS AND SHORT-TERM INSTRUCTIONAL OBJECTIVES   Student Jimmy C.   Page 2d

Present Level of Performance: 1-2 years Jimmy is able to wave "bye". He does initiate some interaction with adults, but rarely with other peers.

ANNUAL REVIEW STATUS: May be used to review goals/objectives on previous IEP: (A)chieved (C)ontinuing (D)ropped (R)evised

SCHEDULES FOR EVALUATION: Record specific times or designated intervals for evaluation:
(A)nnually (S)emester (Q)uarterly (C)ard marking (M)onthly (W)eekly (D)aily

EVALUATION PROCEDURES: (A)ttendance (B)ehavioral observation-documented (C)ompletion of assignments (R)eport card/progress report (P)erformance-based measures Tests: 1-Author/publisher; 2-Criterion/obj.; 3-Norm-referenced; 4-Teacher-made

PERFORMANCE CRITERIA: Incorporate into the short-term objective or write here
Examples: To a given grade level or developmental age; Accuracy (80%); Production (3 items/hr); Rate (4 out of 5 times)

Social / Emotional Skills

	PERFORMANCE CRITERIA	PROCEDURE	SCHEDULE	STATUS
The student will improve ability to FOLLOW RULES AND PROCEDURES				
☐ Follows school and classroom rules				
☐ Attends class regularly and on time				
☐ Takes care of facilities/materials				
☐				
☐				
The student will improve PERSONAL SKILLS:				
☐ Identifies/states causes of feelings				
☐ Expresses feelings appropriately				
☐ Maintains self-control under stress	MT 1/sx	B	A	C
☐ Identifies opinions/likes/dislikes of self/others				
☐ Identifies expectations/responsibilities of self/others				
☐ Identifies personal goals				
☐ Uses acceptable language with peers/adults				
☐ Uses appropriate dress/hygiene				
☐ Attempts new activities/adapts to change	MT 1/sx	B	A	C
☐ Improves behavior (Specify:)				
☐				
☐				
The student will improve INTERPERSONAL SKILLS:				
☐ Uses appropriate conversation skills (e.g., eye contact, proper distance):				
☐ Participates in group discussions/activities	MT 1/sx	B	A	R
☐ Works appropriately with peers and adults	MT 1/sx	B	A	C
☐ Learns to compromise/negotiate				
☐ Learns problem-solving and decision making skills				
☐ Seeks assistance from adults as needed				
☐ Interacts courteously with peers/adults				
☐ Behaves appropriately with peers				
☐				
☐				

The instructional/performance objectives from the MCEC curriculum might be:

A) INCREASE RESPONSES TO MUSIC
1. Quiets when music stimuli is presented
3. Moves rhythmically in response to pulse of music
5. Accepts sounds of various instruments
7. Accepts by touch sound vibrations from musical/ nonmusical source (i.e., drum head, guitar body, wood)
10. Start and stops a musical response

E) IMPROVE GROUP MUSIC PARTICIPATION SKILLS
1. Sits in group quietly, arms/legs in own space)
4. follows musical directions
6. Demonstrates awareness of others

D) IMPROVE INSTRUMENT MANIPULATION
1. Shakes a shaker-type instrument upon request
2. Taps drum or tambourine
9. Indicates preference for a musical instrument when given a choice of 2

F) GENERALIZE ISOLATED SKILLS IN DIFFERENT SETTING
1. Functionally applies isolated skills from the classroom & other environments in the music setting regarding: communication, academic, motor, emotional, and social skills

Figure 4. Sample IEP/Curriculum Goals and Objectives

Student Name: _Jimmy C._   Page 3

━━━━━━ Least Restrictive Environment Considerations ━━━━━━

1. Is this student currently attending a school with students who are not impaired? ☐ Yes ☒ No, Explain. _Jimmy is enrolled_ _in a center based program_

2. Is this student currently attending the school she/ he would if not impaired? ☐ Yes ☒ No, Explain. _Jimmy is enrolled_ _in a center based program_

3. What supplemental aids or services were considered before the student was placed OR continued in special education programs and / or services? _Jimmy is to be enrolled in a center based program which is at the request_ _of his parents. All supplemental aides and services were_ _considered (aide/accessibility/setting/curriculum/support services)._

4. Describe other LRE options considered and provide reasons those options were rejected. _Inclusion and cross categorical classrooms in local buildings_ _were considered. Student's emotional and educational needs_ _would not be met in those settings._

5. List those activities in which the student will be participating with students who are not impaired as determined appropriate in academic, non-academic, and extracurricular services and activities. _Jimmy regularly participates in church/Sunday school_ _activities_

6. What supplemental aids and services are necessary to enable the student to participate in general education programs? _Jimmy would need a full time aide, OT, Speech, music therapy._ _Specific needs for student and setting would be determined by_ _the MAPs process if inclusion were to be pursued._

━━━━━━ Student's Placement ━━━━━━

☞ **Categorical Program**

☐ R340.1738 - SMI	☐ R340.1739 - TMI	☐ R340.1740 - EMI	☐ R340.1741 - EI	☐ MSD
☐ R340.1742 - HI	☐ R340.1743 - VI	☐ R340.1744 - POHI	☐ R340.1747 - LD	☐ MSB
☐ R340.1748 - SXI	☐ R340.1754 - PPI	☐ R340.1756 - SLI	☒ R340.1758 - AI	

For MSD and MSB use procedures for placement as indicated in R340.1742 and R340.1743.

Is secondary program departmentalized? ☐ Yes ☐ No

Hours/Periods Per Week: __30__ Proposed Initiation Date: __3/24/94__ (mo/day/yr or first day of school) Duration: __1 yr.__ (mo/yr or one school year)

If the above categorical program does not correspond with the student's primary disability, the IEPC must provide a rationale. The rationale is: _____

This placement can only occur if the parent/guardian/surrogate gives consent to the alternative placement (page 5).

☞ **Resource Program:** ☐ R340.1749a (elementary) ☐ R340.1749b (secondary) Departmentalized? ☐ Yes ☐ No

Hours/Periods Per /Week: _____ Proposed Initiation Date: _____ (mo/day/yr or first day of school) Duration: _____ (mo/yr or one school year)

Teacher's Endorsement: _____
If the resource teacher's endorsement does not correspond with the student's primary disability, the need for a teacher consultant with corresponding endorsement must be considered to assist the resource teacher. Are these services needed? ☐ Yes ☐ No

☞ **Ancillary and Other Related Services**

Rule Number and Name of Service	Type of Service (Direct or Consultation)	Amount of Time (number and length of session)	Proposed Initiation Date (mo/day/yr or 1st day of school)	Duration (mo/yr or 1 school yr)
R.340. 1701 Occup. Ther.	Direct	1x30min 1:1 + 1x30min group	3/26/94	1 school yr
R.340. 1701 Music Therapy	Direct	1x20min 1:1 + 1x20min group	3/26/94	1 school yr.
R.340. 1745 Speech	Direct	1x15min 1:1 + 1x30min group	3/26/94	1 school yr.
R.340.				
R.340.				
R.340.				
R.340.				
R.340.				

Instructions/ Information on back of page

Figure 5. Monroe County Intermediate School District IEP, Page 3

serve as a model for other Michigan districts (Monroe County Intermediate School District, 1993a). The author participated in developing the MCEC's transition model.

When considering the student's life or "exit" goals for transition at the IEP, the IEPC has the opportunity to gain a unified view of where the student hopes to be upon completion of school. Annual goals should be addressing the skill areas the student will need to fulfill his life goals. This affords the music therapist the opportunity to explain the relevance of music therapy goals to nonmusical gains. For example, if the teenage student diagnosed with autism has "supported living in a group home" as a part of his transition plan, it will be important for him to have effective means for expression, communication, functional use of skills, as many independent daily living and leisure skills as possible, social skills, tolerance for change and sensory input, and effective strategies to deal with stress.

Note that the IEPC, which draws up the transition plan, may invite a representative from a local agency to the planning meeting, such as the student's case worker from the community mental health agency. The team defines the plan by filling out the MCEC transition forms (see Figure 6, MCEC Transition Plan Forms). The expected level of support upon exiting school is checked under each of the listed domains in column 1. The life/exit goals are spelled out in column 2. The annual objectives which will move the student closer to the exit goals are defined in columns 3 and 4, with the responsible persons and agencies noted in columns 5 and 6.

Music Therapy Interventions

In her review of the literature, Edgerton (1994) found that structured intervention approaches were predominantly recommended. However, her research findings, related to the communicative behaviors of children with autism, suggest that gains in communication can be made using low-structured intervention, specifically, therapeutically applied improvisational music. Nordoff and Robbins (1964, 1968, 1971, 1977) and Alvin and Warwick (1992) have documented the efficacy of using improvisational music in programming for students with autism. The literature relating to autism is filled with references to the unusual attraction and responses of children with autism to musical stimuli (Applebaum, Egel, Koegel, & Imhoff, 1979; Grandin & Scariano, 1986; Kolko, Anderson, & Campbell, 1980; Rimland, 1964; Sherwin, 1953; Toigo, 1992). Edgerton's (1994) review of studies relating to autism lists the following areas as favorably affected by music therapy: "Prosocial behaviors, attention span, self-expression, mental age, spontaneous speech, vocal imitation skills, interpersonal relationships, task accuracy, and shopping skills" (p. 34).

The attempts of individuals with autism to interact appropriately with people and objects are sometimes awkward and difficult. Despite impairments in the ability to understand social situations (Volkman, 1987), decode meaning from nondirect verbal or nonverbal communications (Hermelin, 1978), and sensory perception abnormalities, the person with autism continues to look for ways to have human contact. Music therapy interventions often can facilitate the individual with autism in establishing appropriate contact with people and objects.

Individual and Group Treatment Model

The individual music therapy session strengthens the student-therapist rapport. Once a beginning or connecting song is established, there is guided exploration and exposure to various

TRANSITION PLAN

Page 1 of 2

STUDENT NAME: Sarah T. AGE: 18 PROJECTED EXIT DATE: 2001
BUILDING: M.C.E.C. GRADE: 13 IEP DATE: 5-22-93

(1) Life Domains	(2) Post Secondary Life/Exit Goals	(3) Annual Objectives Or Competencies	(4) Actions to Achieve Objectives/Competencies	(5) Persons to Do Actions	(6) Interagency Linkages
Leisure and Recreation ☐ Independent ☒ Support Needed ☐ No services needed at this time (explain reason in column 2)→	Sarah will participate in comm. rec./leisure activities	Sarah will participate in Spec. Olympics Sarah will participate in school based comm. activities	Sign up for a participate in Spec. Olympics bowling a Regional meet Sarah will part. in school dances and assemblies. She will attend gatherings with other students.	Mrs. T. Mrs. May Mrs. May A. Snell	ISD C.S.D.D.
Community Involvement ☐ Independent ☒ Support Needed ☐ No services needed at this time (explain reason in column 2)→	Sarah will access the community on a regular basis.	Sarah will participate in Community based Education Obtain a Mich. I.D. Card	Sarah will participate in outings to resturants, grocery stores, field trips, etc. with classmates. apply for with State of MI.	Mrs. May Mrs. T.	MCEC Mrs. T. will assist

Page 2 of 2

STUDENT NAME: Sarah T. IEP DATE: 5-22-93

(1) Life Domains	(2) Post Secondary Life/Exit Goals	(3) Annual Objectives Or Competencies	(4) Actions to Achieve Objectives/Competencies	(5) Persons to Do Actions	(6) Interagency Linkages
Employment ☐ Independent ☒ Support Needed ☐ No services needed at this time (explain reason in column 2)→	Sarah will work in a sheltered workshop or supported employment setting upon completion of her education program.	Sarah will participate in work activity at school.	Sarah will attend CSDD one to three days per work, accompanied by staff	Mrs. May Mr. Peel	ISD C.S.D.D
Daily Living ☐ Independent ☒ Support Needed ☐ No services needed at this time (explain reason in column 2)→	Sarah will live successfully in a family setting or supervised group home.	Sarah will interact with peers on a regular basis	Sarah will take part in Music Therapy groups with T.M.I. classes Sarah will participate with a larger group at C.S.D.D.	A. Snell Mrs. May Mrs. May M. Peel	MCISD C.S.D.D.

Important: A copy of this plan must be attached to each of the four(4) copies of the IEPC report

Figure 6. Monroe County Educational Center Transition Plan Forms

sounds and instruments. Musical preferences are discovered. Rocking songs and "calming" songs are reinforced and the proper use of instruments is modeled and encouraged. After there is exposure, demonstration, and exploration, choices are allowed. Since offering too many instruments or activities may be overly stimulating, the student is given choices between two items (or more when appropriate). To prepare the student for a group experience the therapist establishes the concept of "my turn" and "your turn." Basic rules or limits are defined for the student, such as staying seated during a "sitting song" and moving or playing the instruments only in the designated area during a "moving song." To help with transitions between experiences, an ending or "time to change" song/musical phrase is established (i.e., "We're all done" sung on a V–I cadence).

As basic skills are reinforced and expanded upon, the music therapist encourages their use in the group setting (i.e., music therapy session with classroom peers/staff) as soon as possible. At first, this is done by using the same greeting/ending songs and the same 1:1 session experiences adapted for a group setting. Acceptance of and participation in a group setting might be a significant accomplishment for the student who has a severe inability to adapt to change and a low tolerance for sensory input.

Change within the familiar music experience is introduced at a level the student can handle. The change may be as subtle as a tempo, accompaniment, or key change. Changes in the words or directions are gradually introduced while increasing the demand for social interaction. As the student is guided through these or other changes, the connecting song and "time to change" passages are used. The music therapist then begins to expand the student's repertoire to include multiple connecting/calming/changing songs. Gestures are coupled with these "transitional" music therapy interventions so that eventually the musical stimuli may not have to be present. When the student is able to handle more significant differences, such as a total change in session structure (i.e., no greeting song, all new musical experiences), he or she is perhaps ready to participate in group music therapy with different peers independent of the classroom staff.

When a student is not progressively tolerating more change over a long span of time, he or she can still be exposed to new peers and situations. For instance, the therapist can bring visiting peers into the structured music therapy session (i.e., other students from the building, visiting students from regular education schools). A staff member can accompany the student to observe other music therapy groups. The music therapist strategically inserts the familiar music experiences into the "new" group's session plans.

Case Examples

"Ron," a 19-year-old student with low functioning autism, did not have functional verbal language skills and needed supervision/assistance in basic activities of daily living. However, he could sing the ends of musical phrases with melodic accuracy. During 1:1 music therapy, he could engage in improvisational music on the drums when accompanied on the piano by the therapist for sustained periods of time. During speech, he was given a choice between a visit to vocal choir or some other activity by using a picture communication system. Ron frequently chose to attend choir and the speech pathologist soon did not need to stay with him during the visits. He learned to join in with some of the musical experiences and accepted interaction from other choir members.

"Jason," a 17-year-old student with low-functioning autism, did not have functional language skills but could be independent in some of the activities of daily living, such as following a routine and retrieving items of need. He could chant one to two words at the end of a familiar phrase and could match changes in duration, tempo, or dynamics of live music when playing percussion instruments. He attended Rhythm Band independently and was generally able to tolerate the sounds associated with such a group. He learned to take turns in a larger group, play four-step rhythm patterns on the drum set, and decrease stereotypical behaviors (i.e., arm flapping). One day he became distressed at the end of Rhythm Band. He displayed screaming and arm flapping, blocking the exit so no one could leave. Even though beginning/ending songs were not used in Rhythm Band, the therapist played the "Good-bye Song" from his individual and small group sessions. He accepted the song by calmly rocking in unison with his peers. After the V–I "All done" cadence, he became distressed again. He pointed his finger to indicate that he wanted the song sung to each person. The therapist did not honor the request, but repeated the last phrase of the song and required Jason to sing "all done." He then stood up and left the room without further incident.

"Jerry," a 10-year-old student with high-functioning autism, had verbal language skills, but echolalia interfered with functional language. He had severely impaired social skills, was resistant to change, and was preoccupied with subjects such as electricity, traffic signs, and cartoon characters. He was able to sing, imitate simple rhythm patterns, match musical dynamics, move creatively to music, and identify tonal/mood changes in recorded music. He received 1:1, small group music therapy and was soon able to attend music with a TMI classroom and be a member of a movement group at the center-based program. He learned to perform a majority of the performance objectives in the music therapy curriculum. Eventually he was placed in a cross-categorical classroom at his neighborhood school. The music therapist continued to provide group therapy using familiar and new musical experiences to aid in the development and generalization of social skills. Soon music therapy was provided to him in a mainstreamed subject (i.e., spelling/writing). Today he receives music therapy in the inclusion setting with his classmates during science or history. Consultation is provided to the classroom teacher and music teacher. Jason earns A's and B's on his report card without an adapted curriculum. While many gains have been made, social skills continue to be significantly impaired.

Suggested Techniques

The student with autism in a self-contained classroom with low functional skills often needs to develop attention span, in-seat behavior, purposeful use of objects, self-control, tolerance for sensory input, and acceptance of change. Beginning communication and interaction skills also need to be developed. By providing structured and low-structured (i.e., improvisation) music therapy interventions, the student with autism can be supported to experience periods of satisfying concentrated use of abilities in a social atmosphere. This can be done by involving the student in experiences in which each action or interaction has a meaningful relationship to the musical stimuli. Consider the following suggestions:

- Establish transition songs, i.e., beginning, ending, calming , and "time to change" songs
- Couple gestures with the transition songs so that future elimination of the musical cue might be possible
- Use familiar music and transition songs/cues in new situations to calm and encourage generalization of skills
- Expand repertoire of transition songs
- Establish "my turn"/"your turn" to help encourage manageable group skills and awareness of others
- Develop and expand basic music interaction skills and encourage their application in a social context
- Support and encourage rhythmic and/or vocal synchronization (exact or approximate) with others
- Use AGE APPROPRIATE music
- Use a variety of music and instruments, as tolerated
- Use both structured and improvisational music interventions
- Encourage the use of two or more skills simultaneously *if* the student is able to tolerate it (i.e., reading and melodic singing; social skills and music/motor skills)
- Help student indicate likes/dislikes of self and others, provide some form of "choices" in each session to provide another way for student have control of life situations
- Use gentle physical support if needed (i.e., touch shoulder, support elbow), then fade out physical support when possible
- Use visual representations of music, commands, feelings, places, people, etc.
- Support generalization of goals/objectives established by other professionals
- Communicate and consult with staff/others regarding the student's responses to music and how these responses relate to nonmusical skills and indicate hidden potential
- Breakdown and teach/define gestural social skills and rules
- Be aware of the continuum of placements/services available and help support movement toward increased independence and socialization
- Define music therapy's relationship to annual and long term goals outlined in the Transition Plan

Coda

Autism presents great obstacles in effective social interaction and sensory processing, which often causes a lack of functional use of skills and isolation from society. The Monroe County Educational Center offers one program model, among many, to address the unique educational needs of individuals with autism and related disorders. Music therapy is but one component of an ever changing collaborative effort to assist MCEC students with autism to successfully prepare for adult life. By assessing music related behaviors and recognizing their relationship to nonmusical abilities in communication, academic, motor, emotional, and social areas, music therapy interventions can assist the student with autism in bridging the gap between isolated skills and their functional social applications. In cooperation with other related services and a variety of approaches, music therapy techniques can ease the individual's movement into settings which provide the greatest opportunity for independence and realization of life goals.

References

Ackerly, M. (1988). What's in a name? In E. Schopler & G. Mesibov (Eds.), *Diagnosis and assessment in autism* (pp. 59–70). New York: Plenum Press.

Alper, S. (1981). Utilizing community jobs in developing vocational curriculums for severely handicapped youth. *Education and Training of the Mentally Retarded, 16*(3), 217–224.

Alvin, J., & Warwick, A. (1992). *Music therapy for the autistic child* (Rev. ed.). London: Oxford Press.

American Psychiatric Association. (1987). *Diagnostic and statistical manual of mental disorders* (3rd ed., rev.). Washington, DC: Author.

American Psychiatric Association. (1994). *Diagnostic and statistical manual of mental disorders* (4th ed.). Washington, DC: Author.

Applebaum, E., Egel, A. L., Koegel, R. L., & Imhoff, B. (1979). Measuring musical abilities of autistic children. *Journal of Autism and Developmental Disorders, 9*, 279–285.

Autism Society of America. (1995). *What is autism?* [Brochure]. Bethesda, MD: Author.

Ayres, A. J. (1979). *Sensory integration and the child.* Los Angeles: Western Psychological Services.

Bagley, C., & McGeein, V. (1989). The taxonomy and course of childhood autism. *Perceptual and Motor Skills, 69*, 1264–1266.

Baldwin, R. (1994). *A story to tell, special education in Michigan's upper peninsula 1902–1975.* Marquette, MI: Lake Superior Press.

Biklin, D. (1992). *Schooling without labels.* Philadelphia: Temple University Press.

Boone, P. (1980). *The diagnostic assessment of music related expression and behavior.* Pottstown, PA: Author.

Boxhill, E. H. (1985). *Music therapy for the developmentally disabled.* Austin, TX: PRO-ED.

Center for Quality Special Education [CQSE]. (1993). *Special education program outcomes guide: Autism.* Lansing, MI: Disability Research Systems, Inc., & Michigan Department of Education.

Clarizio, H., & McCoy, G. F. (1983). *Behavior disorders in children.* New York: Harper Row.

DeMyer, M. K. (1979). *Parents and children in autism.* Washington, DC: V.H. Winston and Sons.

Edgerton, C. (1994). The effect of improvisational music therapy on the communicative behaviors of autistic children. *Journal of Music Therapy, 31*(1), 31–62.

Grandin, T. (1988). My experiences as an autistic child and review of selected literature. *Journal of Orthomolecular Psychiatry, 13*, 144–174.

Grandin, T. (1995). *Thinking in pictures.* New York, NY: Doubleday.

Grandin, T., & Scariano, M. M. (1986). *Emergence: Labeled autistic.* Novato, CA: Arena Press.

Hermelin, B. (1978). Images and language. In M. Rutter & E. Schopleer (Eds.), *Autism: A reappraisal of concepts and treatment* (pp. 141–154). New York: Plenum Press.

Holovka, E. A., & Domsic, M. E. (1976). *The revised index of autistic behavior.* Muskegon, MI: Muskegon Area Intermediate School District.

Kanner, L. (1943). Autistic disturbances of affective contact. *Nervous Child, 2,* 217–250.

Kolko, D. J., Anderson, L., & Campbell, M. (1980). Sensory preference and overselective responding in autistic children. *Journal of Autism and Developmental Disorders, 10,* 259–271.

Krug, D. A., Arick, J. A. & Almond, P. J. (1984). *The autistic behavior composite checklist and profile.* Tucson, AZ: Communication Skill Builders, Inc.

Kurita, H. (1985), Infantile autism with speech loss before the age of thirty months. *Journal of the American Academy of Child Psychiatry, 24,* 191–196.

Michigan Department of Education & Michigan Jobs Commission. (1995). *Fundamentals of transition.* Lansing, MI: Author.

Michigan State Board of Education. (1994a). *Revised administrative rules for special education* (Rev. ed.). Lansing, MI: Author.

Michigan State Board of Education. (1994b). *The special education delivery system task force final report.* Lansing, MI: Author.

Monroe County Educational Center. (1994). *MCEC transition planning packet.* Monroe, MI: Monroe County Intermediate School District.

Monroe County Intermediate School District. (1990). *Curriculum guide for trainable mentally impaired students: A sequence of annual goals, short term instructional objectives, and performance objectives.* Monroe, MI: Author.

Monroe County Intermediate School District. (1993a). *Building bridges to the future: A parent's guide to the process of transition services planning* [Brochure]. Monroe, MI: Author.

Monroe County Intermediate School District. (1993b). *MCISD individual educational planning committee and multidisciplinary evaluation forms packet.* Monroe, MI: Author.

Nordoff, P., & Robbins, C. (1964). Music therapy and personality change in autistic children. *Journal of the American Institute of Homeopathy, 57,* 305–310.

Nordoff, P., & Robbins, C. (1968). Improvised music as therapy for autistic children. In E. T. Gaston (Ed.), *Music in therapy* (pp. 191–193). New York: MacMillan.

Nordoff, P., & Robbins, C. (1971). *Therapy in music for handicapped children.* New York: St. Martin's Press.

Nordoff, P., & Robbins, C. (1977). *Creative music therapy.* New York: John Day.

Olley, J. G. (1987). Classroom structure and autism. In D. Cohen & A. Donnellan (Eds.), *Handbook of autism and pervasive developmental disorders* (pp. 411–417). Silver Spring, MD: V. H. Winston and Sons.

Paul, R. (1987). Communication. In D. Cohen & A. Donnellan (Eds.), *Handbook of autism and pervasive developmental disorders* (pp. 61–84). Silver Spring, MD: V. H. Winston and Sons.

Rimland, B. (1964). *Infantile autism.* New York: Appleton-Century.

Schopler, E., & Mesibov, G. B. (1983). *Autism in adolescents and adults.* New York: Plenum Press.

Schopler, E., & Mesibov, G. B. (1985). *Communication problems in autism.* New York: Plenum Press.

Schopler, E., & Mesibov, G. B. (Eds.). (1988). *Diagnosis and assessment of autism.* New York: Plenum Press.

Schopler, E., Reichler, R. J., & Renner, B. R. (1986). *The childhood autism rating scale.* Los Angeles, CA: Western Psychological Services.

Sherwin, A. C. (1953). Reactions to music of autistic (schizophrenic) children. *American Journal of Psychiatry, 109,* 823–831.

Snell, A. M. (1990). Music therapy curriculum. *Curriculum guide for trainable mentally impaired students: A sequence of annual goals, short term instructional objectives, and performance objectives* (pp. 48–59). Monroe, MI: Monroe County Intermediate School District.

Snell, A. M. (1991). "Shake Their Hand." Unpublished song.

Snell, A. M. (1995). *Monroe County Intermediate School District's continuum of placements* [chart]. Monroe, MI: Author.

Thaut, M. (1984). A music therapy treatment model for autistic children. *Music Therapy Perspectives, 1,* 7–13.

Toigo, D. (1992). Autism: Integrating a personal perspective with music therapy practice. *Music Therapy Perspectives, 10,* 13–20.

Tsai, L. Y., & Scott-Miller, D. (1988). Higher functioning autistic disorder. *Focus on autistic behavior, 2*(6), 1–8.

U.S. Congress. (1990). *Individuals with Disabilities Education Act.* Public Law 101–476.

Volkman, F. R. (1987). Social development. In D. Cohen & A. Donnellan (Eds.), *Handbook of autism and developmental disorders* (pp. 41–60). Silver Spring, MD: V.H. Winston and Sons.

Appendix

MONROE COUNTY INTERMEDIATE SCHOOL DISTRICT
ANNUAL GOALS AND SHORT-TERM INSTRUCTIONAL OBJECTIVES - MUSIC THERAPY
STUDENT_____PLACEMENT_____DATE_____

MUSIC THERAPIST_____

ANNUAL GOAL: THE STUDENT WILL DEVELOP/IMPROVE EXPRESSION IN THE MUSIC SETTING

A. *EVALUATION PROCEDURES*	B. *SUCCESS CRITERIA*	C. *ASSISTANCE LEVEL*
1. Observation	1. With 100% Accuracy	1. Passively cooperating
2. Standardized Test	2. With 75% Accuracy	2. With physical assistance
3. Teacher Made Test	3. With 50% Accuracy	3. With physical prompts
4. Developmental Profile	4. With 25% Accuracy	4. With imitation
5. Skill Inventory	5. With____% Accuracy	5. With verbal and/or gestural prompt
6. Curriculum	6. Maintain present	6. With repeated requests, no prompts
7. Other_____	level of functioning	7. Independently w/wo adaptive device
	7. Standard Score of_____	8. Maintain Skill

A. B. C.   A) *INCREASE RESPONSES TO MUSIC*

___ ___ ___ 1. Quiets when music stimuli is present
___ ___ ___ 2. Exhibits movements related to music stimuli (i.e., startle, eye contact, etc.)
___ ___ ___ 3. Moves rhythmically in response to pulse of music (i.e., tap, rock, clap, etc.)
___ ___ ___ 4. Exhibits spontaneous singing or humming
___ ___ ___ 5. Accepts sound of various instruments representative of each instrumental family
___ ___ ___ 6. Touches/holds instruments from each instrumental family
___ ___ ___ 7. Accepts by touch sound vibrations from musical/nonmusical sources (i.e., drum head, strings, amplifier, wood, etc.)
___ ___ ___ 8. Locates hidden sound
___ ___ ___ 9. Matches individual rhythm instruments by sound: a. drum
                        b. sticks
                        c. bell
                        d. maraca
                        e. other
___ ___ ___ 10. Start and stops a musical response
___ ___ ___ 11. Matches/anticipates changes in duration, tempo, or dynamics of music (i.e., stop/go, loud/soft)
___ ___ ___ 12. Indicates likes/dislikes of musical stimuli (i.e., smile, frown, verbalize opinion)
___ ___ ___ 13. Names/indicates 3 or more favorite songs
___ ___ ___ 14. Identifies at least 3 musical styles (i.e., Pop/Rock, Country, Classical)
___ ___ ___ 15. Identifies tonal/mood changes in live or recorded music
___ ___ ___ 16. Labels at least 2 musical passages with a feeling (i.e., happy, sad, etc.)
___ ___ ___ 17. Expresses feelings musically by engaging in improvisation, dance, creative movement, song writing, or by choosing a song

B) *IMPROVE MUSIC VOCALIZATION SKILLS*

___ ___ ___ 1. Imitates chanted/sung syllables (i.e., la, ba, da, ma, ha)
___ ___ ___ 2. Sustains vowel sounds for 2 to 4 beats
___ ___ ___ 3. Imitates chanted/sung word/sound in a reoccurring phrase

A. B. C.

___ ___ ___ 4. Sings/chants 3 word phrase in a song
___ ___ ___ 5. Sings/chants 4 or more word phrase in a song
___ ___ ___ 6. Sings/chants an entire song
___ ___ ___ 7. Sings/chants by rote
___ ___ ___ 8. Sings/chants by memory
___ ___ ___ 9. Sings/chants to match changes in tempo and dynamics,
                        a. long/short   b. loud/soft   c. fast/slow
___ ___ ___ 10. Vocally produces high/low sounds upon request
___ ___ ___ 11. Sings directionally
___ ___ ___ 12. Matches isolated pitches
___ ___ ___ 13. Sings melodically
___ ___ ___ 14. Sings/chants rhythmically in duple and triple meter
___ ___ ___ 15. Sings/chants while clapping, stomping or other type of rhythmic motor movement
___ ___ ___ 16. Sings/chants while producing given beat on an instrument
___ ___ ___ 17. Clearly pronounces word while singing/chanting
___ ___ ___ 18. Sings/chants answer in a musical call and response
___ ___ ___ 19. Chooses singing style or song to communicate feelings
___ ___ ___ 20. Sings/chants a simple improvisational 2 to 8 beat passage

C. *IMPROVE MUSICAL MOVEMENT SKILLS*

___ ___ ___ 1. Imitates 2 to 5 non-locomotor musical movements
___ ___ ___ 2. Imitates at least 10 non-locomotor musical movements
___ ___ ___ 3. Performs structured locomotor musical movement
                        a. leader dancing
                        b. circle dancing
                        c. marching
                        d. line or train dances
                        e. partner dancing
                        f. fast/rock dancing
___ ___ ___ 4. Maintains motor movement with a steady beat for 4 to 8 beats
___ ___ ___ 5. Maintains motor movement with a steady beat for an entire song
___ ___ ___ 6. Performs rhythmic body movements in duple and triple meters (i.e., clapping, stomping, patching, other)
___ ___ ___ 7. Applies directional movement skills to musical movement
___ ___ ___ 8. Imitates peers' movements
___ ___ ___ 9. Performs 2 to 5 original musical movements
___ ___ ___ 10. Improvises movements to match tempo, mood, and dynamics
___ ___ ___ 11. Labels at least 2 movements with a feeling (i.e., happy, sad, etc.)
___ ___ ___ 12. Expresses emotions through interpretive dance, creative movement, or by choosing from at least 3 given movements

MONROE COUNTY INTERMEDIATE SCHOOL DISTRICT
ANNUAL GOALS AND SHORT-TERM INSTRUCTIONAL OBJECTIVES - MUSIC THERAPY
STUDENT_____PLACEMENT_____DATE_____

MUSIC THERAPIST_____

ANNUAL GOAL: THE STUDENT WILL DEVELOP/IMPROVE EXPRESSION IN THE MUSIC SETTING

A. *EVALUATION PROCEDURES*
1. Observation
2. Standardized Test
3. Teacher Made Test
4. Developmental Profile
5. Skill Inventory
6. Curriculum
7. Other_____

B. *SUCCESS CRITERIA*
1. With 100% Accuracy
2. With 75% Accuracy
3. With 50% Accuracy
4. With 25% Accuracy
5. With____% Accuracy
6. Maintain present level of functioning
7. Standard Score of_____

C. *ASSISTANCE LEVEL*
1. Passively cooperating
2. With physical assistance
3. With physical prompts
4. With imitation
5. With verbal and/or gestural prompt
6. With repeated requests, no prompts
7. Independently w/wo adaptive device
8. Maintain Skill

D) *IMPROVE INSTRUMENT MANIPULATION*

A. B. C.
1. Shakes a shaker-type instrument upon request
2. Taps drum or tambourine
3. Strums a stringed instrument
4. Plays keyboard instrument with one finger
5. Plays two part instrument
6. Plays advanced rhythm instrument
   a. xylophone   d. afuche/cabasa
   b. castanets   e. other
   c. finger cymbols _
7. Indicates recognition/ names rhythm instruments
   a. drum   g. woodblock
   b. bells   h. triagnle
   c. rhythm sticks i. tone bell or chimes
   d maracas   j. cymbol
   e. autoharp/guitar k. other
   f tambourine
8. Indicates preference for a musical instrument when given a choice of 2
9. Indicates preference for a musical instrument when given a choice of 3 or more
10. Maintains instrument play with a steady beat for 4 to 8 beats
11. Maintains instrument play with a steady beat for the length of an entire song
12. Plays instrument to match changes in tempo and dynamics of music
13. Repeats two instrument sound sequence
14. Repeats 3 or more instrument sound sequence
15. Matches rhythm pattern, 3 or more equal beats
16. Repeats 3 beat unequal rhythm pattern (____)
17. Repeats 4 or more beat unequal rhythm pattern (____)
18. Performs ostinato rhythm pattern for a given duration (_____)
19. Performs instrumental question/answer interaction
20. Labels various ways to play instruments (i.e , fast, slow, loud, soft) with a feeling (happy, sad, etc.)
21. Expresses emotions musically by choosing an instrument, choosing a playing style, or instrumental improvisation

E) *IMPROVE SOCIAL/EMOTIONAL SKILLS IN GROUP MUSIC*

A. B. C
1. Sits in group quietly, arms & legs in own space.
2. Attends to therapist/instructor
3. Chooses to participate in group music 100% of the time
4. Follows musical directions
5. Handles music equipment properly
6. Demonstrates awareness of others
7. Takes turns within structure of musical exchange
8. Adapts behavior to appropriately participate when a disability or other condition exists
9. Attempts new musical activities/adapts to changing dynamics
10. Interacts musically with peers
11. Becomes active member of a special music group (i.e., choir, rhythm band, dance, chimes, or other groups)
12. Attends music sessions independently
13. Assumes responsibilities in group music
14. Exhibits self control during music when experiencing happiness, anger, frustration, excitement, etc.
15. Performs in a music group on at least 2 occasions
16. Exhibits appropriate audience behavior (i.e., sits quietly, claps at proper times, dresses appropriately, etc.)
17. Assumes musical leadership role
18. Shares musical expression of feelings with others

F) *GENERALIZE ISOLATED SKILLS IN DIFFERENT SETTINGS*

1. Functionally applies isolated skills from the classroom & other environments in the music setting regarding:
   (Circle all that apply) a. communication   d. emotional
                            b. academic   e. social
                            c. motor
2. Functionally applies music related behavior, independent of the music setting , with musical stimuli present:
   (Circle one) I. With music therapist assistance
                II. Without music therapist assistance (consultation only)
   Circle all that apply regarding: a. communication   d emotional
                                     b academic   e. social
                                     c. motor
3. Functionally applies music related behavior, independent of the music setting, without musical stimuli present regarding:
   (Circle one) I With music therapist assistance
                II. Without music therapist assistance (consultation only)
   Circle all that apply regarding: a. communication c. motor   e. social
                                     b. academic   d. emotional

Music Therapy for Learners With Learning Disabilities in a Private Day School

Ned D. Gladfelter

Description of the Population

THOSE who work with children categorized as learning disabled realize that no two children with this diagnosis are identical. Because of this, there are a variety of definitions used from state to state to describe this population. Public Law 101–476, the Individuals with Disabilities Education Act (IDEA), defines a learning disability as a "disorder in one or more of the basic psychological processes involved in understanding or in using spoken or written language, which may manifest itself in an imperfect ability to listen, think, speak, read, write, spell, or to do mathematical calculations" (National Information Center for Children and Youth with Disabilities [NICHCY], 1993). The term includes such conditions as perceptual handicaps, brain injury, attention-deficit hyperactivity disorders, dyslexia, and developmental aphasia. In accordance with the law, learning disabilities do not include learning problems that are "primarily the result of visual, hearing, or motor disabilities; mental retardation; or environmental, cultural, or economic disadvantage" (NICHCY, 1993). Although persons with a learning disability can have normal or above average intelligence, the manner in which the individual selects, retains, and expresses information is negatively affected. Each child with a learning disability is unique, and can display a different combination and severity of problems. Some of the most frequently displayed problems include: short attention span; difficulty following directions; poor memory; difficulties with sequencing; inadequate ability to discriminate between and among letters, numerals, or sounds; poor reading ability; coordination problems; disorganization; and numerous other problems which may affect the sensory systems (Learning Disabilities Association of America, 1994).

There are many children with learning disabilities in schools across the nation. Given the proper attention and assistance, they can be successful in their school environment. If a learning disability is not diagnosed and proper corrective measures taken, the child will often perform poorly in school, become angry and frustrated, and be faced with continued failure. Some of these children may need more specialized, individual attention that is not available in many school settings. They are likely to benefit from the one-on-one attention that is only available in a school with small class sizes and a variety of support staff trained to teach children with learning disabilities. This is where a special school setting, such as the Pilot School, can be helpful.

The Pilot School

At the Pilot School in Wilmington, Delaware, approximately 155 students, ranging in age from 5–14 years, receive individual attention to assist them in dealing with their learning problems. This independent day school attracts students from northern Delaware and bordering counties in Pennsylvania, New Jersey, and Maryland. Students are referred by many different sources, including surrounding agencies as well as private and public schools. Once admitted to the Pilot School, the children are assigned to one of three divisions. Children from 5 to 9 years of age are in the lower division, children ages 10 and 11 make up the middle division, and children ages 12 to 14 are in the upper division. In the lower and middle divisions, the students remain with their classroom group much of the school day, receiving a majority of their instruction from their homeroom teacher. In the upper division, however, the students move from one classroom to another to attend classes with teachers who specialize in each academic area. In order to prevent the academic lapses that can occur over a long summer holiday, the Pilot School year begins in September and continues until mid-July. Students generally attend the school for 1–8 years, with an average stay of 3 years, before returning to a regular school. A small percentage of the population continues in a special education school setting after leaving Pilot.

The Pilot School specializes in identifying each child's limitations and assisting him or her to grow into a successful and productive individual. Since every child who attends the Pilot School has unique needs, the school focuses on meeting the needs of the child, rather than on following a particular teaching method or educational approach. To better focus on each individual student, the class sizes are small (approximately 6 students per class) and ungraded. Children work at their own pace, with their own material, and on their own programs and goals. Emphasis is placed on building self-esteem and confidence, and providing the child with adequate problem solving and coping skills, in order to facilitate the return to a regular classroom as soon as possible.

The Pilot School has a language-based curriculum which focuses on developing the reading, writing, spelling, speaking, and listening skills of each student. Children also receive instruction in the same subject areas they would study in a regular school including language arts, mathematics, science, social studies, art, music, drama, health, and physical education. In addition, training in basic skills such as gross and fine motor skills, visual and auditory perception, memory skills, and speech and language therapy is provided for children who have deficits in those areas.

Music Therapy Program

Every student attending the Pilot School participates in the music therapy program under the direction of a registered, board-certified music therapist who also holds a degree in music education. The amount of contact each student has with the music therapy program depends on the needs and interests of each child.

Every student takes part in a *group music therapy* session with their homeroom class on a weekly basis. Sessions, which run for the entire school year, are approximately 45 minutes in length. During these weekly group sessions, the students take part in activities which include singing, playing instruments, rhythm activities, music listening, music writing, drama exercises, and creative movement. Through participation in these activities, the following group program goals are addressed:

- Building self-esteem through successful experiences
- Developing and refining auditory processing skills
- Encouraging attention to task
- Enhancing speech and language skills
- Improving fine and gross motor skills
- Promoting academic concepts
- Developing appropriate social skills
- Expanding leisure-time activities

In addition to attending weekly sessions with their class, some students are selected to participate in *individual music therapy* sessions with the therapist so they can receive additional attention in their deficit areas. These students are referred to the music therapist by the classroom teachers and division chairpersons. Those referred often have more severe disabilities than the traditional Pilot School student. By attending individual music therapy, children are provided with an additional resource to strengthen below-average skills. Individuals referred attend a weekly 30-minute session throughout the school year. Activities in these sessions are specifically tailored to meet the needs of each individual student. Goals for the individual music sessions, as well as more specific areas that are often addressed during the individual sessions, might include:

- Improving visual perception—Correctly identifying symbols used in academic areas (letters, numbers, music notation)
- Improving auditory memory—Developing ability to sequence information in a specified order, following verbal directions, and understanding lyrics
- Enhancing expressive and receptive language skills—Articulating vowel and consonant sounds, speaking fluently while singing and speaking
- Reinforcing basic academic concepts—Understanding directional words such as left, right, forward, backward, beside, behind, high, and low
- Enhancing self-esteem—Successfully participating in a variety of music activities
- Strengthening specific academic information—Monetary values, multiplication tables, addition, subtraction, colors, and shapes
- Developing fine or gross motor skills needed for specific tasks—Holding a pencil, holding mallets and striking an instrument

Due to the large number of students seen by the music therapist each week, it is not possible to create specific student goals for each child in the group sessions. Specific goals are only developed for the students receiving individual music therapy services.

Students at the Pilot School also have the opportunity to take part in special music groups throughout the course of the year. These special music groups provide the children with necessary skills to become involved in similar groups at other schools after leaving the Pilot School. For example, through participation in large choral groups, the students learn to focus their visual and auditory attention on a director so they can participate successfully during rehearsals. They also learn when to communicate with their peers so as not to be disruptive in the rehearsals. Participation in these music groups offers students a variety of opportunities for exposure and involvement in activities designed to help them discover their strengths and instill the confidence needed to succeed in school.

Two of the special music groups involve singing. Singing is considered to be a very valuable experience at the Pilot School because it assists in the sequencing of verbal ideas, reinforces sight vocabulary, enhances pronunciation, modifies speech behaviors, improves auditory awareness, and involves memory training.

Middle Wing Glee Club—The glee club is a voluntary vocal group for all students in the middle wing. The club rehearses once a week and performs for their peers at school functions. The objectives of the glee club are to: (a) promote positive self-esteem through successful experiences, (b) learn to function as part of a large group, (c) develop poise and self-confidence, and (d) develop interest in singing through exposure to appropriate vocal techniques.

Upper Wing Chorus—The upper wing chorus is a voluntary activity for all students. Rehearsals are scheduled once each week and the chorus performs at school functions and community events several times each year. The objectives of the chorus are to: (a) develop social skills through participation in group activities and community events, (b) promote positive self-esteem through successful experiences, (c) develop poise and self-confidence, and (d) enhance singing ability through exposure to appropriate vocal techniques.

Instrumental Ensemble "Early Morning Jammers"—The instrumental ensemble meets once a week before the start of the school day, hence the name, "Early Morning Jammers." The ensemble consists of students who show interest in developing skill on a particular instrument. In this traditional rock group, which includes keyboards, drum set, guitars, wind instruments, and vocalists, band members rehearse songs from the 1950s–1990s and perform for their peers at school functions and in the community. As part of the ensemble, the band members are able to: (a) develop skill on a particular instrument, providing an appropriate leisure-time activity that can be used throughout life; (b) develop the social skills and cooperative efforts needed to play with other instrumentalists; (c) gain a more positive sense of self-esteem through successful experiences; and (d) gain exposure to a variety of musical styles.

All group and individual music therapy sessions are held in a fully-equipped music room designed specifically for music sessions. The room, which is carpeted and climate-controlled, has ample natural and electric lighting that can be manipulated with blinds to reduce external distractions. The room is set up in three sections, so that the students and therapist can move around with ease while being surrounded by a minimal amount of distractions in any one area.

On one side of the room there is a large, round table with chairs, which comfortably seats up to eight people, located by a chalkboard and bulletin board. In the center of the room is a large open space for movement activities. The remaining third of the room consists of a complete drum set, congas and bongos, seven electronic keyboards of various-sized keys (each with headphones), a computer with sequencing abilities, an acoustic piano, and an entire wall of private, storage space which conceals guitars (classical, folk, and electric) of various sizes, Orff and rhythm instruments, autoharps, tone chimes, a stereo-sound system, various recordings of music, and a wide variety of books and sheet music.

The equipment used to furnish the music room is a collection of both donated and purchased items. The drum set, electronic keyboards, and guitars are especially useful in the sessions and have proven to be an essential part of the music therapy program. The drum set, in particular, motivates many of the students to take part in rhythm activities which can develop fine and gross motor skills, improve coordination, and develop auditory memory. In addition, playing the drum set can enhance the understanding of concepts such as left and right, and allows the students to express themselves through improvisation.

The electronic keyboards are also quite useful in the music sessions. The keyboards provide stimulating sounds, rhythms, and effects which can be used in many music activities. Students can play familiar melodies or create original works with relative ease while improving fine motor and auditory processing skills. Since many of the children also have access to some type of keyboard instrument at home, a positive exposure to the instrument during music sessions at school may encourage interest and improve self-esteem. Because of the variety of ability levels in one class of students with learning disabilities, there is a keyboard available for each person in a class. By having several keyboards with both half and full-sized keys, children of all ages, and with varying degrees of fine motor dexterity can successfully create music. Each keyboard is also equipped with a set of headphones so that the students can work individually without distraction. In addition to helping the students focus on the task at the keyboard, it enables the therapist to move among the students, giving them individual attention in a group setting.

Since most school-aged students relate to some type of guitar playing, electric, folk, and classical guitars are often used in the music sessions, particularly with the older students. Although playing the guitar is generally more of a challenge than playing the drum or keyboard for many of the children, this instrument has wide appeal due to influences from television and live concerts. Visual, motor, and auditory skills are all integrated as the children create music on the guitar. As with the keyboards, it is helpful to have both full and half-sized guitars so that students of all ages can participate in guitar activities.

Not only does the music therapist have a great amount of direct contact with the students in this setting, there is also opportunity for interaction with the classroom teachers as well. This enables both the music therapist and classroom teacher to utilize each other as consultants in order to integrate music activities into the regular classroom and academic material into the music sessions. Some examples of this interdisciplinary approach are included in Table 1. When the classroom teachers and music therapists use such an integrated approach, it allows the children to experience important concepts and information in an exciting way, with a variety of repetition so more effective learning can occur.

Assessment

The music therapist in this setting gathers information about the students in a variety of ways. For those children returning to Pilot from the previous year, a brief informal assessment is done during the first music session of the school year. During this session, a variety of music activities are presented to each group of peers, so the therapist can gain insight into their academic, social, perceptual, and musical abilities.

For those students who are new (approximately 30 each school year), the therapist speaks with the classroom teacher and looks through each new file for background information before

Table 1

Interdisciplinary Activities Created for Students With Learning Disabilities

Academic Area	Activity
Reading	After a class read a story book with their homeroom teacher, the music therapist assisted the class in creating sound effects and music to accompany the story. The story was then recorded for students, staff, and parents to enjoy.
Math	To supplement an upper wing math lesson, the math teacher asked the music therapist to give a brief lecture/demonstration about note values and time signatures so the class could see how numbers and ratios are used outside of the math classroom.
Writing	Poems written in an English class were brought to the music session where the students combined them with chord progressions to create original songs that they could perform.
Math	To assist those having difficulty learning times tables, the therapist created drum set activities which reinforced counting by groups of 2's, 3's, and 4's.
Science	When the science teacher was teaching a unit about tropical rain forests, the music therapist enhanced the students' knowledge of animals, tribes, and other rain forest facts through the production of a rain forest musical. Students memorized lyrics and performed on stage using rain forest props created in their art classes.
Physical Ed.	The music therapist assisted the physical education staff by creating live music on the piano and drums for movement activities and exercises during physical education classes.

working with the child in the first music session. The school psychologist, speech therapist, and educational diagnostician, who assess each student upon admission, also provide valuable information. Once information is collected from these sources, the therapist gathers further information directly from the student using the Music Therapy Assessment (see Figure 1) as a guide.

Student: _____   Date: _____

Skill	Test	Un Able	Need Imp.	Sat.
Auditory Perception Skills				
Sound Awareness	Reaction to Sound and Silence Starting and Stopping to Sound Cues			
Sound Localization	Locates source of sound with visual clue or gesture.			
Sound Discrimination	Intensity (Dynamics - Loud/Soft)			
	Duration: Rhythm (Long/Short)			
	Pitch (Same/Different High/Low)			
Auditory Memory Skills	Can imitate rhythm patterns accurately			
	Recalls words to songs			
Visual Perception Skills	Focus: Locates instruments Moves hand to objects			
	Tracking: Follows written symbols across page			
Motor Skills Gross Motor	Maintains rhythm and balance in locomotor activities			
	Demonstrates awareness of body parts			
	Comprehends directional words.			
	Coordinates hands and feet while playing drum set			
Fine Motor	Coordinates eye/hand movements in action songs			
	Demonstrates adequate finger strength and separation when playing piano			
	Has strength in left hand to finger guitar chords			
	Can depress key with one hand while strumming strings on autoharp			

Skill	Test	Un Able	Need Imp.	Sat.
Social Skills				
Attention Span	Maintains interest in activities			
Cooperation	Follows directions/cues			
	Uses materials approp.			
Self Esteem	Accepts challenges			
	Contributes ideas/skills			

Musical Interests:

Instruments:

Styles of Music:

Reading/Math/Language Skills:

Comments:

Figure 1. Music Therapy Assessment, The Pilot School

This assessment, which is completed in the music room during the first month of the school year, provides specific information about each student and reveals how they respond to a variety of musical stimuli. Musical interests and abilities are also noted, helping the therapist to plan activities and sessions that will be beneficial for the student.

To evaluate the child's perceptual skills in a musical environment, the therapist engages the child in a variety of short activities which include movement, playing rhythm and keyboard instruments, and vocal exercises. During the course of these music activities, the therapist gains valuable information about the students' auditory and visual perception skills, fine and gross motor skills, and social skills. The language and academic skills (which were acquired by the music therapist from the classroom teacher and speech therapist before the assessment) are also briefly noted. Below is a sample session that may be used for the music therapy assessment. The skill being assessed is in parentheses.

Example of Assessment Procedures

After greeting the student and briefly discussing the child's musical tastes and other interests, the therapist introduces the child to several percussion instruments, such as the conga, hand drum, triangle, tambourine, and maraca. The student is shown how to produce a sound on each instrument, and is encouraged to explore each instrument to become familiar with the sound. The therapist then uses these instruments in several activities.

- First the therapist has the child create a movement, such as hopping, marching, or standing "frozen," for each different sound. The student then does the appropriate movement while each instrument is played by the therapist (Sound Awareness and Discrimination).

- The child is then asked to cover his or her eyes and point to the sound source when an instrument is played (Sound Localization).

- The student plays a favorite rhythm instruments as the therapist gives verbal cues and/or hand gestures for various dynamic levels such as loud and soft (Sound Discrimination).

- The student then is asked to imitate rhythm patterns initiated by the therapist (Auditory Memory). The therapist may ask the student to create his or her own rhythm patterns (Self Esteem).

- The rhythm instruments are set aside and the therapist introduces the drum set. The student is shown how to hold the drum sticks (Fine Motor Skill) and is encouraged to explore the different drums, from the snare drum through the tom toms and cymbals (Visual Perception). He or she is then asked to imitate rhythm patterns initiated by the therapist (Auditory Memory) on the drum set.

- The therapist introduces a basic rock beat on the drum set using one foot on the bass drum and one hand on the snare drum (Motor Skills–Coordination Among Hands and Feet, Directional Concepts–Left/Right, Forward/Backward). More advanced drum patterns may be attempted depending on the ability level of the student.

- The therapist next moves to the piano with the student. The therapist sings through several familiar songs encouraging the child to sing along (Auditory Memory). The therapist listens to see if the child is able to sing on key and may even have them match a few pitches while singing. Echo songs (Auditory Perception and Memory) and action songs (Fine and Gross Motor Skills) may be included. Written words to the songs may also be used to see if the individual can follow the words across the page (Visual Perception-Tracking).

- The therapist shows the student a series of letters, from A through G, written on a page. He or she is asked to identify a letter (Visual Perception), and to locate it on a piano keyboard which has the letters printed on the keys. The student is then asked to play the appropriate piano key (Fine Motor Skill). A simple, familiar melody may be written out for the student to play on the piano. Adapted notation could use a number system, where students identify a written number and play a corresponding key with the same number.

- The session could end with a brief introduction to the guitar or autoharp. For the older students, a nylon string, classical guitar is used in the assessment session since it is generally easier for most students to produce a clean sound when fingering a note with the left hand. They are then shown how to hold the guitar, how to produce a single note, and how to strum a simplified, one-finger chord (Motor Skills). For the younger students, the autoharp is used instead of the guitar since most younger children don't have the finger strength and coordination to play the guitar.

Throughout the entire session, the therapist notes social skills such as the child's attention span, ability to follow directions, willingness to take risks, and contribute ideas. The child's abilities are noted on the assessment form.

Relationship to the IEP

To ensure that each student receives proper attention in his/her deficit areas, an Individual Education Plan (IEP) is developed at the beginning of each school year. The IEP is based upon evaluative data and input from the classroom teacher, division chairperson, school psychologist, educational diagnostician, and family members. It is updated at least three times a year by the classroom teacher. The student's progress in his/her IEP is discussed with the parent/guardian of the child in three separate conferences throughout the school year. The division chairperson, classroom teacher, and any other staff members who have direct contact with the child may attend these conferences. Since the music therapist works with every child in the school, it is not possible to attend each one of these conferences. Instead, each classroom teacher routinely gathers verbal and written information about their student's progress in the music sessions directly from the therapist before the conference occurs. This information is then shared with those attending the conference. On occasion the music therapist will attend a conference to share specific issues about a student.

In addition to the academic IEP, a music therapy IEP is created for the students who attend individual music therapy sessions. During the first month of school, the music therapist meets with each child who will be attending individual music therapy sessions. The therapist assesses the students and develops the music therapy IEP by mid-October. The music therapy IEP states specific goals and objectives with corresponding music activities. The music therapy IEP is updated four times during the school year to provide family members and other staff members with specific feedback on the student's progress in the music therapy sessions. It is included in the student's file, along with the academic IEP and other information about the student. Figure 2 shows a music therapy IEP for a hypothetical child with learning disabilities. The hypothetical child in this example is an 8-year-old boy with attention-deficit/hyperactivity disorder and dyslexia. He has been enrolled in the Pilot School since age 7 and he reads at the first grade level. Visual symbols are challenging, and he experiences frustration when writing and reading. He is unsure of directional words such as left and right. He enjoys physical activities and has very advanced motor coordination skills. He shows much interest in percussion activities, particularly the drum set, and his auditory memory skills are excellent.

Progress Report

Each student's progress in the group music therapy sessions is reported on a mid-year and end-of-year progress report. This report is included in the student's file and shared with the parents/guardians at the next conference. A sample progress report can be seen in Figure 3. The progress report includes a checklist which identifies attitudes and behaviors of the child. Written comments about progress on the music therapy goals are reported by the therapist, along with comments on progress and behavior in any special music groups in which they may be involved.

The hypothetical student mentioned in Figure 3 is a female, 11 years of age, who has been attending the Pilot School since age 9. Next year she will be returning to a Catholic school as a 6th grader. When she arrived at Pilot three years ago, she had difficulty interacting with her peers and her lack of social skills were creating behavior problems with her classmates. Because of previous failure in school, she had a low sense of self-esteem and put little effort into school work. During her years at Pilot, she experienced success in school, which helped her to begin to realize that it was possible to enjoy school. She also gained the organizational and study skills necessary to keep her school work organized, which helped in all of her academic areas. In addition, she had the opportunity to take part in many small group situations with her peers, which helped her to develop the social skills to interact positively with others. Figure 3 reveals her progress in the group music therapy sessions during her final year at the Pilot School.

Unique Role of Music Therapy

The music therapy program at the Pilot School offers every student, regardless of ability level, the chance to participate in some form of musical activity with success. The music therapy program complements the other academic areas and programs in the school while providing the students with another arena in which they can feel good about their participation in school.

Music is one area in which about every child seems to want to get involved. In addition to the group and individual music therapy sessions, the special music groups are popular with practically every Pilot student. These groups not only give them the chance to develop some of their musical ability in their voices or on an instrument, but they provide the students with the opportunity to share their musical talent with others in the school and community. The children

Annual Goals	Short-Term Objectives	Specific Educational Services	Criteria/ Evaluation Procedures	Status of Objective			
				Dec.	Mar.	June	Summer School
To improve visual perception	1. Extinguish letter reversals by correctly identifying the letters of the alphabet, and placing cardboard figures of each letter in the appropriate direction and order during music activities.	Individual Music Therapy once a week for 1/2 hour for the entire school year.	Letters placed with 100% accuracy during the "ABC Song" and "BINGO"				
	2. Spell simple words and names requested in the lyrics of songs using both the cardboard letters and writing skills.	Individual Music Therapy once a week for 1/2 hour for the entire school year.	Spell 100% of words accurately during the song "Spell Some Names/Words"				
	3. Enhance visual tracking skills used in reading by following the printed notes of a melody across a page while playing the melody on a keyboard or xylophone.	Individual Music Therapy once a week for 1/2 hour for the entire school year.	Successful performance of "Hot Cross Buns" and "Lean On Me" on keyboard or xylophone.				
To reinforce academic concepts	1. Concepts of left and right will be enhanced through exposure to rhythm activities using both hands and drum sticks on the bongos and drum set.	Individual Music Therapy once a week for 1/2 hour for the entire school year.	Perform 4-beat drum patterns which use a combination of left and right hands in a specified order (LRLL or RLRR)				
To enhance self-esteem	1. Learn to play a basic rock beat on the drum set and then use this rock beat to accompany a favorite song.	Individual Music Therapy once a week for 1/2 hour for the entire school year.	Video recording of the student playing a rock beat on the drum set to accompany a favorite song.				
To encourage attention to task	1. Remain focused for a given amount of time while playing different melodies on the bells. Increase the duration of time spent on task as the difficulty of the melody is increased.	Individual Music Therapy once a week for 1/2 hour for the entire school year.	Amount of minutes spent focusing on reading a melody played on bells: By December Easy Melody - 5 minutes By March Intermediate Melody - 10 min. By June Advanced Melody - 15 min.				

Figure 2. Music Therapy IEP for Hypothetical Child With Learning Disabilities

Program Goals for Music Therapy Groups Include:

Building self-esteem through successful experiences
Developing and refining auditory processing skills
Enhancing speech and language skills
Improving fine and gross motor skills

Encouraging attention to task
Developing appropriate social skills
Promoting academic concepts
Expanding leisure-time activities

Activities Include:

Instrument playing, Music listening, Movement activities, Singing, Writing music and lyrics, & Creative drama activities

Class Attitudes and Behaviors:	Mid-year	End-of-Year
Follows Directions	S	S
Participates in Activities	S	E
Interacts Appropriately With Peers	S	E
Can Work Independently	N	S
Accepts Praise and Encouragement	E	E
Respects Musical Equipment	E	E

E = Excellent
S = Satisfactory
N = Needs Improvement

Comments:

Mid-year: *This student willingly participates in each music therapy session. She does not hesitate to get involved, and she seems to enjoy the activities, particularly when she is interacting with the group members. On occasion, she gets distracted and becomes immature with her peers and needs to be refocused. When working independently at an instrument, or at a pencil and paper task, she has much difficulty remaining focused on the given task for more than a minute. She seems to give up on herself quite easily, and needs to be encouraged to put forth effort. When the therapist provides her with easy to accomplish, one-step tasks, interspersed with much positive verbal reinforcement, she seems to stay more motivated and on task for longer periods of time. It should also be noted that she sings on key quite well, and she shows an interest in singing.*

End of Year: *As the year progressed, this student seemed to feel better about her abilities in the music sessions. She began to show more effort and determination on her own, and she depended less on the therapists prompts to stay on task. She also acted more appropriately with her peers, engaging in appropriate mature dialogue that contributed to the activities. The development of her singing voice gave her the confidence to successfully sing a solo with the Glee Club this year. The positive attention she received from her family, friends, and teachers from this performance seemed to increase her self-esteem. She even mentioned that she will audition for the choir at her new school next year.*

This Student Also Participates In:
_X_Middle Wing Glee Club
____Upper Wing Chorus
____Early Morning Jammers
____Individual Music Therapy

Figure 3. Group Music Therapy Progress Report

in these groups learn that they must each work together so they can progress toward a common performance goal. Throughout the year, those involved in the special music groups have several opportunities to perform for audiences of their peers, teachers, families, and friends. Not only do these groups perform at the Pilot School, but these special groups have performed at other schools, malls, bar mitzvahs, and conferences.

Every student in the entire school takes part in a musical production around the winter holidays. The entire school, students and staff, work together cooperatively to create a festive performance in which every student is highlighted. This helps to create a feeling of unity among all of the students and staff in the school. The sense of accomplishment and pride in their achievements can be seen and heard by the students and their families in this performance.

During the month of March, the Pilot School celebrates "Music In Our School Month." On each day of the month, there is some type of musical performance by either a student, staff member, parent, or friend of the Pilot School. All styles of music, and all ability levels of performance, are encouraged for the celebration. Performances have included recorder duets and trios by both students and professional recorder groups, rock guitar demonstrations, harmonica and accordion players, folk singers, choral groups, concert bands and jazz bands from local schools, classical and jazz piano performances, opera singers, and drum soloists, to name a few. The students not only learn how to become respectful audience members by attending each performance, but many of them have the opportunity to get involved and work toward a performance goal . Parents and students who have performed together seem to enjoy the unique musical experience. By observing such a wide array of music performances, the students can see that people of all ages and backgrounds value music throughout their lives. It also exposes the students to a variety of musical styles, all performed live by musicians whom they can question to learn new information.

The program at the Pilot School has been developed by a music therapist with a dual degree in music education. Because of this background, and because of the fact that some of the children attending Pilot for many years have no other exposure to a music program, the therapist does incorporate some music education into the therapy sessions when appropriate. The overall focus of the program uses musical activities to accomplish the nonmusical goals stated earlier in this chapter. However, there are situations such as the special music groups, where a performance-oriented musical goal is desired. In some of these group situations, the therapist will encourage students who are functioning at a high cognitive level, or who have previous musical experience, to use appropriate music notation rather than adapted music. Students are also encouraged to sing correctly and accurately on key, with the aid of Kodaly hand signals. By being exposed to some of the techniques typically used by music educators, it is believed that the children will be able to more likely make a successful transition back into a regular music education setting.

It is believed that through exposure to the music therapy program at the Pilot School, the child with learning disabilities will have another avenue to explore which will assist them in their quest to become a successful and productive individual.

Tips

Below are some suggestions which may be of use when working with students with learning disabilities in a music environment:

- Try to limit the size of your music group (6 students or less) so that it will be easier to address the variety of learning problems and learning styles that you will encounter. Individualize your sessions as much as possible, offering several levels of participation within a session.

- When working with large groups of students, strategically seat certain students in locations which reduce distractions. Keep the distance between yourself and a highly distractible student to a minimum (3 feet or less).

- Since some students will be challenged to stay focused on an activity, set up the room where the therapy session is to occur with a minimum amount of distractions.

- Keep sessions structured and place materials and equipment not being used out of sight, if possible. To help structure the environment, place carpet squares on the floor to assist the children in defining their space.

- Because many students have difficulty understanding sequences of events, keep verbal directions simple, specific, and to the point.

- Be sure that you have the students' attention before giving directions. Use the music, rather than talking to grab their attention. Students can easily learn that a short chord progression played on the piano means to stop talking and focus on the therapist.

- Help keep the students organized by establishing a predictable schedule of activities.

- Present concepts and new material using more than one of the senses (visual, auditory, and kinesthetic) to enhance the students ability to understand the information. For example, when introducing singing activities, use Kodaly hand signs that correspond to the syllables being sung. This gives the students both auditory and visual cues which may assist them to better sing on key. Also, try starting with the music (auditory stimulus) first, and then introduce the visual symbols that coincide with what they are hearing.

- Since some students may need the freedom to move around more than usual during the music sessions, devise a plan for those students so they can have this freedom without disrupting the other group members. For example, allow them to stand while others are doing desk work.

- Live music seems to be quite effective with this population since the students can visually see the music being produced in addition to just hearing it. Through live performance, the therapist can also modify a variety of musical elements (tempo, pitch, rhythm, and dynamics) so the students can be more successful in the music activities.

- Present small pieces of new information at a time. Repetition with some variety can help ensure success and interest in the activities.

- Set verbal time limits for some activities to assist the students in managing their time appropriately ("You have 3 minutes to practice your melody. . . .You have 1 more minute". . .etc.).

- Have many large, clearly identifiable cards with symbols (such as letters, numbers, punctuation, and music notation) available to use in the sessions. Providing the students with visual reinforcement of these symbols may help the children to understand them more fully.

- Use an overhead projector to focus an entire group on song lyrics or visual symbols. With the projector, you can enlarge visual symbols, reduce the field of vision, and point to words to help them better focus on specific areas.

- On some occasions, you may want the students to get involved quickly when they play "by ear" in a musical situation (without the use of written symbols). However, on other occasions adapted music can be helpful, and provide the students with practice in visual tracking, an important skill used in reading. Guitar tablature, chord charts, letters above lyrics, colors or numbers which correspond to certain pitches, and pictures of the piano keyboards with dots on the intended keys are all useful visual devices.

- Use laminated charts so you and the students can create spontaneous visual symbols of any size and color during the music sessions.

- Since students will often complain about not getting to play a favorite instrument, have the students rotate through all of the instruments during an activity to allow every student the opportunity to explore each instrument being used.

- When creating original song lyrics, reduce the amount of handwriting by having the students fill in blanks with individual words rather than having them write entire sentences.

- Some students have difficulty filtering out other sounds in a group music situation, creating additional stress for these children. Provide them with headphones to help keep them focused on the specific auditory sound.

- Get advice and suggestions from the other professional staff in your setting. What do they find effective? What assessments do they use? How can you adapt their ideas to conform to your music situation? Can you work together to reinforce some specific skills?

- Work with the classroom teachers to integrate information from a topic the students are studying into the music sessions. Give the teachers suggestions for music activities that they can use in their classroom.

- Recognize the children's strengths by providing a brief time at the end of a session for the students with extra musical talent to perform for their peers.

- Keep the music sessions enjoyable. Reinforce positive behaviors and provide opportunities for success to help build the student's self-esteem. Use music to help them have more success in an academic area that they find challenging so the student can gain confidence in that academic area.

References

Learning Disabilities Association of America. (1994). *When learning is a problem*, Pittsburgh, PA: Author.

National Information Center for Children and Youth with Disabilities. (1993). *Fact sheet number 7*. Washington, DC: Author.

MUSIC THERAPY FOR LEARNERS WHO ARE DEAF/HARD OF HEARING*

Alice-Ann Darrow
Heather A. Schunk

A Note to the Reader: Throughout this chapter, we will use the abbreviation "D/HH" to denote the term "deaf and/or hard-of-hearing." We choose to use "deaf and/or hard-of-hearing" rather than "hearing impaired" because it is the terminology most often used by deaf adults. Many deaf adults view "hearing impaired" as a negative term denoting "broken or defective"; however, many professionals and parents of deaf children, particularly those who are hearing, frequently use the term "hearing impaired." Further, because those who are deaf and/or hard-of-hearing do not view their degree of hearing as a disability, it is not seen as pejorative in the Deaf culture to use the descriptors "deaf" or "hard-of-hearing" before references to the individuals. Music therapists should be sensitive to the terminology used by their students, their students' parents, as well as teachers and other professionals working in the school.

Introduction

THE role of the music therapist in school programs for students who are deaf and/or hard-of-hearing (D/HH) is often multidimensional. Music therapists working in deaf education programs must be flexible and sensitive to the overall goals and objectives of the program. The nature of therapeutic goals and objectives is heavily dependent upon the school's philosophy regarding deaf education. There are two diverse philosophical approaches to educating students who are deaf and/or hard-of-hearing. The proponents of each approach have been at odds for many years. The primary controversy exists between those who support oral approaches and those who support manual communication approaches. Further controversies exist over specific methodologies utilized within each of these two major approaches. Music therapists must take into account the overall goals of the deaf education program and design their music therapy program objectives accordingly.

Given the educational environment, the music therapist should also include program objectives which address not only therapeutic goals, but also the musical education of D/HH students, particularly if they are not mainstreamed into regular music classes. Fortunately, many music therapy and music educational goals overlap. Both types of goals can often be met through similar classroom activities. Music therapy goals center around the communication needs

---

* Parts of the chapter may be found in other resources on the same topic by the first author.

of D/HH students (Darrow, 1989), particularly in relation to language development (Gfeller & Darrow, 1987). Music education goals center around D/HH students' need for avenues of self-expression as well as their educational and personal development in relation to the larger hearing world (Darrow, 1995).

The frequent communication problems that D/HH children experience are a result of their status as a linguistic minority within the society of hearing persons who use spoken language as their primary means of communication. Left to socialize within their own subculture, D/HH children communicate freely and with all the expressiveness of any person using spoken language. Communication problems arise when D/HH children must interact with hearing individuals. These problems center around differences in their development of language and in their styles of communication.

Children who are born deaf and/or hard-of-hearing are neglected in language input, which must necessarily precede language output. Most young children receive language passively, soaking up the spoken word of their parents, older siblings, the television media, and even the conversations of strangers they encounter in public (Gfeller, 1992). In a similar way, a small percentage (about 10%) of infants who are deaf and/or hard-of-hearing are born to deaf parents, and they may develop a strong foundation for language development if they are exposed to the native, visual, and manual language of deaf people in the United States: ASL (American Sign Language). Still, they are apt to struggle with the spoken and written forms of English, the language of America's majority culture. deaf and/or hard-of-hearing children of hearing parents, however, are usually completely shut off from language in those early stages. As a result, they can encounter more pronounced communication barriers and exhibit an even greater delay in language development. For most deaf and/or hard-of-hearing children, the primary challenge is developing language in an often deprived language environment. Beyond that, for those who intend to and are able to learn spoken English, additional challenges include speech perception and production (Gfeller, 1992).

In the educational environment, the function of music in teaching language deserves attention. Music is communication. Music participation not only serves to mediate communication by organizing people into interactive behavior, but it also provides structure for both spoken and visual languages. "Music activity and active listening to music can produce functions supporting the acquisition of language, of attention and perception, the transfer of movement to sound and of sound to movement, such as an experience of the unity of language, music and movement" (Bang, 1986, p. 25). Darrow (1985) identifies some elements of music that parallel inherent qualities of spoken language, such as rhythm, intensity, duration, accents, pitch, and intonation. Rhythm, intensity, duration, accents, and inflection are also characteristic of signed language.

Beyond the facilitative aspects of music, there is the inherent value of music as a motivator which further supports the use of music therapy with deaf and/or hard-of-hearing children. Music therapy provides a creative, expressive, self-esteem-building, group-oriented, and reinforcing medium in which D/HH children can learn. Thus, music is significant in establishing a positive learning and therapeutic environment for children who often are presented with exceptional challenges in their educational experiences.

The ability to adapt music therapy procedures to the learning characteristics and communication styles of deaf and/or hard-of-hearing children requires specialized preparation. Along with some prerequisite skills, there is considerable background information that the music therapist must have in order to work successfully with these students. Background information in the following areas should be particularly helpful to the music therapist: speech and hearing science, audiology, aural habitation, manual and oral communication methods, and the impact of hearing loss on language development. An additional important area of background study is Deaf culture. Sensitivity to, and respect for, the culture of the Deaf community is essential to working successfully with children who are deaf and/or hard-of-hearing.

Deaf Culture

Culture embodies the beliefs, experiences, and practices of an integrated group of people. These commonalities unify and strengthen the individual members who find understanding from and belonging with others like themselves. Cultural affiliation gives purpose for and insight into the collective values, needs, and ways of achieving group goals (Rutherford, 1988). Through their endeavors, subgroups develop distinct behaviors which are functional for survival within a larger world community. For people who do not hear to be able to survive in a sound-reliant world, they draw together to engage in a silent society. According to Rutherford (1988, pp. 134–135), some clear evidence of the Deaf as a distinct community include a high "endogamous marriage rate," "the existence of a formal societal structure," and "material artifacts." Beyond these characteristics, however, the key feature which defines and maintains virtually all cultures is language. It is through language that people are able to socialize, and thereby they transmit group customs, mores and expectations. Deaf people thus emerge as a unique group with strong solidarity and identity.

Indeed, what makes deaf people a cultural group instead of simply a loose organization of people with a similar sensory loss is the fact that their adaptation includes language. An environment created solely by a sensory deprivation does not make a culture. Blind people find themselves in a visual void. This similarity in circumstance certainly provides for a strong group bonding of individuals of similar experience; it does not, however, form a culture. Blind people are vision-impaired members of the variety of America's linguistic communities. What does form a culture for deaf people is the fact that the adaptation to a visual world has by human necessity included a visual language. In the United States this is American Sign Language. (Rutherford, 1988, p. 132)

American Sign Language (ASL) is the native language of Deaf people. It originated in the early 19th century through the efforts of Laurent Clerc, a deaf French educator, and the Reverend Thomas Gallaudet, an American, who saw the need for deaf education in the United States. It has not been until recently, however, that ASL has gained recognition as an independent, manual/visual language with its own grammar, syntax and rules. Through the research of William Stokoe in the late 1960s and early 1970s, the myths of ASL being broken English and impeding the development of any language for its users were finally dispelled.

The development of the body of linguistic research related to American Sign Language resulted in an attitudinal shift which moved from viewing deafness as a pathological inability to identifying it as a cultural difference. Increasingly, deaf people are seen as a linguistic minority within the hearing world. They are not defective or impaired people who are intellectually or cognitively inferior to those who do hear. They can be equally brilliant, witty, or expressive.

Past misconceptions about the language and the abilities of those who are deaf built many barriers and obstacles to mutual understanding and interaction between Deaf and hearing communities. This has had an impact on the educational and political experiences of the deaf. They feel that traditionally hearing educators and leaders have made decisions about the teaching practices and social position of those who are deaf without consideration for the special needs and views of the group itself. As a result, deaf people are compelled to advance their group's acceptance within the hearing world to gain respect and rights. They have made great strides in exerting their issues by educating the public about their language, social and political organizations, and rich legacy of Deaf folklore, art, and literature. For further readings on Deaf culture, see the Resource section.

Music and Deaf Culture

In respect for the Deaf community, it is important to discuss the role of music in a cultural context. This means expanding the conventional constructs through which music involvement is traditionally defined. The adaptability of music allows it to be molded into the ways deaf people experience it so as to make it useful and cherished in ways both similar and dissimilar to hearing uses. It is important to note that very few individuals actually have no hearing.. Usually, Deaf and/or hard-of-hearing people have some degree of residual, or existing, hearing; therefore, there are certain frequencies, timbres, and intensities of music which can be auditorily detected. Music can also be expressed visually and tactually. Aspects of music participation among deaf people include vibrations, rhythm, movement, and expression. There are deaf instrumentalists, rock bands, concert fans, country dancers, and more. Research, however, indicates that it is erroneous to assume that all deaf people value music (Darrow, 1993). Some individuals reject music as a hearing value and find no use for it in their lives. This caution is noted in discussing the implications of music therapy with deaf and/or hard-of-hearing children. Music therapists must recognize and understand their students' place within or outside of Deaf culture.

Those who uphold the values of Deaf culture and use ASL take pride in their cultural identity and they describe themselves as "Deaf" with a capital "D." There are others, however, who do not share the language or social ties and thus function more in the hearing world. These individuals are more apt to describe themselves as "deaf" with a lower case "d" or with the term "hard-of-hearing." For the purposes of this chapter, we will attempt to address music therapy implications as they apply to these combined groups of individuals. They will be referred to in the encompassing category of deaf and/or hard-of-hearing persons (D/HH).

Terminology Related to Deafness

There are numerous terms used in the field of deaf education. We have included selected terms below. Knowledge of these terms is essential to working effectively with D/HH students and interacting credibly with other professionals.

Types of Hearing Loss

There are four types of hearing loss, each of which can result in different possibilities for remediation:

Conductive Hearing Losses are caused by diseases or obstructions in the outer or middle ear (the conduction pathways for sound to reach the inner ear). Conductive hearing losses usually affect all frequencies of hearing and do not result in severe losses. Because of this, a person with a conductive hearing loss usually is able to use a hearing aid with success.

Sensorineural Hearing Losses result from damage to the delicate sensory hair cells of the inner ear or the nerves which supply it. These hearing losses can range from mild to profound deafness. They often affect certain frequencies more than others, and this results in distorted perception even when the sound level is increased. The distortion accompanying some forms of sensorineural hearing loss is so severe that successful use of a hearing aid is impossible.

Mixed Hearing Losses are those in which there is a problem in the outer or middle ear and in the inner ear.

Central Hearing Losses result from damage or impairment to the nerves or nuclei of the central nervous system, either in the pathway to the brain or in the brain itself.

Onset of Deafness

The onset of deafness varies from person to person, and it holds implications for an individual's language development.

Congenital Deafness: when a person is born deaf.

Adventitious Deafness: when deafness occurs sometime after birth, usually as a result of an accident or illness.

Prelingual Deafness: when deafness occurs before the acquisition of language (usually before 3 years of age). Such a person will have no language frame of reference when learning to speak, write, or speechread.

Postlingual Deafness: when deafness occurs after the acquisition of language (usually after 3 years of age). In most cases, persons who have lost their hearing after this age have a relatively strong language base.

Classifications of Hearing Loss

Hearing Level Effect on the Clinical Environment

An individual's hearing loss is generally described in terms of slight, mild, moderate, severe, and profound, based on their average hearing level, in decibels, throughout the frequencies most important for understanding speech (500 to 2,000 Hz). Each level of hearing loss will have a differential effect on the client's interaction with the clinical environment. Table 1 outlines the effects each level of hearing loss will have on the clinical environment.

Descriptive Terms

Deaf (with a capital "D")—people who share a language— American Sign Language— and a culture.

deaf (with a lower case "d")—individuals who are oral, or often those who lose their hearing adventitiously through illness, accidents, or old age. This groups does not have access to the language, heritage, beliefs, and practices of deaf people.

Hard-of-hearing—a condition in which one's residual hearing is functional for processing speech—usually with the help of a hearing aid (Padden & Humphries, 1988).

Table 1

Effect of Hearing Loss on the Environment

Degree of Loss	Effect on Environment
Slight loss (27 to 40 dB)	May have difficulty hearing faint or distant speech. May experience some difficulty with language arts.
Mild loss (41 to 55 dB)	Understands conversational speech at a distance of 3 to 5 feet. May miss as much as 50% of conversation if not face-to-face. May have limited vocabulary and speech irregularities.
Moderate loss (56 to 70 dB)	Can understand loud conversation only. Will have difficulty in group discussions. Is likely to have impaired speech, limited vocabulary, and difficulty in language use and comprehension.
Severe loss (71 to 90 dB)	May hear loud voices about 1 foot from ear. May be able to identify environmental sounds. May be able to discriminate vowels, but not consonants. Speech and language likely to be impaired or to deteriorate.
Profound loss (91 dB or more)	More aware of vibrations than tonal patterns. Relies on vision rather than hearing as primary means of communication. Speech and language likely to be impaired or to deteriorate. Speech and language unlikely to develop spontaneously if loss is prelingual.

(Heward & Orlansky, 1988, pp. 259–260)

Terms Related to the Measurement of Hearing

Since music therapists are concerned with the response of the human ear to music stimuli, it is helpful to know those terms that relate to the measurement of hearing. Sound consists of vibrations that travel in waves, generally through the air. Sound waves can vibrate at different speeds as they travel through the air. The faster the wave vibrates, the higher the pitch. Frequency is the number of vibrations produced per second and is measured in Hertz. One vibration per second equals one Hertz. The frequency of a sound is a physical reality while pitch is our subjective judgment of its frequency. Table 2 gives familiar frequency ranges.

Table 2

Frequency Ranges in Hertz

Frequency Range	Hertz
normal hearing:	20 – 20,000 Hz
normal speech:	500 – 2000 Hz
the piano:	27.5 – 4186 Hz

The duration of sound has to do with its continuance in time. The aural discrimination of varying lengths of sound is the basis of rhythm perception. Intensity is the amount of energy in a sound wave. Intensity is a quantitative measurement of sound. Loudness is our subjective judgment of this measurement. The intensity of sound is measured in decibels. Zero decibels (0 dB) is the quietest audible sound while sounds above 120–140 dB can actually cause pain to the ears. Table 3 gives some common decibel ranges:

Table 3

Decibel Ranges of Common Sound Sources

Decibel Levels	Sound Source	Musical Levels
0 dB	just audible sound	
20 dB	soft rustle of leaves	
30 dB	quiet whisper	background music
40 dB	soft speech	p
50 dB	normal conversation	mp
60 dB	loud conversation	mf
80 dB	shouting	f
90 dB	heavy traffic	marching band
100 dB	riveter 35 feet away	
120 dB	jet engine	

Audiology, the science of hearing, has made great strides in the development of instruments which assist in the detection and assessment of hearing loss. Audiologists measure the degree of hearing loss by generating sounds at specific frequencies and intensities on an audiometer, and then measuring an individual's response to these sounds. By viewing these responses displayed graphically on an audiogram, the music therapist can determine the aural accessibility of music stimuli and the degree of amplification required in the clinic setting.

Fortunately for us as music therapists, our medium, music, is usually more aurally accessible to D/HH individuals than speech. Music is generally more intense than conversational speech, employs many more frequencies than normal speech, and is composed of notes which are greater in duration than speech sounds. This is why even individuals with severe hearing losses will still be able to listen to and enjoy music, yet they may have difficulty in aurally processing speech (Darrow, 1990).

Communication Methods

In the United States, D/HH persons use a variety of methods and symbol systems for communication. These communication styles represent differing philosophies, and supporters of the controversial theories are sometimes at odds. These methods and philosophies include American Sign Language, Fingerspelling, Manual Communication, Oral Communication, Cued Speech, Simultaneous Communication, and Total Communication.

American Sign Language—ASL is a natural language with its own grammar and syntax. It is a beautiful and graceful visual-gestural language which developed naturally among deaf people and is used widely in the United States and several other countries. The signs in ASL are word-like units which have both concrete and abstract meanings. Signs are made by either one or both hands assuming distinctive shapes in particular locations and executing specified movements. The use of spatial relations, direction, orientation, and movement of the hands, as well as facial expression and body shift make up the grammar of ASL.

Fingerspelling—A manual alphabet is merely an alternative form of a written alphabet with hand shapes and positions corresponding to the letters of the written alphabet. In a very real sense, fingerspelling is "writing in the air." In a fingerspelling conversation, one person spells the message letter by letter to a second person who reads it and responds by spelling a reply. The use of fingerspelling as the primary mode of communication in combination with spoken English is known as the Rochester Method.

Manual Communication—The term "manual communication" includes a combination of sign language and fingerspelling used for both expressive and receptive communication. A number of manual communication systems combine sign language and fingerspelling with the grammar and syntax of standard English. There are four major systems in this group: (a) Seeing Essential English (SEE), (b) Signing Exact English (SEE II), (c) Linguistics of Visual English (LOVE), and (d) Signed English.

Oral Communication—This term denotes the use of speech and speech-reading as the primary means of communicating. Educators who believe in the Oral Communication philosophy, teach speech and speech-reading exclusively using appropriate amplification and the D/HH person's residual hearing.

Cued Speech—Cued Speech is a system of communication in which eight hand movements supplement the information being spoken. This is not a form of sign language. The hand "cue" is used to indicate, visually, the exact pronunciation of every syllable spoken. With Cued Speech, a person with hearing loss can see all the words a hearing person hears. It is a speech-based method of communication aimed at taking guesswork out of speech-reading.

Simultaneous Communication—This term is used to denote the combined use of speech, signs, and fingerspelling. An individual receives the message both by speech-reading what is being said and by reading the signs and fingerspelling simultaneously.

Total Communication—Total Communication is a philosophy of communication which implies acceptance, understanding, and use of all methods of communication to assist the D/HH child in acquiring language.

Historically, proponents of the various systems have been at odds. There is increasing consensus that whatever system or method works most successfully for the individual should be used to allow the person who has a hearing loss access to clear and understandable communication.

Additional Information

Inclusive background information regarding children who are deaf and/or hard-of-hearing cannot, of course, be included within this chapter. Music therapists working with D/HH children should request inservice as needed. Suggested topics for inservice might include the following:

1. Sign language instruction
2. Deaf culture
3. Current literature in deaf issues
4. D/HH musicians
5. Psychosocial aspects of deafness
6. Seminar offerings in basic hearing science
7. Parts and functions of the ear
8. Introduction to hearing aids and other assistive listening devices
9. Methods of nonverbal communication
10. Speechreading concepts
11. Causes and prevention of deafness

Additional information can be obtained from organizations related to deafness and through the Internet. For a listing of these organizations and Internet resources, see the Resource section.

Adaptations in the Music Therapy Setting

There are two primary aspects of the music therapy setting for which adaptations should be made in order to meet the needs of children who are deaf and/or hard-of-hearing. The purpose of these adaptations is to facilitate communication. Aspects of the music therapy setting which require adaptations are the physical environment and interpersonal communication.

Adaptations to the Physical Environment

1. Unnecessary noise, such as air conditioners or outdoor traffic, should be eliminated or minimized.
2. The clinical setting should have good lighting.
3. Clinic room fixtures such as draperies, carpeting, and upholstery should be used to absorb unnecessary noise.
4. Seating should be in a circle for group activities.
5. If the D/HH children wear hearing aids, they should be positioned with their hearing aids toward the group.
6. The speaker's face must be clearly seen.
7. Optimal speechreading distance should be kept at 6 feet.
8. If necessary, additional assistive communication devices such as microphones, visual aides, tactile aides, sign language interpreters, and appropriate technological aides should be added to the physical environment.

Adaptations in Interpersonal Communication

One-to-One Communication

1. Get the D/HH person's attention before speaking. A tap on the shoulder, a wave, or other visual sign of soliciting attention.
2. Speak slowly and clearly; however, exaggeration and overemphasis of words distorts lip movements, making speechreading more difficult. Speechreading is a skill not all deaf persons are able to acquire. Only about ⅓ to ¼ of all speech is visible on the lips, and even the best speechreaders can't read everything although they can pick up contextual clues to fill in some of the gaps.
3. Look directly at the person when you speak. Even a slight turn of the head can obscure the D/HH person's view. Other distracting factors affecting communication include mustaches obscuring the lips, smoking, chewing gum, and putting your hand in front of your face.
4. Don't be embarrassed about communicating via paper and pencil. Getting the message across is more important than the medium used.
5. Try to maintain eye contact with the D/HH person. Eye contact helps convey the feeling of direct communication. If an interpreter is present, continue to talk directly to the D/HH person who can turn to the interpreter if the need arises.
6. If you are having some difficulty getting an idea across, try to rephrase a thought or restate a sentence, rather than repeating exactly the same words. Sometimes a particular group of lip movements is difficult to speechread.
7. Use pantomime, body language, and facial expression to help communicate.

Group Situations and Meetings

1. Seat the D/HH person near the speaker where he or she can see the speaker's face.
2. Try to avoid standing in front of a light source, such as window. The bright background and shadows created on the face make it almost impossible to speechread.

3. Aid the D/HH person in following a lecture, movie, or filmstrip by providing a brief outline or script printout. This can be provided in advance or accompanied by lighting for the D/HH person.

4. In a training situation, try to provide new vocabulary in advance. It is almost impossible to speechread unfamiliar words.

5. Use visual aids. They can be a tremendous help to D/HH persons. Vision is a D/HH person's primary channel for receiving information. Make full use of overhead projectors, chalkboards, films, diagrams, charts, and other visual media where appropriate.

6. Try to avoid unnecessary pacing and speaking while writing on the chalkboard or lecturing. It is difficult to speechread a person in motion and impossible from the side or from the back.

7. Slow down the pace of communication slightly. This often helps to facilitate understanding. Many speakers tend to talk too fast. Try to allow a little extra time for the D/HH person to assimilate the information and respond.

8. Make sure the D/HH person is not left out when vital information is presented. Write out any changes in meeting times, special arrangements, additional instructions. Allow extra time when pointing out the location of materials, referring to manuals and other media, because the D/HH person must look, then return attention for further instruction.

9. Repeat questions of statements from the back of the room. Deaf and/or hard of hearing persons are cut off from whatever is not in their visual field. Since it is often necessary to know the question in order to fully understand the answer, questions or statements should be repeated.

(NTID at RID, no date)

Music Therapy Objectives

The term "therapy" usually implies the remedial treatment of a disease or other physical or mental disorder. The Deaf community has made great strides in recent years to depathologize their disability. Deafness is no longer viewed as a medical condition, a deficit in need of treatment. The only true handicap related to deafness is being cut off from the usual means of acquiring and transmitting language. As a result, most D/HH individuals communicate manually rather than orally. They regard this alternative form of communication as their only "difference." The loss of hearing, however, has many implications for the development of communication skills. Consequently, music therapy remains a viable educational intervention for children who are D/HH. The range of goals which are targeted for this population comprise the following categories of therapeutic objectives: *linguistic, behavioral, academic, motor skills, social interaction skills,* and *self-concept.*

Linguistic

The main focus of educational programs for D/HH children is the acquisition of English. Whereas some educators have recently argued that this rigid focus on English is unhealthy and that more attention should be given to learning history, science, math, etc.—through any available means of communication—it is still generally true that the majority of a D/HH child's time and energy in school is spent on developing skills in English. (Baker-Shenk & Cokely, 1991, p. 63)

With the focused training of English literacy being the critical chore in deaf education, music therapy serves as a motivating and engaging method of successfully achieving linguistic objectives. Through music therapy, other academic goals can be incorporated into activities relating to language development to enhance the educational foundation of D/HH children. The design of these applications can be further influenced by the needs and priorities of the individual student, as discussed in the section on Deaf culture. Therefore, the linguistic objectives for D/HH children fit into two distinct categories: developing aural-oral English literacy and learning English as a second language through American Sign Language.

Aural-Oral English

The spoken language objectives for music therapy with clients who have a significant hearing loss, are related to communication: (a) auditory training, (b) speech production, and (c) language development of children who have a hearing loss.

Auditory training. The goal of auditory training is to teach the complex task of listening. The ability of individuals to use their hearing for the purpose of listening varies. Good hearing does not necessarily insure skilled listening; conversely, poor hearing does not necessarily indicate an inability to listen. Listening is a mental process; hearing is a physical process. It is the function of the ear to collect auditory stimuli and deliver them to the brain; at which time the brain takes over and hearing becomes listening (Darrow, 1990). The development of good listening skills allows the D/HH individual to use their residual hearing to the maximum extent possible. When D/HH individuals learn to interpret the sounds around them, they also increase the rate and quality of their social and communicative development.

Training the ear to listen requires: (a) analysis of the desired auditory task, (b) the structuring of successive approximations to the desired goal, and (c) regular and systematic evaluation of the client's auditory skill level. Auditory training should consist of sequential listening exercises. Nearly all auditory tasks can be broken down into four very basic levels of aural processing (Erber & Hirsh, 1978). These levels of aural processing follow as well as ways of integrating music to determine a client's present level.

1. Detection—the listener determines the presence or absence, initiation or termination of music stimuli.
2. Discrimination—the listener perceives differences in music stimuli (such as fast and slow, high and low).
3. Identification—the listener appropriately applies labels (such as forte or piano, woodwind or brass) to music stimuli.
4. Comprehension—the listener makes critical judgments regarding music stimuli (such as judgments concerning form, harmony, or texture).

Most D/HH individuals develop detection and discrimination skills through normal interaction with the environment. It is the third and fourth levels of auditory processing, identification and comprehension, that require the attention of the music therapist.

There are a number of other listening behaviors that are subsumed within these four basic levels of auditory processing. These additional listening behaviors are prerequisites to auditory comprehension. Derek Sanders (1977) developed a hierarchy of auditory processing which should assist the music therapist in developing sequential listening objectives for a wide range of clients. The hierarchy was developed with the processing of the speech signal in mind; however, music applications can be made and are given in each of the hierarchical steps. Speech and music contain many common properties, though perhaps identified by different names. In music, reference is made to intonation, tempo, accent, and rhythm. Speech counterparts are speech inflection, rate, stress, and speech rhythm. Once again, proficiency at the first four levels of the hierarchy is usually acquired naturally. The remaining six levels of auditory processing should provide a guide for music listening experiences.

1. Awareness of acoustic stimuli
    Is the client aware that music is in the environment ?
2. Localization
    Can the client identify the location of the musical sound source ?
3. Attention
    Can the client attend to the music over time ?
4. Discrimination between speech and nonspeech
    Can the client discriminate between music and nonmusic sounds ?
5. Auditory discrimination
    Can the client discriminate between the timbre of different instruments or the entrance and exit of specific instruments within the total music context (figure/ground discrimination) ?
6. Suprasegmental discrimination
    Can the client make discriminations about the expressive qualities of the music (dynamics, tempo, phrasing) ?
7. Segmental discrimination
    Can the client make discriminations about changes in pitch ?
8. Auditory memory
    Can the client remember what instruments were heard ?
9. Auditory sequential memory
    Can the client remember in what order the instruments were heard ?
10. Auditory synthesis
    Can the client make critical judgments regarding form, texture, harmony ?
                                                                                (Darrow & Gfeller, 1988)

There are controversial views regarding the transfer of music listening skills to linguistic use; however, teaching a client to develop a focused and analytical attention to sound will undoubtedly transfer to the development of good listening habits, regardless of the source of sound stimuli. Although we can do little to improve D/HH individuals' ability to hear, we can do much to improve their ability to listen. Our goal is to increase the amount of information they receive through the sense of hearing. We do this by teaching them to interpret the sounds they hear. Listening, like any other skill, must be practiced through regular, sequential listening exercises.

The ear is a valuable listening device; and music, a powerful medium through which listening skills can be taught, practiced, . . . and rewarded.

Language acquisition and development. Language is the means by which people communicate. Native languages are generally learned auditorily, with ease, and over a relatively short period of time. Aural exposure to language is the most important ingredient in the development of communication skills. Without adequate aural exposure to language, D/HH children essentially learn a "foreign" language with only the assistance of nonverbal cues such as facial expression, body language, and small movements of the lips—on which approximately only one third of all speech is visible. It is understandable that, without alternative forms of communication such as sign language, D/HH children are at a tremendous disadvantage during the process of language development. Even children with mild hearing impairments experience difficulty with the fine discriminations that must be made in comprehending language.

Other more subtle forms of language, such as sarcasm and play-on-words, are dependent on the aural processing of speech. Many verbal behaviors are also learned auditorily; some of these include social customs such as "please" and "thank you," use of compliments, and avoidance of inappropriate questions. Young children are generally able to comprehend various words or phrases long before they are able to use them appropriately, demonstrating the importance of exposure as an antecedent to expression. Every professional involved in the habilitation of young D/HH children, including music therapists, should have among their objectives the acquisition and development of language.

The two fundamental components of language with which the music therapist is most likely to work are vocabulary knowledge and word-class usage (Gfeller & Darrow; 1987). Receptive and expressive skills, as well as reading and writing skills, should be employed as a part of instructional strategies. In order to foster language development to the fullest extent possible, methods of achieving these goals should not be confined solely to lesson objectives, but to every procedure employed in the music therapy setting. The music therapist can make most interactions an opportunity for learning language (Rickard, Robbins, & Robbins, 1990).

For young D/HH clients, the most important language objective will be the increased and appropriate use of vocabulary. Developing vocabulary skills is not as simple as defining words. Word meaning in a single context measures only one component of vocabulary knowledge. Words often have multiple meanings and serve separate language functions. D/HH children tend to know fewer words and to use them in a singular context (Davis & Hardick, 1981). A D/HH child may know the word "kid" in its noun form, a child or young goat, but not in its verb, adverb, or adjective form. It is the therapist's task to introduce vocabulary words, their multiple meanings, and their proper use in as many circumstances as possible: in song texts, song writing, informal conversation, and contrived situations. The therapist's choice of target words should be made in consultation with the child's classroom teacher or professionals who specialize in the language development of D/HH children.

D/HH children may also experience difficulty with word-class usage. D/HH children with a moderate degree of residual hearing tend to use most word classes adequately with the exception of adverbs, pronouns, and auxiliaries; D/HH children with minimal residual hearing use fewer words in all classes than children with no hearing loss. A characteristic of most D/HH children's language is a tendency to overuse nouns and articles, thus, the speculation that impaired hearing interferes with the function of words as well as understanding of their meaning (Davis & Hardick, 1981). The music therapist must attempt to provide good models of word usage, opportunities for variety of word use, and corrective feedback. Again, this can be accomplished through the study of song texts, informal conversation, or contrived situations. Additional approaches are activities such as song writing, song signing, and small group ensembles where communication is essential (Gfeller, 1987; Gfeller, 1990). Gfeller and Baumann (1988) give suggestions for the assessment of language skills in music therapy.

Speech production and reception. Speech production is acquired and controlled through the auditory system. Children learn to speak by imitating the sounds of others. The degree to which these sounds are available to the D/HH child will directly influence the quality of speech production and the ability to receive the speech signal. The aspects of speech which are most severely affected by impaired hearing are phonation, rhythm, and articulation. D/HH children often do not associate breath control with the power source needed for fluid speech; consequently, they may breathe in the middle of words or phrases. Errors of rhythm constitute one of the most deviate aspects of D/HH individuals' speech. The speech is generally slower, the syllables prolonged, and stress placed on inappropriate syllables. Speech intelligibility varies widely among D/HH individuals; however, even individuals with very little hearing are capable of developing intelligible speech.

Hearing one's own voice allows the speaker the aural feedback necessary to self-correct pronunciation of words, adjust vocal inflection and imitate speech rhythm. D/HH children are dependent on corrective feedback and instruction in remedial strategies from others. The music therapist can provide assistance in both of these areas. Music therapy objectives may include, though not be limited to, the following: vocal intonation, vocal quality, speech fluency, and speech intelligibility. In speech, the melodic elements such as rhythm, intonation, rate, and stress are referred to as the prosodic features of speech. These prosodic features convey important contextual information. Music activities such as singing can aid in the recognition and development of these melodic aspects of speech (Darrow & Cohen, 1991; Darrow & Starmer, 1986). Appropriate procedures include free vocalization, vocal imitation, rhythmic vocalization, and work on vocal phrasing and dynamics. Traditional music activities such as pitch matching practice, singing songs and vocal exercises, and following notated melodic contours, are also helpful (Bang, 1977).

The remediation of poor vocal quality can also be enhanced through traditional music activities. A breathy quality can be alleviated by vocalise that exercise the diaphragm; a nasal quality can be minimized by incorporating vocal exercises that utilize the head voice. The volume of a client's voice can be monitored during music therapy by teaching and practicing the use of expressive terms such as piano and forte, decrescendo and crescendo .

Speech fluency and articulation are not as easily influenced by the use of music therapy techniques (Gfeller, 1986). Speech fluency can be improved by the rhythmic chanting and singing of syllables, syllable combinations, words, word combinations, phrases, and finally, complete sentences. Articulatory problems constitute the greatest challenge for speech and music therapists. Problems with articulation usually involve sound omissions, such as final consonants; substitutions, such as "thoup" instead of "soup"; interjections, such as "boyee" instead of "boy"; and mispronunciation of sounds, such as "sh," "th," or "s." The music therapist can carefully select song literature which focuses on specific speech sounds or words. The therapist should also maintain a record of the number of intelligible words in a given song (Darrow, 1989). Consultation with the client's speech therapist can be extremely helpful in selecting appropriate and realistic objectives. In addition to directed music activities, feedback regarding a client's speech intelligibility should be given by the music therapist during everyday interactions in the clinical setting. Traditional assessments used in speech therapy can also be of use to the music therapist (Darrow & Gfeller, 1988).

English as a Second Language

For children who affiliate with the Deaf community, the approach to language instruction should adhere to the group's philosophy regarding the learning of English. Because ASL is the central facet of Deaf culture, they strongly support it as their native language. Subsequently, they consider English a second language. Educators have attempted to teach English in combination with signing, but typically they ignore the role of ASL and employ English sign systems. These systems have been artificially created and are not generally accepted by members of the Deaf community (Baker-Shenk & Cokely, 1991).

In learning ASL, D/HH children follow rules of grammar and syntax when communicating thoughts and ideas. Therefore, they have an established language base which provides an understanding of the building blocks of language and through which they can learn English. Given this premise, the traditional curriculum in aural-oral language remediation for some of these students may not be viable. It is critical to accept the use of their native language, ASL, for English instruction. Through their complete and independent language, complex concepts are successfully communicated, and thereby, they can learn fundamentals of English and achieve bilingual literacy. In addition to incorporating ASL into practice, the music therapist should seek direction from members of the Deaf community in designing and implementing therapeutic interventions. The best experts on the subject can be found among the cultural members.

The goal of instruction in English as a second language is to develop "communicative competence" (Diaz-Rico & Weed, 1995, p. 13). This refers to a point when the learner can effectively and idiomatically—that is, as a native would—use the language. For children who are D/HH, this process aims at somewhat different outcomes from those of hearing students learning English as a second language. Training in verbal and auditory skills to comprehend and speak English is necessary for children whose first language is Spanish, Russian, Urdu, or another spoken language. When the first language is ASL, however, the required cognitive skills are transmitted manually and visually.

Diaz-Rico and Weed (1995) suggest four areas of desired competence when teaching English as a second language that could apply to spoken and nonspoken English: grammatical, sociolinguistic, discourse, and strategic competence. There are verbal components of the following explanations, however, that would be nonapplicable; they are marked with an asterisk (*). *Grammatical competence* "involves knowing the language code: vocabulary, word formation and meaning, sentence formation, *pronunciation, and spelling" (Diaz-Rico & Weed, 1995, p. 14). *Sociolinguistic competence* refers to comprehending the language in the context of various factors, such as "the status of participants, the purposes of the interaction, and the norms or conventions of interaction" (Diaz-Rico & Weed, 1995, p. 14). Both form and meaning of the discourse should be appropriate. *Discourse competence* "involves the ability to combine and connect *utterances (spoken) and sentences (written) into a meaningful whole" (Diaz-Rico & Weed, 1995, p. 14). *Strategic competence* involves behaviors and techniques which manipulate the language "to compensate for breakdowns in communication" and "to enhance the effectiveness of communication" (Diaz-Rico & Weed, 1995, p. 14).

These complex goals of language remediation warrant clever ways of structuring the educational experience to reinforce comprehension and functional usage. Music has been documented as a key tool for such achievement (Little, 1983; "Teaching and Learning Aids: Musical ESL," 1983). Curriculum for teaching English as a second language (ESL) is complex, and the music therapist is not expected to have all the necessary training to implement such a program. In cooperation with a qualified professional, however, the music therapist has an unlimited resource for supplementing and developing ESL applications. Little (1983) explains that "music cuts across cultural and linguistic boundaries so easily" (p. 41). Although his research involved hearing children, the adaptability of music makes the same statement true in working with D/HH children.

Properties of music, such as rhythm, accents, tempo, and repetition, organize and direct behavior toward educational objectives. These same features support the structure of language. Teaching D/HH children English songs to sign can be useful for practicing syntax, vocabulary, and idioms. Songs also facilitate some of the strategies Diaz-Rico and Weed (1995) emphasize that ESL teachers should employ in order to help students build communicative competence: repetition, memorization, formulaic expressions, elaboration, monitoring one's own errors, appealing for assistance, requesting clarification, and role playing.

Beyond signing English songs, there are other uses of music therapy for teaching ESL to children who are D/HH. Some other applications of music therapy include playing instruments, dancing, songwriting, and performing. Each of these activities can be designed to correspond to specific principles of language. Further, the musical involvements can be organized into skits, games, and storytelling. Numerous books describe the use of skits and games to teach ESL, such as *101 Word Games: For Students of English as a Second or Foreign Language* (McCallum, 1980), *Once Upon a Time: Using Stories in the Language Classroom* (Morgan & Rinvolucri, 1983), and *Skits in English as a Second Language* (Hines, 1973). Unfortunately, there is a dearth of such writings which also incorporate music, and there is virtually none that pertains to teaching ESL to children who are D/HH.

The creative role of the music therapist working with D/HH children not only demands originality in designing goal-directed applications, but it also challenges him or her to draw on a multitude of instructional resources, not limited to musical equipment. Instruments are used, but additional visual and tactile aids must be incorporated, such as picture files, charts and posters, slides, printed material, and costumes (Diaz-Rico & Weed, 1995). These materials can complement the musical structure of the session and serve to facilitate comprehension and to reinforce participation.

As the students' knowledge of English improves, they will have more expertise in conveying English concepts through music. Evidence of their literacy can take the form of written songs or it can be displayed by role-playing the literal and the intended meanings of English idioms through dance. For example, the phrase "let the cat out of the bag" can be performed first in a literal scene with one dancer opening an imaginary bag and letting out another character who dances like a cat. In a second scene, other dancers can convey the concept when one person tells another a secret. Then, the second character dances around anxious to tell someone the news until a third dancer enters and the second "lets the cat out of the bag."

The use of music to teach English as a second language is recommended for this population. In addition to the proven success of this instructional approach it also emphasizes culture-specific adaptations that foster acceptance of the Deaf community and input from its members.

Other Objectives

Clearly, the emphasis of music therapy interventions with D/HH children is on the linguistic objectives. It is important to note, however, the various other therapeutic goals supported by D/HH students' participation in music applications.

Behavioral

1. To increase motivation for learning
2. To improve compliance
3. To increase on-task behavior
4. To improve turn taking
5. To improve sharing

Academic

1. To learn fundamentals of music
2. To improve reading skills
3. To improve writing skills
4. To rehearse and develop additional academic concepts

Motor Skills

1. To develop gross motor skills
2. To improve coordination
3. To improve balance
4. To develop fine motor skills

Social Interaction Skills

1. To increase personal expression
2. To improve interpersonal communication
3. To develop group cooperation

Self-Concept

1. To improve self-esteem
2. To increase opportunities for individual success
3. To develop a sense of group achievement

Music Education Objectives

Some people believe that to be musical, one must have good hearing; however, many D/HH individuals are indeed musical (Darrow, 1985; Darrow, 1987b). The degree of interest in music among D/HH individuals varies as it does among those with normal hearing. Many D/HH students enjoy participating in musical activities. Their education in the arts should not be forfeited for entirely nonmusical goals (Birkenshaw-Fleming, 1990). Music objectives for these students should follow those that are often outlined for normal hearing students. Objectives should include various forms of music participation:

1. Listening to music
2. Singing
3. Playing instruments
4. Moving to music
5. Creating music
6. Reading music

Music education objectives should also include knowledge about masterpieces of music and the elements of music: rhythm, melody, harmony, form, and expression. Traditional approaches to teaching music concepts can be employed with D/HH students (Ford, 1990; Robbins & Robbins, 1980; Robbins & Robbins, 1990; Schatz, 1990). Because of their visual and movement components, music educators of D/HH students have indicated that Orff and Kodaly approaches are particularly useful (Darrow & Gfeller, 1991). D/HH students are at a distinct disadvantage if they are taught music solely through listening. Most D/HH students learn best through active participation in music making. Learning music through performing, reading, and writing music is essential for the students with a hearing loss. Additional adaptive strategies include the use of visual and tactile aides. Almost any aural concept can be represented in some visual way. Using kinesthetic movement, such as having students outline the movement of a melody with their hands, is also helpful for the D/HH student.

Special attention should also be given to amplification of music stimuli (Dalgarno, 1990), the quality of recording equipment and instruments, as well as the suggestions given earlier for adaptation of the physical and communication environment. Every individual, regardless of hearing status, deserves the right to participate in the musical arts and, as a result, to experience a part of our culture. Some D/HH individuals do not consider music a part of Deaf culture and, consequently, look upon musical study as a "hearing value." Many members of the Deaf community, however, do find music to be an important part of their lives (Darrow, 1993).

Adaptive Instructional Strategies

In teaching music, the music therapist must be aware of the use of music with this population as it relates to their strengths and preferences (Darrow, 1991). There are some generalizations that can be made regarding the musical characteristics of D/HH individuals based upon research in music perception and performance. By reading the research and reviewing these characteristics, the music therapist can make the appropriate adaptations in teaching music to students who are D/HH. A bibliography of research related to the D/HH is given in the Resource section. Following are some of the implications for teaching derived from this body of research.

1. Rhythmic abilities tend to be stronger than pitch related abilities.
2. Discrimination of or production of rhythmic patterns is more difficult than beat reproduction.
3. Music stimuli must be presented at appropriate level of amplification.

4.   Tactile perception can, in part, compensate for auditory deficits.
5.   Visual cues, such as tapping the beat, are particularly helpful.
6.   Music skills may be delayed rather than deviant.
7.   Pitch discriminations can be made more easily in lower frequency ranges.
8.   Pitch discrimination skills can be developed with training.
9.   Discrimination skills may be misjudged because of language problems in individuals who are D/HH, which interfere with their ability to describe what is heard.
10. The vocal range of D/HH individuals is often lower and more limited in range.
11. Individuals who are D/HH can benefit both musically and academically from participation in music activities.
12. These individuals are more responsive to the rhythmic aspects of music than the tonal aspects.
13. They may require greater exposure, both in duration and intensity, to music stimuli than do normal hearing individuals in order to meet therapeutic objectives.
14. Sustaining instruments may provide more useful aural feedback than do percussive instruments.
15. Use of moderate tempi assist in greater rhythm performance accuracy.
16. D/HH individuals may perform more accurately by reading standard music notation than by relying on the ear to imitate or learn by rote.
17. D/HH individuals can improve their vocal intonation, both in singing and in speaking by participating in vocal activity.
18. The vocal range of song literature should be taken into consideration with D/HH singers.
19. D/HH individuals are capable of improvements in ear training as are hearing individuals.
20. Vibrotactile stimuli are a useful supplemental tool in the music instruction of D/HH individuals.
21. As with hearing individuals, D/HH individuals can develop an ear more sensitive to sound over time.
22. D/HH individuals could benefit from instruction in the use of musical vocabulary.
23. D/HH individuals exhibit certain musical preferences in regard to sound, source, intensity, and listening conditions.
24. Amplification and sound quality of the musical media should be given particular attention when instructing D/HH individuals.
25. Music instruction can assist in the development of a number of nonmusical behaviors such as speech production, listening, language, social, and academic skills.

Interpreting Songs into Sign

Interpreting songs into sign is a popular activity for D/HH as well as hearing students. Darrow and Gfeller (1991) surveyed public school music educators teaching D/HH students and found that signing songs is a frequent activity in the music classroom. With increasing adoption of the total communication philosophy, students in deaf education programs are finding song signing to be a useful means of sharing cultural values and performing popular music. Signing songs, however, should not be simply "finger play." Many of the elements of music and expressive aspects of music can be illustrated through the signing of music: rhythm, tempo, changes in tempo, style, texture, tone color (male signers for male voices, etc.), form, and dynamics. Careful attention should also be given to the art of interpreting songs into sign. The signing should be as meticulously executed as the singing of the songs. The following guidelines will assist in interpreting songs into sign (Darrow, 1987a):

1. Signs used for song interpretation can reflect volume, pitch (though rarely used), rhythm, and mood, as well as the lexical content by a variety of uses of body language, facial expression, space, and manner of execution.
2. Incorporating rhythm into signs is the most important factor distinguishing musical from nonmusical signing. Signing is paced to match the rhythm of the words.
3. Signs are drawn out or accelerated depending on the duration of the sung word.
4. Fingerspelling is rarely used.
5. Instrumental sections or humming requires the creative uses of mime. The viewer should be aware of what is happening in the music at all times.
6. Figurative language or symbolism require creativity on the part of the signer.
7. Many times a single sign can reflect an entire phrase in a song.
8. Musical signing should transmit emotion as vividly as the audible song.
9. Some interpreters suggest that signs move upward as the melody moves upward, and as the melody moves downward, so should the signs. This adds very little to the performance for the deaf audience.
10. For sections marked *forte,* signs should be larger and executed with more force than sections marked *piano.*
11. *Crescendos* can also be expressed by gradually making signs for larger and more intense. *Decrescendos* likewise should be expressed by gradually making signs smaller and more gently.
12. Signs should also follow the phrasing of the song, flowing one into the next with a slight pause at the end of the phrase.
13. The song style, whether it be classical, folk, rock, country, or pop, can be interpreted through the rhythm of signs, facial expression, body language, and, though unrelated to the signs, the dress of the signer.
14. When groups are performing in sign, special attention should be given to ensemble work. Signs should be synchronized: all hands moving in unison, all signs executed the same way, all signs made in the same amount of space.
15. Signs like voices, should also, blend. No individual signer should stand out among the group. Practice with a mirror or videotape.
16. Use a D/HH individual as your "sign master." Acknowledge him/her in the program.
17. Sign performers should wear solid colors.

Conclusion

Music is a viable treatment modality that transcends physical, emotional, cognitive, and cultural differences in individuals. The sensory and cultural differences of many D/HH children provide unique challenges for the music therapist. For D/HH children, music may not always be an auditory experience, though music can, most assuredly, be a tactual, visual, social, and esthetic experience for these children. By adapting music so that it can be experienced through other senses, the music therapist utilizes alternative pathways to further the academic and musical growth of D/HH children. Many music therapists find that such pathways lead to truly enjoyable and enriching experiences for themselves as well as for D/HH children.

References

Baker-Shenk, C., & Cokely, D. (1991). *American Sign Language: A teacher's resource text on grammar and culture.* Washington, DC: Gallaudet University Press.

Bang, C. (1977). *A music event.* Hicksville, NY: M. Hohner, Inc.

Bang, C. (1986). A world of sound and music. In E. Ruud (Ed.), *Music and health* (pp. 19–36). Oslo, Norway: Norsk Musikforlag.

Birkenshaw-Fleming, L. (1990). Music can make a difference. In A. A. Darrow (Ed.), *Proceedings from the Second National Conference on Music and the Hearing Impaired at Gallaudet University* (pp. 14–20). Lawrence, KS: The University of Kansas.

Dalgarno, G. (1990). Technology to obtain the best musical sound for hearing impaired listeners. In A. A. Darrow (Ed.), *Proceedings from the Second National Conference on Music and the Hearing Impaired at Gallaudet University* (pp. 43–59). Lawrence, KS: The University of Kansas.

Darrow, A. A. (1985). Music for the deaf. *Music Educator's Journal, 71*(6), 33–35.

Darrow, A. A. (1987a). Exploring the art of sign and song. *Music Educators Journal, 74*(1), 32–35.

Darrow, A. A. (1987b). An investigative study: The effect of hearing impairment on music aptitude. *Journal of Music Therapy, 24*, 88–96.

Darrow, A. A. (1989). Music therapy with the hearing impaired. *Music Therapy Perspectives, 6*, 61–70.

Darrow, A. A. (1990). The role of hearing in understanding music. *Music Educators Journal, 77*(4), 24–27.

Darrow, A. A. (1991). An assessment and comparison of hearing impaired children's preference for timbre and musical instruments. *Journal of Music Therapy, 28*, 48–59.

Darrow, A. A. (1993). The role of music in Deaf culture: Implications for music educators. *Journal of Research in Music Education, 41*(2), 93–110.

Darrow, A. A. (1995). Music therapy for hearing impaired clients. In T. Wigram, R. West, & B. Saperston (Eds.), *The art and science of music therapy: A handbook.* Chur, Switzerland: Harwood Academic Publishers.

Darrow, A. A., & Cohen, N. (1991). The effect of programmed pitch practice and private instruction on the vocal reproduction accuracy of hearing impaired children: Two case studies. *Music Therapy Perspectives, 9*, 61–65.

Darrow, A. A., & Gfeller, K. E. (1988). Music therapy with hearing impaired children. In C. A. Furman (Ed.), *Effectiveness of music therapy procedures: Documentation of research and clinical practice.* Washington, DC: National Association of Music Therapy.

Darrow, A. A., & Gfeller, K. E. (1991). A study of public school music programs mainstreaming hearing impaired students. *Journal of Music Therapy, 28*, 48–59.

Darrow, A. A., & Starmer, G. J. (1986). The effect of vocal training on the intonation and rate of hearing impaired children's speech: A pilot study. *Journal of Music Therapy, 23*, 194–201.

Davis, J., & Hardick, E. (1981). *Rehabilitative audiology for children and adults.* New York: John Wiley & Sons.

Diaz-Rico, L. T., & Weed, K. Z. (1995). *The crosscultural, language, and academic development handbook: A complete K–12 reference guide.* Needham Heights, MA: Allyn & Bacon.

Erber, N. P., & Hirsh, I. J. (1978). Auditory training. In H. Davis & S. R. Silverman (Eds.), *Hearing and deafness,* Chicago, IL: Holt, Rinehart and Winston.

Ford, T. A. (1990). Development of rhythmic concepts and skills. In A. A. Darrow (Ed.), *Proceedings from the Second National Conference on Music and the Hearing Impaired at Gallaudet University* (pp. 21–30). Lawrence, KS: The University of Kansas.

Gfeller, K. E. (1986). Music as a remedial tool for improving speech rhythm in the hearing impaired: Clinical and research considerations. *Music Education for the Handicapped Bulletin, 2,* 3–19.

Gfeller, K. E. (1987). Songwriting as a tool for reading and language remediation. *Music Therapy, 6*(2), 28–38.

Gfeller, K. E. (1990). A cognitive-linguistic approach to language development for preschool children with hearing impairments. *Music Therapy Perspectives, 8,* 47–51.

Gfeller, K. E. (1992). Music therapy in the treatment of sensory disorders. In W. B. Davis, K. E. Gfeller, & M. H. Thaut (Eds.), *An introduction to music therapy theory and practice* (pp. 209–233). Dubuque, IA: Wm. C. Brown Publishers.

Gfeller, K. E., & Baumann, A. (1988). Assessment procedures for music therapy with hearing impaired children: Language development. *Journal of Music Therapy, 25,* 192–205.

Gfeller, K. E., & Darrow, A. A. (1987). Music as a remedial tool in the language education of hearing impaired children. *The Arts in Psychotherapy, 14,* 229–23.

Heward, W. L., & Orlansky, M. D. (1988). *Exceptional children.* Columbus, OH: Merrill Publishing Co.

Hines, M. E. (1973). *Skits in English as a second language.* New York: Regents Publishing Company, Inc.

Little, J. (1983). Pop and rock music in the ESL classroom. *TESL TALK, 14*(4), 40–44.

McCallum, G. P. (1980). *101 word games: For students of English as a second or foreign language.* New York: Oxford University Press.

Morgan, J., & Rinvolucri, M. (1983). *Once upon a time: Using stories in the language classroom.* Cambridge, Great Britain: Cambridge University Press.

NTID at RID (no date). *Communicating with the Deaf.* Rochester, NY: National Technical Institute for the Deaf.

Padden, C., & Humphries, T. (1988). *Deaf in America: Voices from a culture.* Cambridge, MA: Harvard University Press.

Rickard, P., Robbins, C., & Robbins, C. (1990). Experiences in developing a creative language arts program. In A. A. Darrow (Ed.), *Proceedings from the Second National Conference on Music and the Hearing Impaired at Gallaudet University* (pp. 11–13). Lawrence, KS: The University of Kansas.

Robbins, C., & Robbins, C. (1980). *Music for the hearing impaired: A resource manual and curriculum guide.* St. Louis, MO: Magnamusic-Baton.

Robbins, C., & Robbins, C. (1990). Musical activities with young deaf children. In A. A. Darrow (Ed.), *Proceedings from the Second National Conference on Music and the Hearing Impaired at Gallaudet University* (pp. 8–10). Lawrence, KS: The University of Kansas.

Rutherford, S. D. (1988). The culture of American Deaf people. *Sign Language Studies, 59,* 109–147.

Sanders, D. A. (1977). *Auditory perception of speech.* Englewood Cliffs, NJ: Prentice-Hall, Inc.

Schatz, V. (1990). Using percussion to teach music concepts and enhance music and movement experiences. In A. A. Darrow (Ed.), *Proceedings from the Second National Conference on Music and the Hearing Impaired at Gallaudet University* (pp. 85–92). Lawrence, KS: The University of Kansas.

Teaching and learning aids: Musical ESL. (1983). *TESL TALK, 14*(1–2), 180–185.

Music Therapy for Learners Who Are Mainstreamed in a District-wide (K–12) Program

Jane E. Hughes
Brenda J. Robbins

Description of the Model

THE district-wide music therapy program exemplified here is within the Leon County School District's Exceptional Student Education program. Located in Tallahassee, Florida, the Leon County Schools serve approximately 38,000 students. Of this number, almost 7,900 students receive some type of services through Exceptional Student Education (ESE), sometimes referred to as "special education." ESE is an integral part of the total school program with schools, special services, related state and local agencies, and the community being utilized to provide quality programs for students. The school district's philosophy is to educate exceptional students to their maximum potential in the least restrictive environment. Music therapy has been a comprehensive special service offered through ESE since 1978. Approximately 1,200 students in grades PreK through high school and beyond and 100 teachers currently receive some type of service from music therapists and their interns each year. The primary purpose of the music therapy program is to assist students to benefit from their educational experience.

In Leon County, the term *mainstreaming* describes the placing of students with disabilities into general education settings. Other terms sometimes used by state and local school systems are *inclusion, continuum of services,* and *regular education initiative.* The legal mandate is found in PL 94–142 and the more recent Individuals with Disabilities Education Act (IDEA). While terms such as *mainstreaming* and *inclusion* are in common usage, the legal terminology references the *least restrictive environment.* Under this mandate no exceptional student is taught apart from other students without evidence that segregation is for the exceptional student's benefit or is necessary due to difficulties involved in providing a program for the student in a regular class. Such difficulties might include items that may have a harmful effect such as injury to others or self, excessive disruptive behavior, student safety, health status or lack of progress. Whenever possible, students are educated in the school they would normally attend, and every effort is made to educate them with their regular education peers. Most ESE students, no matter what their degree of disability, attend the district's regular elementary, middle, and high schools with others of the same age. In addition to the regular schools, the district maintains two small ESE center schools where students, though attending self-contained schools, still have interaction with their regular education peers through special programs provided by the schools. (See

Examples 7 and 8, p. 242). Educational placement decisions are based on individual instructional needs as outlined in Individual Education Plans (IEPs). The IEP cover sheet specifies the type and amount of participation in regular (or mainstream) education (see Figure 1).

Since music therapy is provided within the scope of the IEP, mainstreaming is a major focus of the program. In addition to addressing learning needs in traditional curriculum subject areas such as language arts, social studies, and music, the district's music therapists often work within mainstreaming initiatives such as community-based instruction (CBI), cooperative collaboration, team teaching, transition, career preparation, employment training, and prosocial skills development. Music therapists use music to address needs in any curriculum area considered important to student growth (Alley, 1979).

Music therapists consult with classroom teachers and other professionals in the development of music therapy interventions based on the assessed needs of individuals as specified by their IEPs. Psychologists and other evaluation specialists and classroom teachers perform the assessments for the IEPs. Several types of evaluative measures are used in the development of IEPs including psychological, medical, and curriculum-based assessments. In the Leon County School District, music therapists collaborate closely with educators to develop, implement, and report the results of interventions, but they are not directly involved in primary assessment for IEPs. They can, however, recommend IEP modifications based on music therapy program data. Typical goal areas chosen for music therapy intervention include the following: integration with nonhandicapped peers; developmental language, and school readiness in young children; auditory training and communication in students with speech and hearing impairments; affective education and prosocial skills development in students with emotional or behavior disorders; dexterity and mobility training in students with physical challenges; and community-based skills in students with mental retardation.

The comprehensive ESE music therapy program is planned and implemented by two Registered Music Therapists who are state certified in music education. (Florida music therapists must hold state professional educator certification in order to work in professional [as opposed to paraprofessional] public school positions. Most music therapists working in Florida public schools are certified in music education. However, some are certified in other education areas such as special education or early childhood. The certification issue differs from state to state because each state establishes its own certification rules and regulations). Music therapy also provides additional staff for the district by participation in the American Music Therapy Association Clinical Training Program. As many as four music therapy interns work district-wide at any given time during the year, serving hundreds of students who would not otherwise receive music therapy. Music therapists and interns serve students from the following education areas: adult basic education, alternative education, attention deficit hyperactive disorders, autism, early intervention, educable mentally handicapped, emotionally handicapped, gifted, hearing impaired, hospital homebound, juvenile offenders, learning disabilities, physically impaired, prekindergarten (PreK) varying exceptionalities, profoundly handicapped, speech and language impaired, teenage parent program, trainable mentally handicapped, and visually impaired. Age groups range from infancy through adult. Direct services to students occur in large groups, small groups, or individually, in inclusive or self-contained groupings, and in many different physical settings. The settings might be classrooms and other space in regular schools, special center schools, private preschools, juvenile detention centers, or the community at large.

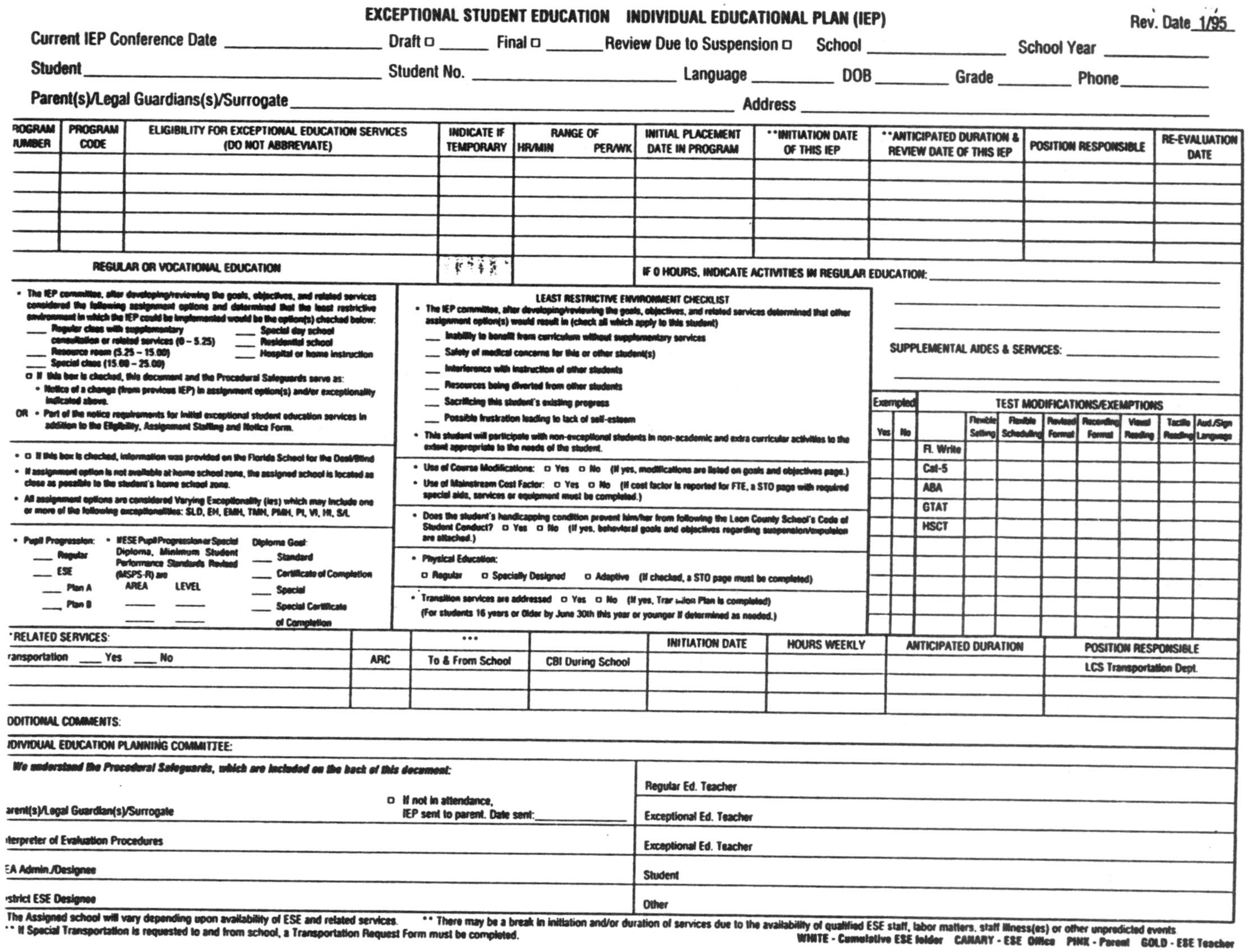
EXCEPTIONAL STUDENT EDUCATION INDIVIDUAL EDUCATIONAL PLAN (IEP)

Rev. Date 1/95

Current IEP Conference Date ______ Draft □ ______ Final □ ______ Review Due to Suspension □ School ______ School Year ______

Student ______ Student No. ______ Language ______ DOB ______ Grade ______ Phone ______

Parent(s)/Legal Guardians(s)/Surrogate ______ Address ______

ROGRAM NUMBER	PROGRAM CODE	ELIGIBILITY FOR EXCEPTIONAL EDUCATION SERVICES (DO NOT ABBREVIATE)	INDICATE IF TEMPORARY	RANGE OF HR/MIN PER/WK	INITIAL PLACEMENT DATE IN PROGRAM	**INITIATION DATE OF THIS IEP	**ANTICIPATED DURATION & REVIEW DATE OF THIS IEP	POSITION RESPONSIBLE	RE-EVALUATION DATE

REGULAR OR VOCATIONAL EDUCATION

IF 0 HOURS, INDICATE ACTIVITIES IN REGULAR EDUCATION: ______

- The IEP committee, after developing/reviewing the goals, objectives, and related services considered the following assignment options and determined that the least restrictive environment in which the IEP could be implemented would be the option(s) checked below:
  - ___ Regular class with supplementary consultation or related services (0 – 5.25)
  - ___ Resource room (5.25 – 15.00)
  - ___ Special class (15.00 – 25.00)
  - ___ Special day school
  - ___ Residential school
  - ___ Hospital or home instruction

□ If this box is checked, this document and the Procedural Safeguards serve as:
- Notice of a change (from previous IEP) in assignment option(s) and/or exceptionality indicated above.

OR • Part of the notice requirements for initial exceptional student education services in addition to the Eligibility, Assignment Staffing and Notice Form.

- □ If this box is checked, information was provided on the Florida School for the Deaf/Blind
- If assignment option is not available at home school zone, the assigned school is located as close as possible to the student's home school zone.
- All assignment options are considered Varying Exceptionality (ies) which may include one or more of the following exceptionalities: SLD, EH, EMH, TMH, PMH, PI, VI, HI, S/L

- Pupil Progression: ___ Regular ___ ESE ___ Plan A ___ Plan B
- If ESE Pupil Progression or Special Diploma, Minimum Student Performance Standards Revised (MSPS-R) are AREA ______ LEVEL ______
- Diploma Goal: ___ Standard ___ Certificate of Completion ___ Special ___ Special Certificate of Completion

LEAST RESTRICTIVE ENVIRONMENT CHECKLIST

- The IEP committee, after developing/reviewing the goals, objectives, and related services determined that other assignment option(s) would result in (check all which apply to this student)
  - ___ Inability to benefit from curriculum without supplementary services
  - ___ Safety of medical concerns for this or other student(s)
  - ___ Interference with instruction of other students
  - ___ Resources being diverted from other students
  - ___ Sacrificing this student's existing progress
  - ___ Possible frustration leading to lack of self-esteem
- This student will participate with non-exceptional students in non-academic and extra curricular activities to the extent appropriate to the needs of the student.

- Use of Course Modifications: □ Yes □ No (If yes, modifications are listed on goals and objectives page.)
- Use of Mainstream Cost Factor: □ Yes □ No (If cost factor is reported for FTE, a STO page with required special aids, services or equipment must be completed.)

- Does the student's handicapping condition prevent him/her from following the Leon County School's Code of Student Conduct? □ Yes □ No (If yes, behavioral goals and objectives regarding suspension/expulsion are attached.)

- Physical Education: □ Regular □ Specially Designed □ Adaptive (If checked, a STO page must be completed)

- Transition services are addressed □ Yes □ No (If yes, Transition Plan is completed) (For students 16 years or Older by June 30th this year or younger if determined as needed.)

SUPPLEMENTAL AIDES & SERVICES: ______

Exempted Yes	Exempted No	TEST MODIFICATIONS/EXEMPTIONS	Flexible Setting	Flexible Scheduling	Revised Format	Recording Format	Visual Reading	Tactile Reading	Aud./Sign Language
		Fl. Write							
		Cat-5							
		ABA							
		GTAT							
		HSCT							

*RELATED SERVICES:		***		INITIATION DATE	HOURS WEEKLY	ANTICIPATED DURATION	POSITION RESPONSIBLE
Transportation ___ Yes ___ No	ARC	To & From School	CBI During School				LCS Transportation Dept.

ADDITIONAL COMMENTS:

INDIVIDUAL EDUCATION PLANNING COMMITTEE:

We understand the Procedural Safeguards, which are included on the back of this document:

Parent(s)/Legal Guardian(s)/Surrogate □ If not in attendance, IEP sent to parent. Date sent: ______	Regular Ed. Teacher
Interpreter of Evaluation Procedures	Exceptional Ed. Teacher
LEA Admin./Designee	Exceptional Ed. Teacher
District ESE Designee	Student
	Other

* The Assigned school will vary depending upon availability of ESE and related services. ** There may be a break in initiation and/or duration of services due to the availability of qualified ESE staff, labor matters, staff illness(es) or other unpredicted events
*** If Special Transportation is requested to and from school, a Transportation Request Form must be completed.

WHITE - Cumulative ESE folder CANARY - ESE Office PINK - Parent GOLD - ESE Teacher

Figure 1. Individual Educational Plan, School Board of Leon County, Florida

Each music therapist spends approximately one-half time providing music therapy services directly to students. The other one-half time is spent supervising interns in school locations throughout the district, providing consultation and training for educational staff and parents (see Examples 1–4, pp. 228–235), advising secondary IEP committees on music course electives (see Example 3, p. 230), conducting research, pursuing grants and collaborative projects with community arts providers (see Example 7, p. 242), coordinating practicum experiences for university music students (see Examples 6 and 9, pp. 238, 243), and serving on school improvement teams and advisory councils. Needs-based requests for services come to music therapists from administrators, special, regular and music educators, occupational, physical, and speech therapists, psychologists, guidance counselors, and parents. The two music therapists accept or deny requests based on the availability of staff time and other considerations such as travel time involved, number of students to benefit, administrative requests, potential effectiveness of music intervention, music therapy services received in the past, importance to interns' training program, and opportunities for investigation/research into current educational situations such as Early Intervention (the effect of music intervention on prereading and writing development), and total inclusion schools (the role of music therapy). Upon acceptance, therapists consult with classroom teachers and others as they plan music therapy interventions based on goals already established in the IEP. (Please note: Music therapists also review the music education and professional education research literature in planning interventions.) Music therapy objectives are then developed as indicated for specific skills. The following are typical samples of music therapy objectives written for individuals in the Leon County Schools:

1. Students will stand and sit on cue with the rest of the high school chorus. (students with mental disabilities)
2. Students will improve spatial awareness. (students with vision impairments)
3. Students will demonstrate an awareness of sound and silence. (students with hearing impairments)
4. Students will improve fine motor skills: grasping, holding, and manipulating musical instruments/other objects. (students with physical disabilities)
5. Students will work cooperatively with peers in inclusive/ mainstream settings. (students enrolled in ESE)
6. Students will increase their ability to recognize letters and numbers. (students in PreK)

Funding for the music therapy program comes from the school district. Costs to the district include teachers' salaries plus appropriate supplements for the RMTs; vicinity travel mileage for the RMTs and interns; and funds for office, storage and program space, equipment, materials and supplies, transportation to arts events, and staff development costs including professional conferences for the RMTs and interns. The majority of costs are offset by dollars under PL 94–142, PL 89–313 and Chapter 2 grants. Budgeting for the program comes from ESE's district-wide and individual school budgets. A small amount of additional funding is generated through local and state arts and special activity grants.

The school district benefits in numerous ways from the music therapy program. The needs of students, teachers and parents are addressed, positive attitudes are promoted within the schools and community, and school district goals are implemented. Making others aware of these benefits is considered very important, especially during times of funding cuts in public education. The district's music therapists consistently use a positive, collaborative, active, and student-centered approach that promotes music therapy as a service to be valued among faculty, staff, parents and administrative decision-makers. They also disseminate various types of evaluative data, including periodic whole-program data as well as student data. An example of whole-program evaluation data is that of a survey of perception and attitudes of exceptional student educators toward district-wide music therapy services (Hughes, Robbins, & King, 1988). Survey data demonstrated the high esteem in which music therapy was held by those teachers most directly involved, and documented the overall perception of effectiveness as related to specific music therapy objectives. This data was widely used as a public awareness tool.

Intervention Models

Music therapists provide services throughout the Leon County School District in many different ways. Some of the music therapy programs are planned for district-wide impact while others are more specific to students and settings (Hughes & Robbins, 1992). Examples of both types of services are exemplified in the brief program descriptions found in this chapter.

District-Wide Services

Consultant Services

Consultant services are provided by music therapists upon the request of teachers or administrators to help teachers develop music strategies for mainstreamed and inclusive classrooms. These services may be rendered in a variety of ways. Sometimes music therapists make one-time recommendations to the teachers requesting assistance. This is done after the music therapist observes and assesses the problem in the classroom setting and meets with the requesting teacher. At other times, after observation and assessment, the music therapist and classroom teacher decide that support in the classroom is required. Support may then be provided on a short- or long-term basis by music therapists or designated others. Designated others are usually university music practicum students (see Examples 2 and 9, pp. 229, 243), trained paraprofessionals (see Example 5, p. 238), music volunteers from the community, and ESE resource personnel. Music therapists may also assist IEP teams in music placements (see Example 3, p. 230). The following three examples are typical of these various types of consultant services.

Example 1

Service Provider:	Music Therapist
Course:	First Grade Inclusive Classroom
Students Enrolled:	23

Problem: The teacher complained about her entire class's behavior, especially their transitions between activities and locations. The class was observed by the music therapist during transition to other locations, and in homeroom and music class activities. Students seemed unclear about procedures during transition times and often exhibited unruly behavior. The teacher gave verbal instructions to the students but rarely captured their attention. In addition, a paraprofessional with the class constantly talked aloud to individual students.

Strategies: 1. Condition the children and the paraprofessional to respond with silence to a specific musical signal
2. Give spoken directions only if necessary.
3. Use engaging action songs to direct the class from one place to another and to change pace or mood.
4. Reward appropriate behavior.
5. Communicate regularly with the music teacher in order to learn new action songs.

Outcomes: Music strategies were recommended because the children displayed appropriate and enthusiastic participation during music and movement activities. The music therapist taught the teacher a few short music activities that had been found to be effective in similar circumstances. She also helped the teacher to establish a process for obtaining additional activities from the school's music teacher. A month after the music intervention began, the classroom teacher reported much smoother transitions and a happier classroom atmosphere.

Example 2

Service Providers: Music Therapist and University Music Therapy Practicum Student
Course: Sixth Grade Band
Students Enrolled: 42
Targeted Student: 1 (vision impaired)

Problem: Learning new music was a problem for the sixth grade band student. While her clarinet playing skills were more than adequate, due to her vision impairment she was unable to read music notation at the tempo required by the band director.

Strategies: 1. Provide tutoring sessions once a week to practice new music before it is presented in class.
2. Enlarge clarinet music scores.
3. Suggest collaborative procedures between the band teacher and vision resource teacher.

Outcomes: The music therapist observed in band class and met with the student for individual practice. She found that the student could read enlarged music notation at a very slow tempo and was able to learn her part quickly once she heard it a few times. A university music therapy practicum student was assigned to tutor her over a period of months and to work with her vision resource teacher to develop procedures of support. The band student gradually gained confidence as she herself discovered ways to learn new music with a minimum of assistance. She continued in the band program and eventually went on to play in her high school band.

Example 3

Service Provider:	Music Therapists
Course Descriptions:	High School Music Electives
Recipients:	District ESE staff, school-based ESE staff, parents

Problems: High school music electives in the Leon County Schools were limited in number and variety of offerings. The main music courses offered at all high schools were band, chorus, piano, and guitar. A number of schools also had specialized courses such as steel drum band, world music, introduction to music performance and music technology which were unique to that particular school. Although the district provided a guide book containing two-line course descriptions to students in the spring of each year in order to help them select their courses for the coming year, the descriptions did not always contain enough information on course content and requirements to allow ESE students and their parents and advisors to make informed selections. This was especially true in music performance classes. In the past some ESE students elected courses where they were not successful due to the requirements of that class. Other students were discouraged by parents and/or ESE advisors from enrolling in music at all because of their disability. These problems arose despite the fact that there were elective music courses available in each high school to suit the diverse needs of students wishing to elect music.

Strategies: 1. Selected music teachers at each high school were asked to describe their school's elective music course offerings.
       2. A school-by-school handout with descriptions of each music course's contents and requirements was compiled.
       3. Course descriptions were distributed to district and school ESE staff and parents prior to spring conferences and course selections for the next year.
       4. Updated information was provided and the process was evaluated annually.

Outcomes: District and school ESE staff and parents reported that the handout made them more aware of the course requirements, their responsibilities, and the concerns of the music teachers. Music teachers found that more ESE students were electing music courses and that they were making wiser course selections. Positive attitudes, especially on the part of music teachers, became an important outcome of this service. Music teachers expressed appreciation for the opportunity to describe their courses, to have input into student placement, and to state the need to have enough support for mainstreamed music students. The samples described here reflect the expectations of music teachers for a variety of high school courses (see Figure 2).

Inservice Training

Inservice training for teachers is provided by music therapists on a "needs" basis. Training sessions are offered on topics such as prekindergarten music, mainstreaming in music, use of music in behavior management, therapies and services in inclusive settings, arts in the classroom,

High School Music Course Descriptions
1995-96
Music Teacher Interview Questions

_____   _____
Teacher   **High School**

 Gospel Choir
Inclusive course recommended for a wide range of abilities.

1.   **Prerequisite courses or music skills needed:**
     None but it would be helpful if the student sings in tune.

2.   **Class size** *55-60*
     Room size   *Large Choral Room with permanent risers for chairs*
     Type of students usually enrolled
     Choir includes a variety of students with multicultural backgrounds and an extremely wide range of abilities.

3.   **Individual Skills Required:**

     (1) **Physical**
            Music is taught by rote, therefore good listening skills are required

     (2)   **Social**
            Requires a person who interacts appropriately with peers. Must have self discipline and restraint- no display of anger

     (3) **Academic**
            Reading the text (words) of the music

4.   **Homework?** *Yes, at times - occasional quizzes on theory/fundamentals*

     After-school rehearsals/performances? *Yes- Several performances outside of school are required. (more than other choirs) Students need to arrange their own transportation. Some after-school rehearsals. (grade penalty policy for after-school absences)*

5.   **Type and amount of ESE assistance needed? (specify)**
     Paraprofessional to help students study the music and administer tests and quizzes. (computer bubble sheets are used).

6.   **Comments: (Include recommended ESE : non-ESE ratio)**
     Has a talented, "cool" F SU Graduate Assistant who is trying to build commitment and responsibility to the group. Students with special needs are welcome if they meet the above requirements.

High School Music Course Descriptions
1995-96
Music Teacher Interview Questons

_____   _____

Teacher   **High School**

Introduction to Music
Inclusive course recommended for a wide range of abilities.

1.   **Prerequisite courses or music skills needed:**
      None

2.   **Class size**   *30 students*
      Room size   *Large choral room with permanent risers for chairs*
      Type of students usually enrolled   *10th-12th grade students with a wide variety of abilities and past music experiences.*

3.   **Individual Skills Required:**

      (1)   Physical
            Will play a variety of percussion instruments, move/dance
            Will play guitar for three weeks

      (2)   Social
            Requires participation in group music performance activities- individual concentration- good audience behavior for visiting community and university guest artists/instructors

      (3)   Academic
            Reading: words and some music notation- written tests
            Note taking

4.   **Homework?** *Yes (bringing in articles on community arts current events and other classwork- related assignments) Some extra credit assignments*

      After-school rehearsals/performances?
      None, unless the student is working on an extra credit assignment

5.   **Type and amount of ESE assistance needed? (specify)**
      Would welcome observation and collaboration of ESE personnel as needed for students' success (especially to follow through on class assignments)

6.   **Comments: (Include recommended ESE : non-ESE ratio)**
      About five: twenty five

High School Music Course Descriptions
1995-96
<u>**Music Teacher Interview Questions**</u>

_____   _____
Teacher   **High School**

<u>Beginning Band</u>
Inclusive course recommended for a wide range of abilities.

1. **Prerequisite courses or music skills needed:**
   None- Small instruments (clarinets, flutes, most trombones, etc.) are provided

2. **Class size**   *30 students*
   Room size   *Large band room on one level*
   Type of students usually enrolled   *Variety of grades and abilities*

3. **Individual Skills Required:**

   (1) <u>**Physical**</u>
   Good eye-hand coordination
   For woodwinds- ability to coordinate fingers (9 out of 10 fingers) .

   (2) <u>**Social**</u>
   *Requires working together as a group. Must be able to sit and wait while another
   section works*

   (3) <u>**Academic**</u>
   Can read language
   Understands math (small fractions and counting for rhythmic notation)

4. **Homework?** *No, unless extra study is needed for occasional quizzes and tests- not
   required to play at home*

   After-school rehearsals/performances?
   None (except in school)

5. **Type and amount of ESE assistance needed? (specify)**
   *Would welcome observation and hands-on assistance of ESE personnel in and after class
    as needed for students' success*

6. **Comments: (Include recommended ESE : non-ESE ratio)**
   10% - 15% of total students

High School Music Course Descriptions
1995-96
Music Teacher Interview Questions

Teacher _____   High School _____

Keyboard I
Inclusive course recommended for a wide range of abilities.

1.   Prerequisite courses or music skills needed:
     None required

2.   Class size   *20 maximum*
     Room size   *Moderate classroom size- individual keyboard instruments
     Located in the new building*
     Type of students usually enrolled   *Students in grades 9-12   Many take the
     course to satisfy the Performing Fine Arts graduation requirement- wide variety of
     abilities and backgrounds*

3.   Individual Skills Required:
     (1) Physical
         Motor skills (basic finger dexterity) needed to manipulate keys

     (2) Social
         *Requires a person who is self-disciplined and works independently- avoids
         socializing in class. Most interaction is teacher:student*

     (3) Academic
         *Ability to read simple directions, follow instructions, and concentrate on the
         tasks given*

4.   Homework? *None*
     After-school rehearsals/performances?   *Recitals are scheduled periodically
     during class. Students need to be present in class on those previously scheduled days.
     There are two evening recitals each year.*

5.   Type and amount of ESE assistance needed? (specify)
     *An aide in the piano class every day is essential. The amount of assistance depends on the
     abilities of the students*

6.   Comments: (Include recommended ESE : non-ESE ratio)
     *1) Would like to have a written description of each ESE student's special needs. 2) Would
     appreciate the courtesy of being informed about field trips. 3) Biggest Concern: so many
     CBI students requiring extra assistance in one class section. Would like no more than
     two ESE students per class*

Figure 2. High School Music Course Descriptions

and activities for learning academics through music. District needs are identified through teacher requests, surveys, and observation. As one example, the results of Leon County music teacher surveys conducted over a 3-year span (see sample questionnaire in Figure 3) led to a grant that funded a series of inservice training workshops on cooperative collaboration in mainstreaming for music teachers and ESE teachers together (see Example 4, p. 235) and the development of guidelines for ESE paraprofessionals in the music classroom (see Example 5, p. 238).

The following examples illustrate two types of inservice training programs for school personnel.

Example 4

Service Providers:	Music Therapists and Selected Teachers
Inservice Course:	Music Mainstreaming
Personnel Trained:	ESE, regular education and elementary music

Problems: Surveys of music teachers have identified problems relating to mainstream music classes in many different locales (Atterbury, 1986; Gfeller, Darrow, & Hedden, 1990; Robbins, 1989). Likewise, mainstreaming has not always resulted in positive social or music learning experiences for students in the Leon County Schools. Music teachers report that they are rarely consulted on placement decisions and believe that some students are inappropriately placed in their music classes. Teachers have also expressed concern over a lack of knowledge and skills for working with special populations. Little communication existed between music and ESE teachers and there was even less effective support available for mainstream music classes. The music teachers thought that few available curriculum resources were applicable to their needs.

Strategies: 1. Survey mainstream music teachers to determine concerns.
2. Organize a team of ESE and music teachers to plan the series of inservice workshops.
3. Present three workshops for ESE teachers and music teachers together.

The workshop agendas seen in Figure 4 contain the inservice objectives and activities.

Outcomes: Responses by teachers indicated that inservice objectives were met. According to the ESE teachers' evaluation sheets, their participation in grade level music activities led them to a greater understanding of the response requirements in music performance. Music teachers unanimously agreed that, with input from the ESE teachers, they had new ideas concerning ways to "make a place for everyone" without lessening the quality of the musical experiences. Teachers collaborated during the workshops on issues of concern to teachers and students, and then initiated ongoing communication procedures back at their local school sites.

Questionnaire Items

o   Which ESE areas are represented in your class load?

Emotionally Handicapped (EH) _____   Vision Impaired (VI) _____
Severely Emotionally Disturbed (SED) _____   Hearing Impaired (HI) _____
Special Class _____   Gifted _____
Community Based Instruction (CBI) _____   Speech/Language Impaired (S/L) _____
Profoundly Mentally Handicapped (PMH) _____   Deaf/Blind (D/B) _____
Profoundly Handicapped (PH) _____   PreKindergarten (PreK) _____
Physically Impaired (PI) _____

o   How are they scheduled for music?

Mainstreamed with chronological age peers _____
In self-contained music classes _____
Other _____

o   Were you consulted before ESE students were scheduled into music classes this year?

o   Do you have any contact/communication with ESE teachers concerning your mainstreamed students?

o   Would you like to have more regular contact or a different type of contact?

o   Do any paraprofessionals ever attend music classes with ESE students? Are they helpful?
     Ideally, how would you like them to assist you in your classes?

o   Please number, in priority order, the areas of concern to you based on your present and past students.
     ("1" = greatest concern)

Motivation/Self-Esteem _____   Paying Attention _____   Seeing Relationships _____
Remembering _____   Generalizing _____   Behavior Problems _____
Following Directions _____   Completing Assignments _____   Class Discussion _____
Working in Groups _____   Learning from Lectures _____   Listening _____
Motor Skills _____   Singing _____   Staying on Task _____
Reading Music _____   Organization _____   Reading Words _____
Oral Expression _____   Starting Tasks _____   Learning from Tape Recordings _____
Taking Tests _____   Understanding _____   Writing _____

o   Check areas of concern as relating to you, the music teacher.

Prior knowledge about individual students _____
Communication with ESE teachers _____
Assistance in the music class _____
Assistance in choosing and/or adapting materials/equipment for a wide range of abilities _____
Time to give individual attention to special needs in a large class _____
Educational training in teaching students with special needs _____
Other (please specify) _____

o   If you were offered assistance in teaching mainstreamed music students, which of the following would
     you choose?   (Check all applicable)

_____ Inservice Training for music and ESE teachers together in the Cooperative Consultation Model (a time-efficient
method of on-going communication between teachers which includes necessary background information on students,
their learning needs, social skills, performance in the music class, etc.)
Please comment _____

_____ Consultation services to music and ESE teachers by qualified music specialists (such as regularly scheduled on-site
assistance in the development of strategies to deal with identified behavior problems, adaptive music materials/tech-
niques, assessment of music skill levels, etc.)
Please comment _____

_____ Support in the classroom (by trained paraprofessionals, university music students, volunteers). For example,
someone to attend the music class and then assist students to practice needed music and other skills in the ESE setting for
transfer back to the music class.
Please comment _____

Figure 3. Leon County Music Teacher Survey

INSERVICE FOR MUSIC MAINSTREAMING

Inservice Objectives
1. Teachers will increase awareness of (a) music education (values/subject content/techniques/desired outcomes), and (b) special needs of mainstreamed music students.
2. Teachers will increase knowledge and skills related to the use of Cooperative Consultation for mainstreaming in music.
3. Teachers will enjoy participating together.

AGENDA
November 6, 3:30–5:30 p.m., Sealey Music Room

- Sign-in and refreshments beginning at 3:15
- **Music Education: Values and Outcomes**—Address by June Hinckley, Music Consultant, Florida Department of Education
- **Objectives of the Program**—Jane Hughes
- **Awareness of Students' Special Needs**—Activities led by Diane Johnson, Director, FDLRS/Miccosukee
- **Introduction to the Cooperative Consultation Model**—N. Stokely, ESE; P. Kargel, Sabal Palm; M. A. Sauers, Chaires
- First Steps (Work in School Teams)
- Questions

**Music Teachers: Bring your new FEMEA Curriculum Outline on 11/13/92!

AGENDA
November 13, 3:30–5:30 p.m., Sealey Music Room

- Sign-in and refreshments beginning at 3:15
- "Wonderful World" attention-getter, singing . . . . Patti Shay & Brenda Robbins
- "Names" Grade 5 opener, motor coordination, rhythm, speech . . . . Julie Fredrickson
- **Music Education: Student Experiences**
  Session Overview/FEMEA Curriculum . . . . Jane Hughes
  Grade K–1:   Creative Movement/instruments/drama . . . . Carla Houck
  Grade 2–3:   Listening . . . . Ginny Densmore
  Grade 3–4:   Singing/Orff process/instrumental ostinato . . . . Shirley Kirwin
  Grade 4–5:   Kodaly process/singing/reading . . . . Blair Clawson
  Reinforcing strengths/social interaction in music/paraprofessionals . . . . Brenda Robbins
  Evaluation/grading/student information . . . . Jane Floyd
  Cooperative Consultation: School teams plan together . . . . Nancy Stokely

AGENDA
March 31, 3:45–5:45 p.m., Sealey Music Room

- Sign-in and refreshments beginning at 3:30
Opening Activities . . . . **Leader**
(1) Singing for Fun and Beauty
  - Scotland's Burning (Action Song) . . . . Rebecca Ream
  - Music Is Everywhere (German Folk Round) . . . . Jane Hughes
(2) Announcements
  - Paperwork Deadlines
  - Evaluations
Learning Non-Musical Skills Through Music (Development and Transfer)
(1) Discussion and Experiential Activities . . . . Blair Clawson
(2) Folk Dancing . . . . Brenda Robbins
(3) Creating/Cooperating . . . . Julie Fredrickson
Questions/Comments from Participants
Tips for Using Music in the ESE Classroom (for Satisfying and Music Results)
- Choosing Songs & Recorded Selections
- Children's Singing Ranges
- Using Music in Musical Ways
- Attending
- Auditory Stimuli (avoiding distracting sounds, stimulus overload, etc.)
- Academic Skills (counting, rhymes, language, speech, coordination, etc.)

Figure 4. Inservice for Music Mainstreaming

Example 5

Service Providers:	Music Therapists and ESE Teachers
Inservice:	Paraprofessionals in the Music Class
Personnel Trained:	ESE Paraprofessionals district-wide

Problem: Many ESE paraprofessionals attending music class with their students were not working effectively due to a lack of understanding their role in music's unique setting. It has been found that a list of guidelines can be helpful in clarifying music teachers' expectations to both paraprofessionals and their supervising ESE teachers.

Strategies: 1. Request that music teachers in Leon County and other school districts in Florida and elsewhere fill out a form listing their expectations of the role of paraprofessionals who accompany ESE students to mainstream music classes.
2. Compile and categorize the results.
3. Distribute the guidelines to ESE teachers for their use in training their own paraprofessionals.

The guidelines in Figure 5 were developed by Leon County music therapists and music teachers based on the top "do's" and "don'ts" of almost 100 music teachers from eight different school districts.

Outcomes: The guidelines are now being used by ESE teachers in Leon County to train their paraprofessionals at the beginning of each year, and by music teachers as reminders throughout the year. ESE teachers have also referred to the guidelines in training paraprofessionals for other mainstreamed subject area classes. Music teachers have reported a marked improvement in paraprofessional effectiveness when the guidelines are read and discussed.

Preservice Experiences

Preservice experiences for university music students are coordinated by music therapists who assist in placing the music education and music therapy practicum students with mainstream music teachers. University students fulfill their practicum requirements while gaining valuable first-hand experience with music teachers in mainstream classes. Music teachers identify students who would benefit from tutoring sessions in individual or small group settings. The duration of each practicum is from 6 weeks to 1 semester.

Example 6

Service Providers:	Music Therapists and University Music Professors
Course:	Music Practicum with ESE Students
Students Enrolled:	University Music Education and Music Therapy Students
Students Served:	Selected Mainstream Music Students
Teachers Served:	Music Teachers

Guidelines for Paraprofessionals in the Music Classroom

Things Paraprofessionals Do That Music Teachers Love

- Model desired behaviors by participating in the singing, dancing, playing instruments, etc., as the children are expected to do.
- Sit or move about the room as the activity directs, in order to assist all students, not only those in ESE.
- Actively and enthusiastically participate in all activities.
- Allow students enough time to perform expected task or behavior before assisting. First give them the freedom to try.
- Redirect inappropriate behavior.
- Correct students "up close and personal."
- Assist the music teacher in any way possible by being another pair of hands and eyes.
- Help the music teacher with discipline, while not usurping the music teacher's authority.
- Communicate with the music teacher about any unusual problems before class begins.
- Ask questions in order to clarify instructions or procedures.
- Give suggestions on how materials or parts may be adapted for individual students.
- Serve as a communication link between ESE teacher and music teacher.
- Sign everything in the class for hearing impaired students.
- Physically help students experience an activity by assisting them when needed.
- Outside of music class, make/adapt materials so all children can fully participate.
- Teach prompting/assisting skills to peers. Model the interaction, then allow classmates to interact within personal time frames.

Things Paraprofessionals Do That Drive Music Teachers "Out of Tune"

- Are not on task (reading the paper, grading papers, eating lunch, etc.).
- Look bored, disinterested, irritated, or sleepy.
- Talk to others or the music teacher during class.
- Discuss a student in front of the student.
- Shout instructions or corrections to students during class.
- Use discipline which conflicts with that of the music teacher's.
- Expect "more or better" behavior from the student who is mainstreamed.
- Use rude, condescending, or irritated voices when addressing students.

Figure 5. Guidelines for Paraprofessionals in the Music Classroom

Problem: Because of their unique learning needs, some students require extra assistance in order to perform successfully in music classes with others of their own age. People not trained in music are often unable to effectively teach skills related to music learning, and it is difficult to find enough trained musicians who are available to serve as volunteers. Local university undergraduate music education students usually have few opportunities to work closely with exceptional students, and music therapy students rarely have a chance to work with music teachers in their music classrooms. Leon County music therapists developed a way to bring extra support for students and teachers in mainstream music classes and to provide valuable practicum experiences for music education and therapy students.

Strategies: The practicum cover sheet provides some information about the program's objectives and procedures (see Figure 6).

Outcomes: Preservice music education and music therapy students have served numerous students and teachers in many different schools. ESE students have increased skills related to successful participation in music classes with their peers. Individuals' music progress reports in general have documented the improvement of skills in ESE student performance. The practicum students have been highly praised by music teachers, ESE teachers, and parents for the many benefits they have brought to the students. Likewise, university students have expressed their appreciation for the opportunity to learn about diverse learning needs and relate to individual students in such meaningful and joyful ways.

Community-Based Experiences

Leon County music therapists help to provide experiences for students enrolled in community-based instruction (CBI) and their regular education peers. CBI teaches students with disabilities the practical skills they need through direct application in real life settings. CBI should not be confused with "field trips." Students are selected for CBI based on factors including:

- nonreader or low academic performance
- needs a functional approach to instruction
- long history of poor school performance
- socially immature

CBI is in place throughout the Leon County Schools at all levels. Priority is placed on skills that will help students become as independent as possible. Skills are identified in four areas:

- self-management/home living
- community functioning
- vocational
- recreational/leisure

Music therapists contribute to CBI in numerous ways. They teach social and musical skills for transfer into the community, relay information about community arts events to parents and CBI teachers, make contacts with potential volunteers from the local arts community, and

MUSIC PRACTICUM WITH EXCEPTIONAL STUDENTS
Cover Sheet

_____
University Student

Assignment

_____   _____
School   Telephone

_____   _____
Music Class Time   Indiv./Sm. Group Time

_____
Beginning/Ending Dates

Exceptional Student Education Goal
Exceptional Students will be effectively mainstreamed in age-appropriate music classes.

Objectives of the Practicum
1) To provide experiences for university music education/therapy students in working with mainstreamed music students.
2) To facilitate transfer of skills targeted by the music teacher to both the ESE student and ESE teacher.
3) To document "alternative strategies" for students in music, and provide consultative services.

Supervisors
University Professor   _____
Music Teacher   _____
ESE Teacher/Classroom Teacher   _____

Coordinators
ESE Music Specialists   Jane Hughes and Brenda Robbins 488-5785 OR 488-5786

Tips for Practicum Students
Be Responsible

1) Arrive at assigned school in time to park, report to the main office sign-in, and be at the Music or ESE room at appointed time.
2) If you are ill and <u>must</u> be absent (hopefully not), call the school as soon as you can to notify the teacher involved. This is very important. Review excused absence policy with your professor.
3) Be prepared with a plan and materials for your sessions with individuals and your teaching assignments in the music classroom. Remember to document results each time.
4) Show both the Music and ESE teachers your **Monitor Form** and **Practice Session Planning Form** as soon as the top portion is completed during the second week of the practicum, and periodically discuss your individual/small group activity plans with the ESE teacher to let her know what you are doing (see objective #2 above).
5) Fill in the log completely on your Monitor Form immediately following each music class, individual session or teacher contact. Show your log to the music teacher and ESE teacher as often as possible. Ask for their comments on the "outcomes, comments" portions (see objective #3 above).
6) Share your mainstreaming experiences with your professor.

Figure 6. Music Practicum With Exceptional Students

develop community arts performance programs for students. The following are descriptions of two community-based experiences under the leadership of music therapists. Both programs are for high school students enrolled in CBI.

Example 7

"Studying the Environment Through the Arts" was designed and implemented through the joint efforts of music therapists, classroom teachers, the director of a university dance repertory company, school administrators, the education director of a local natural history museum, a university composer, and school media specialist. The program has provided students with a multi-arts experience in which they can learn about the environment of their local region. The program includes high school students with physical and mental disabilities and university undergraduate dance performance majors of approximately the same age. The focus of the program has been the creation and performance of a multisite and multimovement work called "Earthworks." In creating the first movement, university students worked with the high school students at their ESE center school, at a university dance studio, and at the outdoor museum. The movement was a choreographed dance piece with original music, costumes, sets, and narration. It was performed for a large audience at the museum. Sites for additional movements included a local lakeside and a bird sanctuary.

Example 8

Since 1986, high schoolers in a center school for students with severe mental disabilities have had the opportunity to participate in a choral music education program. The students attend 50-minute choral classes three times each week to learn vocal technique and repertoire. Choral classes are conducted by the school district's music therapists and interns who work at the school on alternating days. The high quality performance of standard choral literature is a major goal of the class. Another goal is to maintain a program in which the center school students benefit from performance in the community with their peers from regular education. The chorus members from the center school are joined by students from a nearby high school for rehearsals and public performances in the Tallahassee community and out of town. Students in the program develop self-discipline, musicianship, social skills, leadership qualities, and many other attributes which contribute to their ability to function productively in the community (Hughes, 1991; Hughes, Robbins, Smith & Kincaid, 1987).

Program Settings

In Leon County, music therapists provide music experiences for ESE students in many different program settings. The program settings exemplified in this chapter include elementary general music, elementary inclusive classrooms, prekindergarten inclusive classrooms, secondary general music, choral music and instrumental music.

Elementary General Music

The music classroom can be a favorable setting in which to mainstream exceptional students. Students with special needs participate in music experiences with others their own age. The music classroom is considered one of the most positive general education environments in which to mainstream exceptional students with their typical peers (Atterbury, 1989). Generally, the music activities can be designed to include a wide range of abilities and rates of learning in students. Students with special needs engage in music learning activities with others through singing, listening, reading and notating music, playing instruments, moving to music, creating, and evaluating.

Music therapists can contribute to the music classroom in several ways. One way in which music therapists work directly with music educators is as consultants in the music classroom to ensure successful and positive learning experiences for students with special needs. The role of music therapists as consultants is described earlier in this chapter.

The following example illustrates consultant services in a mainstreamed elementary general music classroom. Related to this service, music therapists provide assistance through university preservice music students. University music therapy and music education practicum students are assigned to work with music educators and ESE students identified by the music educator as needing additional support in the music classroom. In this example, a university music education practicum student worked with seven students with special needs in grades four and five. These students were chosen by the music educator as needing additional practice in the following problem areas: rhythmic coordination and reading notation. (Refer to preservice experiences for university music students on page 238 for a detailed discussion on preservice experiences for music therapy and music education university students.)

Example 9

        Service Provider: University Music Education Practicum Student
                Course: Fourth and Fifth Grade General Music
     Students Enrolled: 36
    Targeted Students: 7 (learning disabilities and moderate mental retardation)

Problem: 1. Rhythmic Coordination
             2. Reading Notation

Strategies: Students with special needs worked with the university music practicum student once each week to practice skills through singing, clapping, marching, and playing percussion instruments. The music practicum student also worked once a week in the music classroom to assist the music teacher and the seven targeted students needing additional assistance. Sessions were organized around the overall task of producing a music video to demonstrate the students' improved skills. A token system was introduced which allowed the students to purchase parts, instruments, and costumes for the music video.

Outcomes: During the individual practice sessions, the students enjoyed dancing; however, their rhythmic coordination skills were somewhat poor. Group discussion elicited a lot of off task behaviors and it was clear that the students did not know music notes and note values. The students also had difficulty staying on task in the music classroom. The music class was divided into group and center time and, as a result, the students did not have as much time with the teacher on the center time activities. Once the students had an opportunity to get more individualized attention (the general music class consisted of 36+), they were more eager to participate. With additional assistance in the music classroom and individual practice sessions, the students showed much improvement in rhythmic coordination skills, notation reading skills, and social behavior in the music classroom. Making the video was a motivating and rewarding experience for the students. Even though several of these students had received academic warnings in music in the past, not one student received a warning during this particular marking period.

Elementary Inclusive Classroom

Music therapy is provided throughout the district for students in elementary schools where the total inclusion model is in effect. The school district defines inclusive education as an approach to education that allows all students with disabilities to attend their home schools, working in a regular education class, while receiving individualized support.

The following example illustrates the effectiveness of music therapy in a total inclusion setting. Twenty-four to 28 children were in each of the four classes served. Sessions were conducted twice a week for 3 months and lasted for 30 minutes each. Each week, the sessions alternated between small groups of targeted (special needs) children and the entire class. Fifteen children with special needs in grades kindergarten through five were chosen by their teachers to participate in the small groups.

Example 10

Service Provider:	Music Therapy Intern
Course:	Four Total Inclusion Classes (Kindergarten-Second, First, Third, Third-Fifth)
Students Enrolled:	24–28 in each class
Targeted Students:	15 (learning disabilities, attention deficit disorder, hyperactive behavior and severe speech deficiencies)

Problem: For targeted students with special needs:
1. Socialization skills: increasing self control, extending on task behavior, building self esteem, developing leadership abilities
2. Speech/Language and academic skills: increasing vocalizations and letter/sounds, word recognition

For the entire class:
1. Working together as a group, increasing positive responses, following directions, taking turns, improving on task behavior, and developing positive attitudes to increase class unity.

Most of the children had not been participating appropriately within classroom group activities, lacked confidence in their own abilities, and were not well respected by their peers. Several of the classes had severe morale problems due to children not getting along together.

Strategies: The music therapy intern worked separately once a week with a small group of students which included targeted students with special needs and their classroom peers. The children selected for the small sessions were chosen by the classroom teachers. The small group setting was used as a means to develop rapport and trust with each child, to give positive reinforcement, to offer a safe environment for response, to practice the skills before participating with the class, and to assess the ability of each child and how to best initiate leadership roles within the classroom.

Outcomes: At the end of the 3-month period, the targeted children were standing before the entire group leading successful and exciting activities with confidence and much enthusiasm. Comments by the classroom teachers were very supportive of music therapy in the inclusive classroom. The following are typical examples:

"The targeted children gained self confidence and are becoming contributing members in a group."

"I feel that strides were taken in terms of whole-group cooperation."

"This experience with the entire class has been very encouraging to me because it has brought unity among my children."

Prekindergarten Inclusive Classroom

Preparing children for success in school is a major focus in school systems throughout the United States as stated in the National Education Goals. By the year 2000, it is hoped that all children will start school ready to learn (United States Department of Education, 1995). Music therapists and early childhood educators can work collaboratively to accomplish this national goal. In the public school setting, music therapists and early childhood educators need to work together in planning activities that will prepare young children academically, socially, and musically for successful educational experiences. A pilot program integrating exceptional and non-exceptional students through music is described by Hughes, Robbins, McKenzie, and Robb (1990).

In this district, music therapy services are provided for students with special needs in self-contained classrooms, integrated classroom settings, and early intervention classes. The early intervention classes prepare 4-year-old children for readiness to become successful learners in the kindergarten classroom and are comprised of typical children and children with varying exceptionalities (Standley & Hughes, in press). Below is an example of a music therapy program in an early intervention classroom.

Example 11

Service Provider: Music Therapist
Course: Early Intervention Class (PreK) Ages: Four and Five
Students: 35
Targeted Students: 15 (varying exceptionalities)

Problem: 1. Social: increasing acceptable group interaction, following classroom rules

2. Academic: increasing attending, group participation and basic skills (e.g. colors, numbers, letters)
3. Music: maintaining a steady beat, recognizing differences-same & different (form), developing singing voices and song repertoire

Strategies : The music therapist worked with the entire class once a week for 30 minutes. Classroom teachers and paraprofessional participated in all activities. Following each session, the music therapist provided the classroom teacher with a lesson plan and a cassette tape of recorded music selections which enabled the classroom teacher to practice the same activities throughout the week.

Outcomes: All students enjoyed singing, playing instruments, listening, moving, and creating music. Having weekly music therapy sessions enhanced the students positive group interactions. The typical children were good role models for the children with special needs as they all participated in fun music activities. The students not only improved social and academic skills but music skills as well, thus increasing the possibility for successful music experiences in the kindergarten mainstreamed music education classroom. The classroom teachers stated that they appreciated having music activities to do during the week. It was quite evident by the student responses each week that the teachers were using the materials effectively in their classrooms.

Secondary General Music

An innovative secondary general music class was initiated and coordinated by music therapists at the high school level. The course, Introduction to Music Performance, was offered at a local high school to students in grades 9 through 12 as a mainstreamed collaborative model (see Example 12). It addressed the nine content standards in the National Standards for Arts Education (The Consortium of National Arts Education Associations, 1994) and the concepts and intended outcomes specified in the *Introduction to Music Performance: A Secondary School Guide for Florida Schools* (Florida Department of Education, Division of Public Schools, 1989). Special features of this class included guest appearances by various performing artists from the community and universities, and collaborative teaching by the music teacher, music therapists, music therapy interns, and university secondary music education students. Funds for this collaborative model were provided by a state Arts in Education Grant.

Example 12

Service Providers:	Music Therapists, Music Teacher, Music Therapy Interns, Secondary Music Education Practicum Students
Course:	Introduction to Music Performance
Students Enrolled:	26
Targeted Students:	10 (CBI)

Problem: Few music courses of a truly inclusive nature are currently available in regular high schools. High school general music classes offer the rare exception.

Strategies: The class met daily for 50 minutes in the high school choral room. The student enrollment included general students with little music background, advanced music students from choral and instrumental backgrounds, and students enrolled in community-based instruction. (For additional information on community-based instruction refer to p. 240) . Approximately one third of the class members were from exceptional student education.

A variety of performing artists from the community were responsible for teaching two classes each. Presentations were given in the following areas: Folk and Commercial Music; African Dance and Music; Latin American Music; Choral Styles; Technology: Arranging and Composing for TV; Dance/Movement; Concert Percussion; Opera and Music Theater; and Asian Music. Sessions included artists' performances and related participatory activities led by the artists themselves. Between artists' visits, the music teacher, music therapists, and other instructional team members reviewed and prepared for the artists' visits. They also led the class in other music learning activities: exploring sound, organizing sound, defining music and illustrating melody, rhythm, harmony, and form. The intended student outcomes for the class were to:

1. Play or sing simple musical works in a performance situation.
2. Identify common instruments visually and aurally.
3. Create and play simple melodic and rhythmic passages.
4. Identify major music ensembles (e.g., band, orchestra, chorus, jazz combo, swing choir).
5. Name major music eras and composers in each.
6. Identify varied ethnic or cultural musical styles.
7. Explain the importance of music in everyday life.
8. Express personal music tastes with appropriate vocabulary.
9. Identify career opportunities in music.

Outcomes: The intended student outcomes were met in varying degrees for all members of the class (Hughes, 1992). Students as a whole developed a great amount of enthusiasm for the performing artists' presentations. In addition, they indicated increased awareness of arts opportunities available to them in Tallahassee and in the media. They could name a variety of career opportunities in the arts. Perhaps the most pleasing aspect of their growth was evidenced through their spoken words in class. Analysis of their comments indicated that the students (especially the ones with advanced intellectual and musical skills) were broadening their attitudes of open-mindedness toward different kinds of music and different kinds of experiences. The mainstreamed class provided an opportunity for students to participate together through the activities. It allowed some of the students from the CBI class the opportunity to "shine" through their music abilities. Students were asked to evaluate the impact of the community artists on their feelings about music and the course. The written evaluations were quite positive in most respects. Some of the students expressed their feelings better in conversation. A girl from the CBI class told an instructor that "this was the best, most fun class I have ever had!" Another girl, with more advanced skills made a memorable comment during a class discussion of specific types of choral music when another student said, "Gospel is music sung by black people." The girl answered, "I don't care if you are black, white, or Chinese. Anyone can sing Gospel music! It's the style of the music that makes it Gospel, not the singer's color!"

Choral Music

Music therapists in the district provide support upon request to high school choral directors. They work as consultants or directly with the music teacher in the high school mainstreamed choral class. Music therapists also act as liaisons between the choral and special education teachers, and observe and support students in the choral class setting.

In the following example, a music therapy intern developed and field tested curriculum materials to provide support for students and teachers in choral classes. The materials were designed for students on functional curriculums such as CBI. They could also be used in other music courses such as piano and general music.

Example 13

Service Provider:	Music Therapy Intern
Course:	High School Chorus
Students Enrolled:	50
Targeted Students:	4 (CBI)

Problem: At least 30 minutes of choral class time each week was devoted to written work on music fundamentals. The music teachers reported that students from CBI were either doing nothing or were drawing pictures while the rest of the class worked in their music theory workbooks. The teachers wanted music related materials that were age appropriate and within the students' ability.

Strategies: A 90-page music theory workbook was developed by a music therapy intern. In writing the materials, she observed in the choral class and in the CBI class and consulted with all of the teachers involved. She did an extensive review of beginning keyboard theory books and other literature sources before beginning the project.

Outcomes: Four students used the materials successfully during field testing. High school choral teachers have continued to use the adaptive workbook materials with students who need to work at that level. The workbook has also been successfully used in middle school choral and general music classes.

Instrumental Music

Music therapists, music therapy interns, and other trained musicians from the local universities and community are also available to provide support upon request to high school students and teachers in mainstreamed instrumental programs. In this example, another music therapy intern provided support for students and the music teacher in a beginning keyboard class. The class involved approximately 20 students, 9 of whom were identified as students with severe disabilities. The piano teacher had experienced teaching small numbers of mainstreamed students from this population in the past and had developed a caring and supportive attitude toward *all* learners. She also had engaged in university study on the subject of special education.

Example 14

Service Provider:	Music Therapy Intern
Course:	Beginning Keyboard
Students Enrolled:	20
Targeted Students:	9 (severe disabilities)

Problem: There were too many students with very special needs in one class. Most of the nine students were unable to work independently or to perform together with the rest of the class at functional levels. Due to the nature of piano study, all of the students in the class needed some individual assistance during independent practice times. Assistance for all of the students could not be adequately provided by one teacher and an special education paraprofessional, who was not always present. In addition, it was not a class setting conducive to social interaction, and there were instances of inappropriate social behavior on the part of some students.

Strategies: Extra support in the piano classroom was provided 2 days per week for 1 semester by the music therapy intern. She helped any of the students needing assistance, but most of the time was spent working with the students with special needs on social and piano skills. She and the special education paraprofessional developed strategies together which the paraprofessional could use on other days when the music therapy intern was not present. She also collaborated with the piano teacher regarding planning and occasionally consulted with special education personnel.

Outcomes: The music teacher expressed gratitude for the assistance offered by the music therapy intern. It not only provided help for the students and relief for the teacher, but also a line of communication between teacher and special education support personnel. This enabled the teacher to specify her needs, especially as they pertained to scheduling in the best interest of all the students.

Working as a music therapist in a district-wide public school setting can be demanding, challenging, and definitely rewarding. It is also a job that is very comprehensive and full of professional opportunity. It is essential that music therapists stay abreast of current research and other professional literature dealing with issues pertaining to the public schools in order to continually seek out new and exciting ways to educate students with special needs. For the latest information on music mainstreaming and other school related issues, it is recommended that music therapists not only consult music therapy research and clinical publications but also those of other organizations such as The Council for Exceptional Children, Music Educators National Conference, and The National Association for the Education of Young Children. Readers are invited to contact the authors of this chapter for additional information on music therapy in the Leon County School System.

The suggested strategies presented in the Appendix are excerpted from *Introduction to Music Performance: A Secondary School Guide for Florida Schools* (Florida Department of Education, 1989). They have all proven to be effective in elementary and secondary music settings and specifically address the learning needs of students. This section can be used as a quick reference guide by those working with students in mainstreamed music settings.

References

Alley, J. M. (1979). Music in the IEP: Therapy/Education. *Journal of Music Therapy, 16,* 111–127.

Atterbury, B. W. (1986). A survey of present mainstreaming practices in the southern United States. *Journal of Music Therapy, 23,* 202–207.

Atterbury, B. W. (1989). *Mainstreaming exceptional learners in music.* Englewood Cliffs, NJ: Prentice Hall.

The Consortium of National Arts Education Associations. (1994). *National Standards for Arts Education.* Reston, VA: Music Educators National Conference.

Florida Department of Education, Division of Public Schools. (1989). *Introduction to music performance: A secondary school guide for Florida schools.* Tallahassee, FL: Author.

Gfeller, K., Darrow, A. A., & Hedden, S. K. (1990). On the ten-year anniversary of P.L. 94–142. The perceived status of mainstreaming among music educators in the states of Iowa and Kansas. *Journal of Research in Music Education, 38,* 90–101.

Hughes, J. E. (1991). Sing, everyone. *General Music Today, 4,* 8–9.

Hughes, J. E., & Robbins, B. J. (1992). *Mainstreaming in school music, K–12: A model program guide for school districts.* Tallahassee, FL: Author.

Hughes, J. E., Robbins, B. J., & King, R. J. (1988). A survey of perception and attitudes of exceptional student educators toward music therapy services in a county-wide school district. *Journal of Music Therapy, 4,* 26–32.

Hughes, J. E., Robbins, B. J., McKenzie, B. A., & Robb, S. S. (1990). Integrating exceptional and nonexceptional young children through music play: A pilot program. *Music Therapy Perspectives, 8,* 52–55.

Hughes, J. E., Robbins, B. J., Smith, D. S., & Kincade, C. F. (1987). The effect of participation in a public school choral music curriculum on singing ability in trainable mentally handicapped adolescents. *Music Education for the Handicapped 2,* 1–35.

Hughes, W. O. (1992). Two programs for high-risk students. *General Music Today, 5,* 20.

Riegel, R. H., Mayle, J. A., & McCarthy-Henkel, J. (1988). *Beyond maladies and remedies: Suggestions and guidelines for adapting materials for students with special needs in the regular class.* Novi, MI: Author.

Robbins, B. J. (1989). *Florida music educators' attitudes toward mainstreaming.* Unpublished master's thesis, University of Kansas, Lawrence, KS.

Standley, J. M., & Hughes, J. E. (in press). Documenting developmentally appropriate objectives and benefits of a music therapy program for early intervention: A behavioral analysis. *Music Therapy Perspectives.*

United States Department of Education (1995). *A teacher's guide to the U.S. Department of Education.* Washington, DC: Author.

Appendix

The strategies in this section address special needs of individuals in the music settings. They were compiled by the authors from three categories of resources. Categories include:

- the professional experiences of the authors of this chapter.
- the music and ESE teachers, music therapy interns, and university practicum students involved in music mainstreaming in the Leon County Schools.
- the published research and other professional literature.

Music Skills

Skill Area: Singing

Suggested Strategies

- Explore ways in which the voice moves up and down (e.g., compare the voice to an elevator)
- Produce sounds such as sirens, ghosts, owls.
- Use pictures, graphs, physical gestures and instruments to visually and/or aurally display movement of sound
- Use physical gestures (moving arms from high to low and vice versa)
- Provide good vocal models (peers, teachers, paraprofessionals)
- Echo sing phrases or individual tones within the appropriate vocal register
- Listen, think, and hum pitches before singing
- Use a minimum of accompaniment to focus on the vocal line
- Teach ostinatos, echo songs and rounds
- Discuss and demonstrate the differences between the speaking and singing voice
- Explore ways in which to use the voice (whisper, speak, scream, cry, laugh, hum, sing)
- Vocalize using vowel and consonant sounds
- Model deep breathing techniques

- Have the students take deep breaths in and out, laugh, yawn. Feel the muscular action and expansion of the rib cage
- Emphasize the relaxed jaw and open mouth position
- Whisper and speak words clearly
- Emphasize soft singing
- Have students hold an imaginary candle and slowly blow out the flame to improve breath control
- Sing phrases staccato, marcato, legato
- Use songs that elicit free vocalization on open syllables
- Allow the student time to respond vocally
- Use some songs with melodic and rhythmic repetition (e.g., repeated phrases, words or refrain after every verse)
- Find songs within the vocal range of the student having difficulty matching pitches
- Provide outside assistance to practice specific music skills such as solfege syllables and Curwen hand signs used in the Kodaly philosophy of teaching
- Have students put solfege syllables to favorite songs
- Provide several opportunities for students to hear the melody (sing it, outline the melody with your hand, use Curwen hand signs, play it on instruments)
- Incorporate sign language into song activities

- Practice matching pitches using kazoos, step bells, xylophone

Skill Area: Playing Instruments

Suggested Strategies

- Place instruments, visuals (charts, posters, flash cards) and yourself directly in front of the student's line of vision
- Use color coding or braille markings on instruments
- Have mallets in a variety of sizes available so that the student may find one that feels comfortable in his/her hand
- Remove wheelchair trays to enhance physical contact between students during instrument and action song activities
- Allow students with physical limitations to choose their manner of participation (they usually will tell you the successful way)
- Have a peer hold the instrument while the other student plays with his/her dominant hand
- Adapt instruments only after the student has demonstrated that he/she has difficulty manipulating it correctly
- Design rhythm activities that allow the student to respond in his/her own tempo or pattern
- Provide outside assistance to practice rhythm skills
- Echo clap rhythms
- Incorporate movement activities to develop a sense of basic beat and rhythm
- Practice using a variety of percussion instruments
- Use a variety of activities to develop rhythm skills (singing, clapping patterns, moving, playing the recorder and barred instruments, i.e., xylophones)
- Practice verbal and visual cues such as "ready," "begin," and "stop" during all activities

- Model correct playing techniques (peers, paraprofessionals, and teachers)
- Provide several opportunities for students to hear the rhythm patterns (clap it, sing it, play it on instruments)
- Provide outside assistance to practice playing barred instruments
- Use flash cards to teach the letter names on xylophones and other melodic instruments

Suggested Strategies for Recorder
(A wooden or plastic woodwind instrument)

- Provide outside assistance to practice recorder skills
- Use a variety of creative games, notation exercises and familiar songs when practicing recorder
- Provide much repetition
- Use appealing visuals (posters, flash cards, large music staff)
- Use Suzuki precorders for beginning recorder players

Skill Area: Listening

Suggested Strategies

- Keep directions simple—give a series of directions one step at a time (e.g., 1. "Open book"; 2. "Turn to page 1")
- Use movement to reinforce listening to form
- Provide several opportunities for students to hear the melody and rhythm patterns (sing it, clap it, play it on instruments)
- Play a familiar song; have students identify the "mystery tune"
- Sing a portion of a song and stop on a specific word. Students identify that word
- Sing a song. Students listen and sing silently (mouth words)
- Teach rhythm echo activities

- Use call and response songs
- Provide several visuals illustrating form, melody, rhythm, harmony, timbre
- Use activities that are short and simple with much repetition
- Use a multisensory approach (provide movement, visual aids, auditory cues, singing, playing creating)
- Place student closer to the sound source
- Provide visual cues through facial expressions, signs, movements, lights flicking, etc.
- Check with students wearing hearing aids to determine the optimum levels needed for music
- Use a variety of appealing sound sources to capture attention and motivate participation and musical growth

Skill Area: Moving

Suggested Strategies
- Provide sufficient space for wheelchairs
- Design activities that emphasize the students' motor strengths
- Provide activities for the student to develop body skills to move about the classroom with ease and safety
- Allow the student an opportunity to experience movement at his/her own level (moving eyes, fingers, head, hands, etc.)
- Train peers to assist students
- Remove wheelchair trays to enhance physical contact between students during activities
- Develop ways for all students to participate in activities involving dancing and moving through space. Wagons, tricycles, scooterboards, and other devices could be used if wheelchairs are not feasible
- Say and do all movements when first teaching a dance (step right, tap, tap)

- Partners perform side-to-side or face-to-face rather than pushing the wheelchair. Use two peers if necessary—one to push and one to be the partner
- If necessary, design alternative strategies so that all students participate in the same movement activities and reinforce music learning
- Move creatively with scarves, streamers, paper, parachutes, masks, puppets and other motivators

Skill Area: Creating/Composing

Suggested Strategies
- Have students create their own rhythm patterns and accompaniments
- Encourage exploration and improvisation
- Provide a comfortable environment in which students are free to risk sharing new ideas
- Encourage and ensure peer respect
- Design activities where the students can develop their own creative movements
- Use dramatization in the classroom to act out favorite songs, listening selections or environmental events
- Create sound pieces
- Use appealing stories and poems and have students create sound effects
- Use props such as colorful scarves, paper hats and articles from nature

Skill Area: Reading/Writing

Suggested Strategies
- Pair reading notation with visual and auditory cues (pair sound with symbol)
- Sing songs that will assist the student in remembering and understanding note values
- Practice various rhythms by using the verbal music concepts of Kodaly and Orff or any other consistent manner of counting

- Practice the names of the lines and spaces by using an oversized music staff
- Play word association games
- Provide opportunities for repetition with fun ways to practice
- Provide outside assistance to practice reading and notation skills
- Break down the steps into the simplest form possible
- Use a variety of learning and response modes
- Demonstrate and model correct written response first
- Find alternative ways to evaluate the students
- Use repetition and visuals to teach musical language concepts
- Provide rote learning when reading is not possible
- Use clear and uncluttered charts
- ESE teacher provide magnified or braille materials if needed
- Adapt written worksheets if necessary
- Be aware that some students may need to be placed closer to written words and symbols to process the material

General Skills

Skill Area: Participating

Suggested Strategies

- Use a wide range of appealing activities to ensure success
- Have a peer or paraprofessional model appropriate responses
- Have a paraprofessional physically assist the student
- Use a variety of learning and response modes
- Vary classroom groupings (large groups, small groups)
- Place a "peer/buddy" next to the student to model correct responses

- Accept all efforts as praiseworthy
- Assign the student a "buddy" who can spend time with the student in other activities outside of the music class
- Provide individual praise within the group when the student participates
- Provide outside assistance to practice music skills
- Place student between two good role models

Skill Area: Staying On Task

Suggested Strategies

- Use positive reinforcement when the student is on task
- Teach small amounts of materials at a time and gradually increase the number and length of activities
- Provide outside assistance to practice music skills
- Use a multisensory approach (presenting information in many diverse ways)
- Present small tasks to accomplish and reinforce upon completion
- Seat student near teacher or paraprofessional
- Assign a student to be a "buddy/partner"
- Paraprofessional physically assist the student if necessary
- Teacher physically assist student if possible
- Place student in front of the room
- Give verbal cues to encourage the student to attend
- Upon completion of the music class, send a behavior sheet back to the ESE teacher
- ESE teacher reminds student just prior to the class what is expected of him/her in the music class
- ESE teacher provide positive reinforcement in the classroom for good progress at the conclusion of the music class
- Reinforce with verbal praise

- Give directions in multisensory ways (say it, point to it, write it)
- Provide a structured classroom environment
- Give directions more than once during an activity
- Reduce the number of distractions
- Look directly at the student when giving instructions
- Simplify tasks to the level of the student to ensure success
- Assign the student a "buddy" who can also spend time with the student in other fun activities outside of the music class
- Use appealing visual aids
- Provide a variety of fun and appealing activities (singing, moving, playing, creating)

Skill Area: Following Directions

Suggested Strategies

- Look directly at student when giving directions
- Limit the number of new ideas presented at one time
- Demonstrate while giving directions
- Have the student repeat step-by-step instructions as they are given to ensure understanding
- Simplify the tasks to ensure success
- Make your directions simple
- Model correct behaviors and responses
- Give directions in multisensory ways (say it, point to it, write it)
- Give directions more than once during an activity

Skill Area: Reducing Behavior Problems

Suggested Strategies

- Review the rules of appropriate social behavior in the music classroom prior to the class
- Model correct behaviors and responses
- Be firm and always positive
- Be consistent with student expectations, classroom rules, teaching routines and classroom environment
- Have paraprofessional sit next to student to provide assistance if necessary
- Instruct paraprofessional in nonverbal prompting techniques to prevent distractions or interruptions
- Place student next to a good peer role model
- Assign the student a "buddy" who can spend time with the student in other activities outside of the music class
- Recognize student success (social and musical)
- Provide much positive reinforcement for appropriate behavior
- Explain consequences for behaviors
- Use school-wide classroom warnings and time-out procedures
- Send the student back to the classroom only if he/she is very disruptive, making it difficult for other students to learn
- Place student in the front of the room
- Give directions more than once during an activity
- Discreetly use the same positive reinforcement program used in the ESE classroom to achieve the desired behavior in the music classroom
- Find the students' strengths and plan opportunities for success
- Through your own language model, encourage and ensure respect among peers

Skill Area: Improving Motivation

Suggested Strategies
- Place student next to a good role model and friend
- When doing small group work, assign a good role model and friend to that group
- Find the student's strengths and plan chances for small successes
- Provide much positive reinforcement when the student shows an interest
- Provide outside assistance to practice music skills
- Make the student feel comfortable when participating in class activities
- Provide a variety of fun and appealing activities
- Let the student know it is all right to make mistakes
- Relate music concepts to the student's interests and favorite music selections

Skill Area: Increasing Understanding

Suggested Strategies
- Present tasks slowly to allow for success, then gradually increase the level of music difficulty
- Model correct music responses
- Provide outside assistance to practice music skills
- Teach small amount of material at a time
- Place student closer to the teacher
- Provide a variety of activities
- Provide concrete examples
- Use dramatization to increase understanding by acting out song text and listening to musical selections
- Emphasize for the student specific music skills learned in all activities
- Provide much repetition in many fun ways
- Use several appealing visuals
- Provide immediate positive reinforcement

- Give directions clearly

Skill Area: Discussion/ Oral Expression

Suggested Strategies
- Have discussions about the songs
- Accept all efforts as praiseworthy
- Provide praise when student shows interest in the discussion
- Ask questions that require short "yes/no" responses
- Find the student's interest to encourage a greater feeling of comfort
- Use call and response songs
- Use visual aids (posters, rhythm flash cards)

MUSIC THERAPY FOR LEARNERS IN A PUBLIC SCHOOL EARLY EDUCATION CENTER

Amelia Greenwald Furman
Charles E. Furman

FEDERAL laws such as Public Law 94–142 and the Individuals with Disabilities Education Act (IDEA) impact education in every state. The federal mandates, however, are implemented differently in individual states and school districts. Each state sets requirements within the federal framework, and each school district then sets its own policies and procedures. Every school district negotiates a contract with a teachers' union which impacts the delivery of services to children. Further, if the school district has implemented site-based management, then each individual school building designates how services and resources are utilized. In some of the previous chapters, the music therapy programs have been district-wide services. This chapter describes a program that has developed over 5 years in an individual school within a large urban school district.

Background

Minneapolis Public Schools

The largest district in Minnesota, the Minneapolis Public Schools provides educational services for more than 45,000 students. At the present time, 63 of the 102 schools in the district serve elementary students. Early Childhood Special Education (ECSE) services may begin at birth. There are approximately 300 children receiving home-based services between the ages of birth to 3 years in the district. There are 24 ECSE classrooms throughout the district providing services for 450 to 550 students, ages 3 to 5.

Longfellow School

Longfellow was built in 1911 as an elementary school in the Minneapolis Public School System. Throughout the 1980s, the school served as the primary Early Childhood Special Education (ECSE) site for the district. During that time, all the classrooms in the building were self-contained and only for children who were receiving special education services. All students were placed in other schools when they reached kindergarten age. In 1991, several factors influenced a major change in settings where ECSE services were provided: (a) the realization that the least restrictive environment did not mean simply being in a "regular" school building, but with regular children; (b) the move toward having special needs children attend schools in their own neighborhoods; and (c) the growing recognition of the positive impact that inclusion with peers as role models has for special education students (Falvey, Forest, Pearpoint, & Rosenberg, 1994). The Early Childhood Special Education classes were dispersed to 12 sites throughout the district. Longfellow School became an Early Education Center offering regular education classes for students prekindergarten through the second grade. Three ECSE classes remained as part of the Longfellow program.

Current Student Composition

The 370 current students represent the diversity found in the urban setting: African American 40%, Asian 4%, Caucasian 40%, Hispanic 4%, and Native American 12%. The entire school qualifies for Title I funds since more than 70% of the students receive free or reduced lunches. This federal program, *Improving America's Schools*, provides partial funding for additional staff, parent programming, and materials. The focus of the Title I program is to improve children's learning.

Longfellow continues to include several ECSE classes: a toddler room for children under 3, a classroom for 3- and 4-year-old children, a class of children who are deaf/hard-of-hearing, and "inclusion" classes. Full inclusion refers to those classrooms where a child with special needs spends the school day with their nondisabled peers. Approximately 50 children receive ECSE services through these programs. As part of the "regular education" program, there are two "High Five" rooms, each providing two sessions a day for children who turn 5 years of age after September 2 and before December 31. These children go to kindergarten the following year. There are two kindergarten rooms, each also providing two sessions per day. Five first grades and four second grades complete the academic program. Approximately 17% of students between kindergarten and second grade have an Individual Education Plan (IEP). This means almost a fifth of the students qualify for and receive special education services. Early Childhood Family Education (ECFE) teachers provide parent education programs and work with community families. There is also a before-and-after school childcare program in the building.

Management Framework

The Longfellow program began operating with a *shared leadership team,* sometimes referred to as site-based management, in 1990 and continues with this management style today. This is part of an education reform movement leading to a restructured system trying to meet the changing demands of families and the community (Dettmer, Thurston, & Dyck, 1993). The leadership team includes the principal, teacher representatives, staff representatives (clerks, custodian, paraprofessionals), and parent representatives. Some teams also include community business representatives. The purpose of the shared leadership team is to support and refine the goals and mission of Longfellow Early Education Center within the Minneapolis Public School District by:

1. serving as advocates for the students, parents, staff
2. supporting the attainment of the school's goals
3. monitoring and evaluating the progress made toward the achievement of these goals
4. communicating the goals and philosophy of Longfellow to the District administration, parents, staff, and community

The mission of Longfellow Early Education Center is to promote in each child a spirit of independence and inquiry. All children can learn, and this child-centered program is designed to meet the needs of each child based on his or her individual strengths and weaknesses. The goal is to support and promote positive interaction between all children and to be respectful of diversity.

Philosophical Framework

The entire Longfellow program is built upon: (a) the concept of developmentally appropriate practices (i.e., appropriate activities are developed to meet a child's emotional, social, and intellectual needs, not only according to age and grade level, but also at the level they are currently performing [Bredenkamp, 1987]); and (b) the belief that a strong family school partnership will promote optimal student learning. Varying levels of ability, development, and learning styles are expected, accepted, and used to design curriculum (Udvari-Solner, 1994). The curriculum is integrated, and children's learning in traditional subject areas often occurs through "hands-on" projects and learning centers. At Longfellow, teachers feel children learn best when:

1. children are actively involved in their learning through experiencing hands-on exploration of materials.
2. children's play is respected for its value as an appropriate learning tool.
3. the program addresses the needs of the whole child (personal, social, physical, cognitive and aesthetic/creative aspects included).
4. teachers carefully monitor student growth in the classroom on a regular and frequent basis.

Programming

Individual schools have the responsibility to determine what curriculum, texts, and programming they wish to use. Each school has a unique curriculum and programing. This is particularly evident in each school's determination as to what subjects will be taught during classroom teacher preparation time. According to the 1995–1997 Minneapolis Public School Contract Agreement (1995), the normal work day of an elementary teacher includes 55 minutes of preparation time within the defined student day. The contract further states:

It is the intent of the Minneapolis elementary schools to continue to employ specialists in vocal music instruction, art, physical education, media, and other areas to serve the elementary schools. The intent of employing these specialists is to:
1. provide quality instruction in specialized areas for elementary age children.
2. relieve elementary teachers of the necessity for preparation in some subject areas. (p. 157)

Because each school determines its own programming, there is a great deal of difference in curricula among elementary schools. For example, some schools do not have a music program but may offer physical education, media, and science as the classes provided by specialists. One school provides sign language training as a specialist period for students. At the present time, Longfellow teachers have selected dance, music, physical education, and media as the specialist classes.

Music Therapy

Music therapy, provided by a registered music therapist (RMT), has been part of the Longfellow ECSE program for many years. Music therapy has given students positive learning experiences and has been an integral part of the excellence in programming for ECSE students. This position is highly valued by teachers, administration, and parents within the Longfellow setting. The ECSE staff and principal at Longfellow have consistently supported the use of music therapy for providing the teacher preparation time for the ECSE classes. During the first 2 years after Longfellow became an Early Education Center, all ECSE students were seen four times a week by the music therapist, and the High Five students were seen twice a week. Initially, the regular education students did not receive music.

Longfellow has children at many developmental stages and this often creates a challenge for staff. The classroom teachers who transferred to Longfellow to teach in the early education kindergarten to second grade program were very interested in hiring a music specialist who understood developmentally appropriate practices with young children (such as are included in the Music Educators National Conference Position Statement on Early Childhood Education, 1992). Since the typical music therapist has been trained to work with diversity both in age and development, a second music therapist was hired for this position.

The result has been the evolution of a music program with two music therapists that service all the children in the building from ECSE toddlers through all second graders. An important aspect of the music therapy program at Longfellow is the participation of music therapy students from the University of Minnesota. As a result of a longstanding agreement with the University of Minnesota School of Music, undergraduate and graduate students majoring in music therapy are rotated through the ECSE program. Each student works twice a week for an academic quarter. Student clinicians assist with both data collection and session leading. The program has developed through collaboration and teamwork between Longfellow, the university, and teachers from varied disciplines. It provides developmentally appropriate music experiences for all the children, while enriching and generalizing from classroom learning, both for the ECSE children and for the college students as well.

Administrative Framework

Assessment

Interagency collaboration between the Public Health Department, Hennepin County Human Services, and the Minneapolis School District, as required by part H of Public Law 99–457, provides the central intake and referral system for children and families. After an initial screening, the child is referred to the public school Early Childhood Assessment Team.

As shown in Figure 1, the student must first meet criteria in one of three categories: disability, medical diagnosis, or standardized assessment. The final determination is made by considering eligibility plus need for special education services and is based on a recommendation by a team that includes the parent. The assessment team establishes initial goals for children receiving services in the Minneapolis Public Schools.

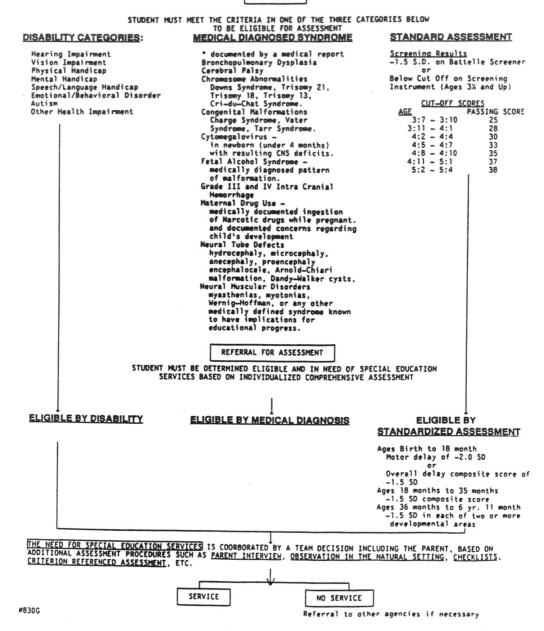

MINNEAPOLIS PUBLIC SCHOOLS
Special Education Department

ENTRY CRITERIA/BIRTH THROUGH SIX YEARS AND 11 MONTHS

SCREENING

STUDENT MUST MEET THE CRITERIA IN ONE OF THE THREE CATEGORIES BELOW
TO BE ELIGIBLE FOR ASSESSMENT

DISABILITY CATEGORIES:

Hearing Impairment
Vision Impairment
Physical Handicap
Mental Handicap
Speech/Language Handicap
Emotional/Behavioral Disorder
Autism
Other Health Impairment

MEDICAL DIAGNOSED SYNDROME

* documented by a medical report
Bronchopulmonary Dysplasia
Cerebral Palsy
Chromosome Abnormalities
  Downs Syndrome, Trisomy 21,
  Trisomy 18, Trisomy 13,
  Cri-du-Chat Syndrome.
Congenital Malformations
  Charge Syndrome, Vater
  Syndrome, Tarr Syndrome.
Cytomegalovirus —
  in newborn (under 4 months)
  with resulting CNS deficits.
Fetal Alcohol Syndrome —
  medically diagnosed pattern
  of malformation.
Grade III and IV Intra Cranial
  Hemorrhage
Maternal Drug Use —
  medically documented ingestion
  of Narcotic drugs while pregnant.
  and documented concerns regarding
  child's development
Neural Tube Defects
  hydrocephaly, microcephaly,
  anecephaly, proencephaly
  encephalocele, Arnold-Chiari
  malformation, Dandy-Walker cysts.
Neural Muscular Disorders
  myasthenias, myotonias,
  Wernig-Hoffman, or any other
  medically defined syndrome known
  to have implications for
  educational progress.

STANDARD ASSESSMENT

Screening Results
-1.5 S.D. on Battelle Screener
  or
Below Cut Off on Screening
Instrument (Ages 3¼ and Up)

CUT-OFF SCORES	
AGE	PASSING SCORE
3:7 — 3:10	25
3:11 — 4:1	28
4:2 — 4:4	30
4:5 — 4:7	33
4:8 — 4:10	35
4:11 — 5:1	37
5:2 — 5:4	38

REFERRAL FOR ASSESSMENT

STUDENT MUST BE DETERMINED ELIGIBLE AND IN NEED OF SPECIAL EDUCATION
SERVICES BASED ON INDIVIDUALIZED COMPREHENSIVE ASSESSMENT

ELIGIBLE BY DISABILITY   **ELIGIBLE BY MEDICAL DIAGNOSIS**   **ELIGIBLE BY STANDARDIZED ASSESSMENT**

Ages Birth to 18 month
  Motor delay of -2.0 SD
    or
  Overall delay composite score of
  -1.5 SD
Ages 18 months to 35 months
  -1.5 SD composite score
Ages 36 months to 6 yr. 11 month
  -1.5 SD in each of two or more
  developmental areas

THE NEED FOR SPECIAL EDUCATION SERVICES IS COORBORATED BY A TEAM DECISION INCLUDING THE PARENT, BASED ON
ADDITIONAL ASSESSMENT PROCEDURES SUCH AS PARENT INTERVIEW, OBSERVATION IN THE NATURAL SETTING, CHECKLISTS,
CRITERION REFERENCED ASSESSMENT, ETC.

SERVICE   NO SERVICE

                           Referral to other agencies if necessary

#830G

Figure 1. Entry Criteria, Minneapolis Public Schools, Special Education Department

Individual Plans

Parents, teachers, and other service providers develop a plan to meet the educational, social, and emotional goals of each child and family. For children from birth until 3 years of age receiving services, the plan is called an Individual Family Service Plan (IFSP). When the child becomes a preschooler (2 years 11 months) the family may choose to continue with an IFSP or change to an Individual Education Plan (IEP). The primary differences are listed in Table 1.

Table 1

Comparison of Individual Family Service Plan (IFSP) and Individual Education Plan (IEP)

Individual Family Service Plan	Individual Education Plan
Addresses the needs of the family as well as the needs of the child.	Addresses the needs of the child and is implemented in the classroom.
Identifies medical and social service needs as well as educational strengths and needs.	Identifies educational strengths and needs.
Ways to meet the school, medical, and social service needs of the child and family are agreed to and written on the plan.	Ways to meet the school needs of the child are agreed to and written on the plan.
Service Coordinator available to help obtain school and non-school services needed.	The school team (teacher, therapists, social worker) available to provide information about different services.
Service Coordinator attends planning meetings and periodic reviews with parent or guardian.	Family attends planning meetings and periodic reviews on their own, but may invite an advocate to attend also.

The trend in Minnesota is to extend the IFSP (rather than the IEP) throughout the early childhood years. Minnesota Statute 120.1701 (12)(b)(4) encourages the use of the IFSP process for children over 3. Some of the reasons for this include: (a) the right to coordinated, interagency family directed services does not end at 3 years of age; (b) as children move into center-based programs, it is important to maintain family participation; and (c) duplication of services by agencies is reduced as a result of interagency agreements and better coordination of services. This trend reflects the current family focus and emphasis on collaborative planning between organizations that is felt to be in the best interest of the student (Bradshaw, 1996).

While the actual goals and objectives to be worked on in the academic setting are very similar for an IEP or IFSP, the style and format of the meeting is different. The IFSP emphasizes the family and the partnership between the family and professionals. The needs of the entire family are considered in an IFSP. The family thoughts page provides family members an opportunity to think about and share their hopes and concerns for their child as well as family needs and strengths. This can be completed before the meeting but is usually handwritten at the meeting to reflect the family's current situation. Much of the IFSP is handwritten because it is written at the meeting with the family's input (see Figure 2).

Child's Name: FAMILY THOUGHTS

Family Considerations and Concerns for the Individualized Family Service Plan

1. Please describe how you see your child. Tell what you most like, any concerns or needs. (Please use the back or additional paper if desired.)

loves music, TV credits, loves his little creatures,
seems to be comprehending speech
concerns- basic communication
peer interaction, attention span, toileting

2. Which of the following do you or other family members feel are important concerns or areas about which you would like more information?

for your child
- [ ] getting around
- [x] communicating
- [x] learning
- [x] eating, nutrition
- [x] sleeping
- [x] toilet learning
- [x] having fun w/other children
- [ ] challenging behaviors/emotions
- [ ] equipment or supplies
- [x] health or dental care
- [ ] pain or discomfort
- [ ] vision
- [ ] hearing
- [x] other hair cuts helping attend Sunday school

for your family
- [ ] meeting other families whose child has similar needs
- [x] planning/expectations for future
- [ ] finding a support group
- [ ] information/ideas for brothers, sisters, friends, relatives, others
- [ ] finding or working with doctors/other specialists
- [ ] coordinating child's medical care
- [ ] coordinating/making appointments,dealing with agencies
- [x] learning about different services and how they work
- [x] information about available resources
- [ ] information about specific special needs
- [ ] explaining professional terms/roles
- [ ] help with transportation (to school, appointments, or vehicle adaptation)
- [x] finding child care for J. or all 3 Kids
- [ ] people who help in your home/care for your child so you can have a break
- [ ] assistance with housing, clothing, jobs, food, telephone
- [ ] assistance in obtaining funds for extra cost of child's special needs

- [ ] help with insurance
- [ ] information about recreational opportunities
- [ ] interpreter -- language:..................
- [ ] other

notes

3. What type of help would you want for your child and family in the months or year ahead?

communicate basic needs, interact with peers, siblings
share mutual toys, increase attention span in group, toileting
information/contact people in the field of autism

4. What else do you think would be helpful for others to know about your child? ...about your family?

Figure 2. Family Thoughts

The team and summary sheet (see Figure 3) emphasizes one of the driving forces behind the IFSP, that is, that all the agencies and personnel involved with a family work together to ensure the needs of the entire family are being met. The family should leave the IFSP meeting with the names and phone numbers of all the people working with their child. This is a major difference from the IEP where the focus is primarily on educational needs and the services that are provided only in the school setting.

Figure 3. IFSP Team and Summary Sheet

Action plans help the family create a list of the information, changes, and tasks that need to be documented but do not require an outcome (see Figure 4).

The IFSP and IEP outcome pages include the goal and objectives. There is little difference between the forms in terms of the information included (see Figures 5 and 6).

The families always decide whom they would like involved in the school conferences, whether an IEP or IFSP is used. Families are welcome to include medical providers, county social workers or case managers, friends, or any person significant in the life of the child to assist in determining appropriate goals for the child and family.

Child's Name   ACTION -   1

	ACTION PLANS for the Child / Family / Team		
Date	Activity or Desired Change	People who can help	Notes

TRANSITION PLANNING CHECKLIST
- ☐ Discussed transition with families
- ☐ Obtained parental consent
- ☐ Notified child study team of transition
- ☐ Convened transition conference
- ☐ Reviewed child's program options from 3rd birthday to end of school year
- ☐ This IFSP includes one or more Transition Outcomes

Figure 4. Action Plan

Integrated Therapy Approach

As much as possible and appropriate, the therapists at Longfellow spend time in the classroom responding to the children and helping them develop functional skills within the classroom routines and working collaboratively with other staff (McWilliam, 1995). As part of the integrated therapy approach, teachers and support staff meet once a week to facilitate communication, thereby improving services and teaching for students (Fullan & Hargreaves, 1991). At Longfellow, the support staff includes the teacher, speech clinician, social worker, occupational therapist, physical therapist, music therapist, developmentally appropriate physical education specialist (DAPE) and an Early Childhood Family Education teacher. At this time, a music therapy intern from the University of Minnesota, completing an AMTA–approved experimental internship, also serves as a contributing member of the support staff. The meeting time helps to ensure that the entire team is aware of changes in the child's life and any modifications in his or her program.

Child's Name   Jane   OUTCOME # 1

Where do we want to be? *(Major Outcome or Goal)*		Periodic Review Date
Jane will sit on her chair without adult help and stay on task for longer periods of time.		Please provide a description of the degree of progress written in the same format as the objective. You should also indicate whether to continue (C), modify/revise (M) or discontinue (D) the objective.

What steps do we need to take? *(Objectives or Subgoals)* include criteria, procedures, and timelines used to determine progress	Service and Person Responsible	
1. During group time, Jane will sit on her chair with the adult only sitting near her (participating independently) for 4 consecutive days by May 1996. 2. During group time Jane will independently stay on task for 15 minutes, for 4 consecutive days, by May 1996.	Mary ECSE teacher Cathy Speech/Language Amy Music Therapist	

Steps the county will take to develop service if unavailable.

Child's Name   Jane   OUTCOME # 2

Where do we want to be? *(Major Outcome or Goal)*		Periodic Review Date:
Jane will begin to express some wants and needs using picture schedules, picture choice boards and verbal imitation.		Please provide a description of the degree of progress written in the same format as the objective. You should also indicate whether to continue (C), modify/revise (M) or discontinue (D) the objective.

What steps do we need to take? *(Objectives or Subgoals)* include criteria, procedures, and timelines used to determine progress	Service and Person Responsible	
1. When present with an array of food pictures, Jane will indicate a choice by pointing to a picture, 2/3 opportunities for 3 days. 2. When presented with an array of song pictures, Jane will indicate a choice by pointing to a picture then participating verbally or physically 2 times during the song 2/3 opportunities for 3 days.	Cathy speech/language intervention in the classroom Amy music therapy sessions in the classroom	

Steps the county will take to develop service if unavailable.

Figure 5. IFSP Goal Sheet

Page 3c of IEP   Learner Name: R.   ED-1078 0.

F.   ANNUAL GOALS, SHORT-TERM INSTRUCTIONAL OBJECTIVES

Use one PAGE 3 for each goal. Thoroughly state the goal. List objectives for the goal, including attainment for each objective. GOAL # ___ OF ___ GOALS

GOAL: During structured time, R will use the Introtalker to choose activities and make requests.

Short-Term Instructional Objectives

OBJECTIVES:

During music, grp, and ind. 1:1 time, R will participate & request activities relating to the structured activity by using the Introtalker with an 8 picure overlay; choosing her desired item given 1 verbal cue 3/4 opport. for 2 consecutive days

During music, grp, and ind. 1:1 time, R will participate & request activities relating to the structured activity by using the Introtalker with an 8 picture overlay; choosing her desired item given 1 verbal cue 4/5 opport. for 3 consecutive days by the IEP.

G.   IEP PERIODIC REVIEW

Date Reviewed: _____   Progress made toward this goal and objectives:

NOTE TO PARENT(S): You are entitled to request a meeting to discuss the results of this review.

Page 3c of IEP   Learner Name: Tom   ED-1078 02

F.   ANNUAL GOALS, SHORT-TERM INSTRUCTIONAL OBJECTIVES

Use one PAGE 3 for each goal. Thoroughly state the goal. List objectives for the goal, including attainment for each objective. GOAL # 2 OF 5 GOALS

GOAL: Tom will go from inconsistent on-task behavior in structured situations to consistent on-task behavior in structured situations.

Short-Term Instructional Objectives

OBJECTIVES:

1. Tom will attend and participate in structured group activities i.e. music, language groups for 10 minutes with 1 verbal prompt 3 out of 4 Days per week for 1 month by periodic review.

2. Tom will attend and participate in structured table activities for 1-3 minutes 3 out of 4 days per week for 1 month by periodic review.

G.   IEP PERIODIC REVIEW

Date Reviewed: _____   Progress made toward this goal and objectives:

NOTE TO PARENT(S): You are entitled to request a meeting to discuss the results of this review.

Figure 6. IEP Goal Sheet

Both the IFSP and IEP are binding, legal documents. Any services written in must be provided as specified. Not all the schools in the district have music therapy programs. Some students move frequently during a year, attending several programs. It is a district administration decision not to have specific music therapy goals written into the IFSP/IEP. Many of the goals and objectives that are written are collaborative, involving more than one discipline, or can be integrated into the child's whole program. Many goals and objectives are written that include music therapy, such as: (a) "Bob will continue to increase his participation during structured group activities from responding with one action and one word to responding with four to five words and imitating four of five actions during songs"; or (b) "Tashawna will sit, focus, and participate in structured activities and groups for 10–15 minutes each of 2 days in 1 week without screaming, touching, or hitting another child." Data to determine whether the objectives have been met are collected from groups facilitated by the music therapist, speech clinician, and classroom teacher.

Some examples of the integrated approach include:

1. In one class the occupational therapist came regularly to music group and adjusted positioning during the session. The child's goal was to increase appropriate sitting during activities. Working together, the occupational therapist and music therapist combined services and the child was able to participate to the fullest extent. The presence of an additional adult ensured that any responses made by the child were reinforced immediately. The use of music as a motivator to set the occasion to practice appropriate skills is utilized over and over again in this age group.
2. The physical therapist identified a child who was resistive to jumping in the physical therapist area but was very willing to participate in jumping during music while "jumping on board a sailing ship" from the song "Going Over the Sea" (Fowke, 1969). This provided an *authentic assessment* that evaluated the child's functioning within a real situation.
3. The speech and language pathologist regularly observes music therapy sessions to obtain information on students' ability to imitate as well as to use spontaneous language.

The above examples all reflect times when the music therapist creates an opportunity for children to practice and to integrate skills developed in therapy settings.

Role of Music Therapy in ECSE Classes

Music therapy sessions provide a motivating environment to work on social, emotional, motor, and cognitive needs. Incorporating into the music group the skills which the occupational therapist, physical therapist, speech clinician, and classroom teacher are currently working on with students is part of the ongoing collaboration between team members. Developing and demonstrating activities that allow all the students to participate at their individual level and yet function as part of the group is another responsibility of the music therapy position.

One of the other functions of the music therapist is that of a resource person to identify skills which are necessary for successful participation as the students progress in school. The music therapist's experience across grade levels for regular classrooms of High Five, kindergarten, and first grade students becomes invaluable as ECSE classes work to prepare students for full inclusion classrooms or to make determinations about programs that would best meet the needs of students.

Service Delivery Models

Toddler Services

Children who turn 3 between September 1 and December 31 and meet the ECSE criteria are eligible for the toddler program. This school-based class meets two times a week for 2½ hours. Six children, a teacher, and a paraprofessional, with additional one-to-one assistants as required (for example, a medically fragile child who must be monitored continually) comprise the class. The music therapist provides a group music session once a week. This is often the first group experience for these students. The main focus of the sessions is exposing the children to the concept of coming to an area, sitting down, focusing on a leader, and using language. The classes are multicategorical so there is a wide range of skills and needs. The songs are simple and involve movements and sign language. For instance, the music therapist sets the occasion by using small puppets, pictures, or instruments. The children are prompted to use words like *me, my turn,* and *more,* or the sign language equivalents, while taking turns doing the activity. The children use the same skill later in the day to respond to the question, "Who wants a snack?" This prepares the students to learn important survival skills for use later in the academic setting, such as volunteering and offering answers.

One aspect of the toddler program that has been especially effective is having "older" helpers during music time. First and second graders are able to cue and encourage the small children. The older students are likely to be more understanding than a young peer if a toddler plays inappropriately with a toy or does not understand the concept of sharing. Additionally, they act as models for appropriate behavior.

Case Example

One first grader, who was a on a behavioral IEP himself, really enjoyed coming and helping with the toddler group. He would regularly call attention to his special friend: "Hey look, Chuckie's clapping by himself!" His dismay was apparent one day when he tried to get his partner to come to group. "Hey—he's not listening to me! I told him to come—what'll we do— he's walking away! He's making me mad!" Since the music therapist also saw the older child in his full inclusion music class, the event could be discussed privately in relation to his own inappropriate behaviors. "Do you always listen? How does that make your teachers feel? What should teachers do to help you follow directions?" The first grader and the music therapist then talked with his classroom teacher about his experience and what he wanted to try to do differently to change his own behavior.

3- and 4-Year-Old Special Education Services

The 3- and 4-year-old ECSE classrooms provide services 4 days a week for 2½ hours. Eight students, a teacher, and paraprofessional, with additional one-to-one paraprofessionals as required, make up each classroom. These classrooms are primarily self-contained and multicategorical (i.e., children of widely varying abilities and needs; it is not uncommon to have a child who is blind and nonambulatory in the same class as a child who is autistic and can read). These students participate in 25-minute music therapy groups two times a week. In order to have the children ready for full inclusion at the kindergarten year, a variety of integrated activities and experiences are structured to assist the students in transferring their skills to new classroom situations (Furman & Furman, 1993).

Longfellow utilizes a *whole language approach* where literacy is taught through natural and meaningful context, much like learning to talk. Children are exposed to words, sounds, and stories through listening, chanting, speaking, singing, reading, and writing. ECSE classroom themes and activities are usually planned by the teacher, music therapist, and speech clinician. Planning together works well and follows the school model of integrated curriculum. A book or several books and poems are often used as the basis for the 3- and 4-year-old classroom themes. For example, instead of using farm animals as a theme, specific children's stories such as "The Big Red Barn" by M. Wise Brown (1989) and "Rosie's Walk" by Pat Hutchins (1968) are used to create an opportunity to study and learn about the characters and events included in the books. In the small ECSE groups, the children learn to look at a book, label pictures, answer questions, sing songs, and participate in music activities related to the story. The use of children's literature can help a child understand what is being sung or talked about (Fallin, 1995; McCoy, 1994).

Classroom themes are often child-directed and reflect their interests, such as dinosaurs, frogs, or, as in the case of one child whose father was a truck driver, trucks. This is an *emergent curriculum* where teachers highlight and extend lessons in response to children's interests.

Integration Techniques

Reverse Mainstreaming

Many ECSE students are very attuned to adults. Their primary learning experiences have occurred in settings with very high adult-to-child ratios. It is important to help the child be ready for the stimulating environment of a classroom full of active students. Reverse mainstreaming, where several students from the High Five program or kindergarten come and participate in the small ECSE music therapy group, is utilized as a first step to help the ECSE children adjust to larger groups. The students come and participate, providing additional models for the ECSE students. It helps the music therapist and other staff have a sense of how much prompting and support the ECSE student is requiring. The additional wait for turns and/or the ability to share their turn provides information as to the child's readiness. The visiting children have the opportunity to meet the ECSE staff and students with a teacher they know and trust. Usually after several music times, the children stay and play in the ECSE room.

Mainstreaming

An important part of ECSE music therapy sessions is mainstreaming experiences in the music classes with High Five or kindergarten students. The ECSE student(s) participate in a music class taught by the music therapist. This allows the child the security of the same music therapist and the familiar activities. The visiting child has time to adjust to a new room and more students during the music group where most of the expectations placed on him or her are familiar and within his or her capabilities. The child is comfortable and successful because the music therapist ensures the success by careful preparation and selection of music and activities. The classroom teacher has the chance to see and meet the child in a comfortable situation where he or she is not trying to limit or require appropriate behavior. The students have the opportunity to meet each other through structured music activities. The purpose of the mainstreaming experiences is to enable the child to practice making a transition to new situations.

Case Example

The ECSE and High Five rooms are connected by a vent so that even though the rooms are not next to each other, the students could hear one child who engaged in a lot of screaming. The High Five students were concerned about this child. The classroom teacher talked to the music therapist about how to reassure her students the ECSE child was all right. Since this child enjoyed music and did very well in structured situations, the music therapist invited him to a High Five music class. After the music group, the class gave a spontaneous and excited report to their teacher: "Hey, he can talk and take turns—he only screamed one time! He's going to come back again and try to use his words the whole time." The music visits gradually extended into invitations to stay and play in the High Five classroom.

High Five Inclusion Program

A self-contained ECSE classroom is too restrictive for some students, yet they are not ready to be in a High Five classroom without significant support. The Longfellow High Five Inclusion Program was developed to meet this need. Four ECSE students were placed in each of the High Five classrooms with 15 regularly enrolled students. An ECSE teacher or paraprofessional was also in the classroom with the teacher. This model was selected based on research which suggested that when strategies to promote interaction between students are facilitated by teachers, special needs students often make the most gains (Humpal, 1991; Jellison, Brooks, & Huck 1984). Because many of these students were previously in the ECSE program, they had a base of knowledge as well as security and familiarity with the music therapist. This familiarity with the basic structure of coming and sitting for music, knowing the hello song, and taking turns meant that skills could be generalized from a small group to the large group instead of trying to learn entirely new skills in a new setting.

Kindergarten and Primary Inclusion

As students move into the primary grades, the music therapist functions in a different role. In a primary setting, the amount of teaming time is different. The student is one of 20 or more in a classroom. The music therapist, who sees the child as part of music for the class, functions often as a resource to the classroom teacher regarding behaviors and/or skills. Signs of regression or failure to use skills previously demonstrated can be quickly noted. The music therapist's familiarity with the students and their social skills is helpful as combinations for classrooms, small group services, or programs are considered.

Case Example

In trying to determine the correct placement for a child who had been in the ECSE program and for whom English was not the native language, the music therapist strongly suggested he be placed in a High Five classroom. (At the time, there was no inclusion model.) The teacher and music therapist had collaborated regarding several students with great success, and she readily agreed to accept the child (Furman, Adamek, & Furman, 1993). After 3 days, during which the child had not said anything and had mainly stood and observed, the teacher said she felt concerned that perhaps she was not the right teacher for this child. As the class lined up and headed outside for the bus, the rain matched her mood. Then, a little voice started singing, "Rain, rain go away" and she thought, "What a good idea to sing—and *WHO* was that singing?" When she turned around, there was Juan, the target child, smiling while singing and signing the song. Soon all the children were singing with Juan. At the bus, the teacher asked how he knew the song, and without hesitating, the child replied, "Amy teach me—want me to teach *you* tomorrow?"

Individual/ Special Sessions

Individual music therapy sessions are not usually scheduled. There is latitude, however, to develop programming that helps meet individual needs.

Case Example

A child who was a former ECSE student began to misbehave during afternoon language times in the spring of first grade. It appeared he was tired by the afternoon and frustrated at how difficult recognizing letters continued to be for him. A program was set up where he could come and be a music therapy "helper" every afternoon if he had met his behavioral objectives in the morning. He came and assisted in a 3- and 4-year-old classroom where the students were working on preacademic skills such as sizes, shapes, and colors. He enjoyed being part of a group where he was the successful role model. He was able to go back to his class after 25 minutes as a music therapy helper, more relaxed and ready to work.

Case Example

A Title V Indian Education Grant (Furman, 1993) was used to provide music therapy sessions to help children develop key skills to ensure a more successful school experience. Fourteen first- and second-grade students, all of whom had difficulty sitting, listening, following directions, and maintaining interpersonal relationships, participated in music therapy groups. Teacher referral and classroom observations showed that the students were on-task and participating in activities less than 50% of the time. Social and classroom skills emphasized in the music groups included: taking turns, attending to a task visually, following directions, interacting with peers, and participating actively in games, including trying new ones. The music sessions worked extremely well in motivating all of the students. Singing and rhythm activities, using a variety of familiar and ethnic instruments, were used to set up the learning situations. By the end of the academic year, the students were able to make verbal choices about what instrument they wanted to play, wait their turn, play in combination with different peers, and listen and echo back rhythms and words to songs. Songs and activities were chosen that required problem solving and presented opportunities for discussion. All of the tasks required concentration and focus on the activity at hand. On the average, all the students were on-task and participated appropriately in the music activities between 70–100% of the time. Final group performances were prepared for the classrooms. These were presented and videotaped. The tapes were given to the classrooms to watch at a later date. The classmates were observed singing along with the tapes and making positive comments to the performers about their respective roles in the music group. The performers gave stickers to their peers at the end of the performance; this was also videotaped. This gave the classmates and performers an opportunity to acknowledge and to relive some positive interactions, instead of the commonly observed negative interactions. Certificates and pictures were given to all of the participants to set the occasion for them to tell others about their successes.

Generalization: Preparing Students for the Full-Inclusion Music Class

The following suggestions have been useful as the staff works with students coming from other programs into Longfellow inclusion classes and in preparing our current students for new experiences.

1. Observe the classroom and music groups of the public schools, daycares, or preschools to ensure you are familiar with the musical, social, behavioral, and academic skills required of successful group members. If the students with whom you work are going to (or coming from) a classroom where the teacher has everyone sit in chairs, for example, it is helpful if the students have experienced that. Some typically expected group skills include: sitting with the group, facing the leader, starting and stopping with the music, naming instruments, raising hands, and waiting turns.
2. Teach the children's songs that are popular for the geographical area as well as basic folk songs (e.g., "Row, Row, Row Your Boat," and "Mary Had a Little Lamb").
3. Review the music curriculum series used locally and try to use songs from that series. Special education students typically do much better with activities and songs that are familiar to them. Thus, "Little Red Caboose" and "Down at the Station" are two songs taught in ECSE so that when the students are in kindergarten and sing those songs with their class, they may be seen as successful and capable (Cassity, 1981). Many of the routines and basic formats utilized in the music education classes have been part of the therapy sessions. The ECSE students know how to hold instruments properly, how to pass instruments, take turns, look at pictures in order to choose songs, and so on.

4. Encourage flexibility! Often children with special needs require repetition for learning to occur but may become locked into a routine which becomes difficult to change. If a teacher decides to sing "*3* Little Monkeys Jumping on the Bed" instead of the more typical "*5* Little Monkeys . . . ," the student needs to be able to adjust to the change. If bells are always used to accompany a certain song, it may be beneficial to try it with some different instruments. Taking turns with different people being first each time and using different orders besides going around the circle right to left helps keep students flexible. Try drawing names or giving verbal prompts, such as "people who are wearing stripes," or "everyone who walked to school today" for designating leaders or for turn taking. This can help the students be ready for the demands future teachers will make upon them.

5. Maintain perspective. In working with and consulting for regular education teachers, always keep in mind that 20 to 30 other children are part of the classroom, needing and deserving the time and attention of the teachers. It is easy to develop too complex a plan that works effectively for meeting the needs of the special education child, forgetting that 25 other children have needs to be met simultaneously.

Summary

Longfellow Early Education Center has developed a music therapy program that allows children to begin receiving services as toddlers. The students then have the opportunity to generalize and transfer these skills throughout their early school career as part of inclusion classes until second grade. Within the building, all the teachers have collaborated to structure smooth transitions using reverse mainstreaming, mainstreaming, and special groupings to maximize each child's readiness for successful inclusion. The success that inclusive programming provides, with familiar environment having consistent teachers over time, is regularly observed firsthand. Through interdisciplinary teaming and individualized programming, the support services and classroom teachers from both special and regular education work together, and with families, to ensure successful educational experiences for all children.

References

Bradshaw, R. (1996). *Use of the IFSP beyond the age of three.* Focus/Discussion Meeting, Minnesota Department of Children, Families and Learning.

Bredenkamp, S. (Ed.). (1987). *Developmentally appropriate practices in early childhood programs serving children from birth through age eight.* Washington: National Association for the Education of Young Children.

Brown, M. W. (1989). *The big red barn.* New York: Harper & Row.

Cassity, M. D. (1981). The influence of a socially valued skill on peer acceptance in a music therapy group. *Journal of Music Therapy, 18,* 148–154.

Dettmer, P., Thurston, L. P., & Dyck, N. (1993). *Consultation, collaboration, and teamwork for students with special needs.* Needham Heights, MA: Allyn and Bacon.

Fallin, J. F. (1995, March). Children's literature as a springboard for music. *Music Educators Journal*, 24–28.

Falvey, M. A., Forest, M., Pearpoint, J., & Rosenberg, R. L. (1994). Building connections. In J. S. Thousand, R. A. Villa, & A. I. Nevin (Eds.), *Creativity and collaborative learning: A practical guide to empowering students and teachers* (pp. 347–368). Baltimore, MD: Paul H. Brookes Publishing Co.

Fowke, E. (1969). *Sally go round the sun.* Toronto: McClelland and Stewart.

Fullan, M., & Hargreaves, A. (1991). *What's worth fighting for? Working together for your school.* Andover, MA: The Regional Laboratory for Educational Improvement.

Furman, A. G. (1993). *Using music therapy to increase socialization and classroom skills with Native American children in a multicultural setting.* Title V Grant Report, Minneapolis Public Schools.

Furman, A. G., Adamek, M. S., & Furman, C. E. (1993). *Music therapy with Native American children to increase communication, socialization, and classroom skills.* Paper presented at the Joint North American Music Therapy Conference, Toronto, November 1993.

Furman, A. G., & Furman, C. E. (1993) Music for children with special needs. In M. Palmer & W. Sims (Eds.), *Music in prekindergarten: Planning and teaching.* Reston, VA: Music Educators National Conference.

Humpal, M. (1991). The effects of an integrated early childhood music program on social interaction among children with handicaps and their typical peers. *Journal of Music Therapy, 28,* 161–175.

Hutchins, P. (1968). *Rosie's walk.* New York: Macmillan Publishing Co.

Jellison, J. A., Brooks, B., & Huck, A. M. (1984). Structuring small groups and music reinforcement to facilitate positive interactions and acceptance of severely handicapped students in the regular music classroom. *Journal of Research in Music Education, 32,* 243–264.

McCoy, C. W. (1994, Spring). Music and children's literature natural partners. *General Music Today,* 15–19.

McWilliam, R. (1995). Integration of therapy and consultative special education: A continuum in early intervention. *Infants and Young Children, 7*(4): 29–38.

Minneapolis Public Schools. (1995). *Teacher Contracts, Agreements, & Policies* July 1, 1995–June 30, 1997, p. 157.

Music Educators National Conference (1992). Position statement on early childhood education. *Soundpost,* 21–22.

Udvari-Solner, A. (1994). A decision-making model for curricular adaptations in cooperative groups. In J. S. Thousand, R. A. Villa, & A. I. Nevin (Eds.), *Creativity and collaborative learning: A practical guide to empowering students and teachers* (pp. 59–78). Baltimore, MD: Paul H. Brookes Publishing Co.

Music Therapy for Learners in an Early Childhood Community Interagency Setting

Marcia Earl Humpal
Jacquelyn A. Dimmick

The Cuyahoga County Board of Mental Retardation and Developmental Disabilities (CCBMR/DD), located in Cleveland, Ohio, serves children and adults with mental retardation or developmental disabilities. CCBMR/DD's William Patrick Day Early Childhood Center and its three satellite centers provide comprehensive, collaborative, prenatal, and early childhood services to families and their children. The Early Childhood Center emphasizes coordinated services through a true partnership of agencies dedicated to meeting the needs of the entire family unit. Music therapy is one of the services that is part of this team effort.

Background

History

In each of Ohio's counties, boards were established to serve individuals with special needs. These boards operated schools and adult training centers for individuals with varying levels or ranges of developmental disabilities and multihandicapping conditions. Local school districts initially referred individuals to these boards if they or the individual's family felt that the student could be best served in a separate educational setting. As time passed, county boards began taking on a more collaborative role in Ohio's educational system. Now their personnel often are being used as teachers or consultants within the local school or community setting.

County boards were impacted by the passage of Public Law 99–457 (Education for All Handicapped Children Act Amendments, 1986). In addition to expanding school programs to young children, the law recognized that some infants and toddlers will need early intervention services because they either have or are at risk for delays that may impact future learning. A major emphasis is placed on serving the needs of the entire family unit. Furthermore, collaboration between agencies, schools, and professionals is highly encouraged to best serve the needs of both the children and their families in a least restrictive environment (Hanline & Hanson, 1989; Ludlow, 1987). PL 102–119, the Individuals with Disabilities Education Act (IDEA, 1992), further specifies services and collaboration and clarifies prior laws.

In 1992, CCBMR/DD, reflecting and supporting the mandates of these laws, opened the William Patrick Day Early Childhood Center. The Center offers a model program with a holistic approach to providing health, nutrition, parenting, and education services to more than 450 young children and their families. Several agencies have programs at the facility including CCBMR/DD (Early Childhood Division), Cleveland Public Schools, Cuyahoga Community College, the Council for Economic Opportunities in Greater Cleveland (Head Start), Family Information Network, Interlink, Maternity and Infant Health Care, WIC (nutrition information for women, infants, and children), Cuyahoga County Early Intervention Local Collaborative Group, Achievement Center for Children (Lekotec program for teaching through play), and United Cerebral Palsy (Adaptive Computer Technology Program). These agencies provide a range of services that promote inclusion and are accessible, culturally sensitive, and affordable to families (Robertson, 1992).

At its inception, William Patrick Day Early Childhood Center was awarded a 5-year federal grant to study how Developmentally Appropriate Practices could be applied to the young child with special needs. Labeled the Transactional Inclusive Program (TRIP), the grant embodies an alternative process that emphasizes a play-based, child-initiated approach (Mahoney & Powell, 1984). TRIP is a guiding force behind the Developmentally Appropriate Practices model central to the center's philosophy. Since William Patrick Day Early Childhood Center exemplifies a dynamic collaborative effort, information gathered via this federal grant may have an impact on the development of and future programming for other early childhood centers.

It is widely accepted that learning is a lifelong commitment for early childhood educators (Vander Ven, 1994) and that these professionals must continue to be good planners, thinkers, collaborators, and be nurturing to the children in their classrooms. Before children arrive at an educational setting, preparation should include thorough plans for human interactions among the children, adults, and between children and adults. Putting this in perspective, early childhood educators need a personal sense of self-understanding in relation to their work. For this reason, professional growth and planning days are vital parts of the Center's schedule. These opportunities help staff stay abreast of current trends and explore best practices for young children.

Role of Music Therapy

For many years, CCBMR/DD has encouraged the integration of children with and without developmental delays into typical early childhood activities. In 1979, its early childhood music mainstream program was developed. A pilot program combined early childhood classes from a separate school for students with disabilities and a class from another preschool for typically developing children. This model has grown into a permanent part of the music curriculum (Dimmick & Humpal, 1989, 1990; Humpal, 1990, 1991; Humpal & Dimmick, 1993) and is at the core of the Center's integrative philosophy.

CCBMR/DD currently employs three full-time music therapists to serve its early childhood population. In addition to their music therapy credentials, all three hold teaching certificates from the State of Ohio. Since William Patrick Day Early Childhood Center is an approved clinical training site of the American Music Therapy Association, up to two music therapy interns per year may also be involved in service delivery. Music therapy is considered a part of the interdisciplinary team approach. The music staff meet regularly with others (such as the classroom teacher, speech-language pathologist, occupational therapist, physical therapist, and adapted physical education instructor) to determine goals and procedures that best meet the individual needs of the children and their families.

Music classes are provided once each week for all students. Service is delivered in inclusion, integrated, reverse mainstream, small group, or individual settings as determined by the individual needs of the child. Service may be conducted jointly with other related services or integrated into playtime. Additionally, music therapists direct sessions for families, provide consultation for classroom teachers, conduct in-services and public relations seminars, and supervise music therapy students.

Preparation

How Children Learn

While working with young children may look easy, those who understand children know that they learn in their own specific ways. Children often seem to distort statements made by an adult or erroneously interpret what they see. They think very concretely and in the here-and-now and often make comparisons that are not true. For example, a child may see a red-headed girl sitting in a wheelchair and conclude that she will someday need to be in a wheelchair because she also has red hair. Since children do not always verbalize what they are thinking or do not know how to express their fears, they should be asked questions to find out exactly what connections they are making. In so doing, the adult may alleviate many of the child's unnecessary fears.

Awareness Training

When CCBMR/DD's original music mainstreaming projects were initiated, two main purposes were identified: to provide positive peer role models for young students with disabilities and to provide for the acceptance and understanding of differences among individuals (Dimmick & Humpal, 1989). With the opening of the Center, music therapy became one of several opportunities for integration. Children now play and learn together in inclusionary, integrated, or reverse mainstreamed classes or at least come together for music, physical education, lunch, and play times. Yet, the need to initially facilitate the ideas of acceptance and understanding is still evident. Therefore, the music therapy department delivers a multifaceted program to prepare students, staff, and parents for inclusionary activities.

There are two basic guidelines that direct this preparation process. First, the awareness training must be carefully planned and geared directly towards the *child's* level of understanding. Additionally, teachers, parents, and other community agency personnel who will be directly or indirectly involved with the Center should participate in the process.

Before children view the music therapy presentation, teacher preparation packets are distributed to all staff. The packets contain inservice training information, program specifics, and activities to use with children prior to and following the disability awareness program itself. Staff are expected to participate in the complete process, actively assisting the music therapists whenever needed, to help decrease any anxiety the children may have. In addition, parents are notified of the program and are given an overview of the entire process. They are welcome (and encouraged!) to attend the presentation *with* their children. It is very important to keep parents informed; when the child asks questions at home, the parent should feel comfortable and able to give correct information.

The main event of the presentation is a puppet show which stresses similarities and differences among individuals. Songs and signing reinforce these concepts. Also included are opportunities for children to try out the actual equipment that the children with disabilities may use to enhance their abilities to function in society. Actual child-size examples of wheelchairs, crutches, walkers, communication devices, adapted toys, or medical apparatus may be demonstrated. The equipment selected to be presented reflects situations the children will most likely encounter in their particular class setting.

Children at this young age generally have short attention spans. Therefore, particular attention is paid to the length of time spent on the entire presentation as well as the length and type of each activity. The total session does not exceed 1 hour, although teachers and parents are encouraged to maintain an ongoing, open dialogue.

Framework

Team Approach

The Early Childhood Center represents a collaborative venture where teamwork is of utmost importance. Whether at home or in the school setting, the child is served by a team that is comprised of several people: the classroom teacher or early childhood specialist, teacher assistant, speech/language pathologist, occupational therapist, physical therapist, adapted physical education instructor, and the music therapist. Other ancillary staff such as the outreach worker, psychologist, or nurse may be included. The parents are essential to the team; their wants and needs are always solicited and addressed.

Good music education/therapy practices take into account the ways in which children acquire musical information, organize and process it, and use it in musical experiences (McDonald & Simons, 1989). This process does not occur independently of other areas of intellectual growth and development. Skill development in children has many correlations to learning. It provides opportunities to enhance listening skills, academic challenges, social experiences, motor planning, and also creativity. Music is *not* a separate entity unto itself. Therefore, assessment information is shared with and by the team; goals are developed to address the "total child." All team members try to work together while implementing service delivery. Music therapy really shines in this treatment approach because it may facilitate all of the other therapies.

Assessment

Since no standard music therapy assessment was available for use in the early childhood setting for children with special needs, such a tool was developed (see Appendix). The authors recognized the normalizing effect of music experiences for the young child and examined musical characteristics of, and program goals for, typically developing young children (Andress, 1989; Andress & Walker, 1992; Bayless & Ramsey, 1991; Boswell, 1984; McDonald & Simons, 1989; Overby, 1991; Palmer & Sims, 1993). From this background, a hierarchy of competencies within each musical area as well as nonmusical skills and stages of play was developed. This multiyear assessment and evaluation checklist examines how the child explores his or her environment through such musical means as singing, sound play, moving, and listening. Creativity is noted throughout each area as well as how participation and engagement levels reflect the child's stage of social play. Space is also provided for anecdotal information considering the child's social, medical, sensory, communication, and motoric abilities and/or needs. Additional room is given for team notes regarding such areas as progress made or adaptations needed, and recording of the IFSP (Individual Family Service Plan) outcome or IEP (Individual Education Plan) objective and its attainment status (Dimmick & Humpal, 1994). Input is gathered by direct observation, by interactive play, and from the entire interdisciplinary team (including the family). Assessment is ongoing and is often paired with a general play-based assessment to determine global goals that address the needs of the whole child through developmentally appropriate practices.

The underlying philosophy of the Center promotes inclusion and builds on the strengths of all children and their families ("William Patrick Day Early Childhood Center," 1992). Therefore, every effort is made to serve children in integrated settings. The music therapy assessment and team discussions help determine what adaptations might be necessary to structure success for the child with special needs. Assessment also may indicate that a child could benefit from individual music therapy service or that he or she might require additional adult assistance in order to adequately function in an inclusive music class. Flexibility of scheduling and cooperation among staff is essential in order for inclusive programming to run smoothly and effectively.

Individual Family Service Plan

The first documentation that the early childhood team uses is the Individual Family Service Plan (IFSP) (see Figures 1–6). This document is used for children from birth to 3 years of age who have or are at risk for developmental delay(s). A collaborative effort among early childhood caregivers and experts developed guidelines to meet the federal mandate of Public Law 99–457 long before the law became a reality (McGonigel & Johnson, 1991). The IFSP clearly emphasizes the family and the partnership between the family and the professionals.

The basic procedure for the IFSP involves a play-based assessment process (with the family and the team). Before the parents/guardians bring their child in for an individual assessment, the interdisciplinary team meets to discuss the role each team member will play during the assessment. Theoretically, at least three individuals are needed during the assessment. One team member is the facilitator and interacts with the child; another team member interacts with the parent and explains the procedure as it is happening. The third person is the observer/recorder. If additional team members are present, they are assigned duties specifically related to the situation (e.g., something as simple as taking care of a sibling in another room to avoid distractions/interruptions). *No one* is supposed to interact with the child except the designated team facilitator. If the child approaches someone else, that person will look down and ignore the child.

The role each team member plays depends upon his or her specific areas of strength and expertise and the needs of the child. It should be noted that any member of the team can be the facilitator. The music therapist, who is well trained in observation and recording techniques, is often called upon to be the observer/recorder. However, the music therapist may also be the facilitator as long as he or she has gone through the training and the situation warrants that responsibility.

Before the assessment begins, each discipline representative tells the recorder specific things that need to be observed and recorded. For example, the speech pathologist may want a frequency count on all two-word phrases spoken by the child in 20 minutes. The teacher may want to know how long the child plays in each area of the room. Does the child go from one area to the next, never stopping to really play with a toy, or does the child sit down, select a toy and explore/play for *x* number of minutes? At the same time, the physical therapist may want to know how the child ambulates around the room.

The play-based assessment format requires the facilitator to be the *guide* who follows the child's play and interacts by imitation and limited speech. The room has been prearranged with toys/objects that might interest the child. When the child goes to a particular toy or part of the room, the facilitator begins the assessment in that area with the toy selected by the child. The child initiates the activity and the adult follows his or her actions. If repetitive actions on a toy are continued, the facilitator may choose to play with the toy differently to discern the action/reaction of the child. The length of time spent with the child depends on his or her attention span and the allotted time frame available.

After the facilitator is finished playing with the child, the team and the parents discuss their observations about the child; the parents are asked to share their major concerns both for themselves and their child (see Figure 3) and formulate a statement of needs (see Figure 4). The IFSP has a separate page for each concern (see Figure 5). At the top of the page, the designated team member writes down the exact words of the parent. For example, "Mom wants Tyler to talk good." The formal writing and strategies are then included on the same page after being discussed and agreed upon by the parent and the team.

The formation of outcomes are based on observation, assessment, and parental concerns. Implementation of strategies/procedures for attainment of the outcomes consider the child's choices during play and strive to encourage play across a variety of environments. Although separate music outcomes are rarely written, music therapy is listed on the IFSP Service Page (see Figure 2). The music therapist follows the IFSP in planning and implementing treatment procedures. Ongoing anecdotal data/notes are taken after each session regarding the child's progress towards intended outcomes. These notes also provide a quick assessment on the effectiveness of the chosen treatment plan.

Each IFSP contains a 90-day review (see Figure 6). At that time all data and notes are shared with the team and parents and a determination is reached as to whether or not an outcome has or has not been achieved by the child. Outcomes may be continued if they have not been achieved. Outcomes that have been achieved may be continued with an increase in the criteria level, or an altogether new outcome may be added to the IFSP.

The above procedure gives the parent tremendous input and the IFSP is written in the spirit for which it was intended. Practically speaking, there are not always enough hours in the day or enough manpower to carry out the procedure in this manner for every toddler entering the program. Shortcuts are sometimes necessary. For example, IFSP play-based assessments take place on Fridays. The music therapist may be a member of at least seven interdisciplinary teams, many of which are for toddlers. The various IFSP meetings, as well as the music master schedule, often overlap, so the music therapist cannot possibly attend all of the assessments. Another staff member may need to do "double duty," or the time spent on the assessment may have to be shortened. Nevertheless, two parts of the process remain consistent: the parents are always involved in writing the outcomes for their child and the team provides the strategies for achievement.

Cuyahoga County Early Intervention Local Collaborative Group
INDIVIDUALIZED FAMILY SERVICE PLAN

Draft 6/91   Date: 9/30/94

Child's Full Name	Date of Birth
Tyler Canoe	11/3/91

PARENT(S)/GUARDIAN INFORMATION:	
Name(s) K. Pinson	Service Coordinator Teacher
Address 3020 S. Green Rd. Cleveland, OH 44124	Referral Source N. Powder
Phone 932-0074	Referral Date 5/24/92

Service Provider	Contact Person / Title	Phone
Cuyahoga C. Bd. of MR/DD	(name), teacher	736-2920

IFSP TEAM/SIGNATURES:

The undersigned agree to exchange information pertinent to the development of an Individualized Family Service Plan for the child and family listed above. Each person understands and agrees to carry out the plan as it applies to his/her role in the provision of services. All matters relating to this child and family are considered privileged and confidential and are treated as such by the undersigned personnel/agencies. The information is available only among the below listed personnel/agencies. This information cannot be re-released to other agencies without the signed consent of the family. This consent may be amended at any time at the request of the family.

x _____

Parent/Guardian   Date   Parent/Guardian   Date

x _____

Service Coordinator

_____ (signature), music therapist   x _____

x _____   x _____

The IFSP was developed with telephone consultation from the following people:

_____   _____

_____   _____

Figure 1. Cuyahoga County Early Intervention Local Collaborative Group,
Individualized Family Service Plan

Page_____

Child's Name _Tyler Canoe_____

Date: _9/94_____

Medicaid #_____

EARLY INTERVENTION SERVICES

CCBMR/DD SERVICES: 9/12/94 - 6/13/95

Transportation	needs vest	☑ YES	☐ NO
Center-Based	4 mornings per week, 2½ hrs.	☑ YES	☐ NO
Home-Based	5 - 7 home visits during year	☐ YES	☑ NO

Date	Related Services: (Signatures, Frequency and Duration)
9/12/94	Speech -- 1 - 4x per month, ½ hr. block times
	Occupational therapist -- 2 - 10x during yr.: 10 - 60 min. block times
	Music therapist -- 1 - 4x per month, ½ hr. block time
	Adapted physical education -- 2 - 4x per month, ½ hr. block time

Appliances/Mechanical Supports/Adaptive Devices/Medical Procedures (Please describe below)

Type of Device/Procedure	Reason	Situation/Schedule Who is Responsible

Figure 2. Individualized Family Service Plan, Early Intervention Services Page

Page ――――

Child's Name: Tyler Canoe

Date: 9/30/94

FAMILY INFORMATION:

Family Member/People who help out: mother's parents

Family Concerns, Priorities, Resources: Attends program for parents at another facility
and at Tyler's school. Wants Tyler to talk more, stop drooling,
and be potty trained.

WHAT MY CHILD CAN DO NOW:

Vision: I feel his eyes are okay.

Hearing: Good

Health: Herpes encephalitis, (treated). Rarely sick.

Posture & Movement: Runs, Walks, climbs stairs using rail (note: same step
placement). Jumps off steps.

Self-Help:

Social/Emotional: Doesn't cry when mom leaves room. Comforts peers. Likes
trucks, tape recorder (puts right up to ear).

Figure 3. Individualized Family Service Plan, Family Information Page

Child's Name ____ Tyler Canoe _____

What My Child Can Do Now:

Communication:

> Babbles, points to items he wants; may scream to get attention
> of adult. Uses single words randomly in imitation.
>
>
> Needs to talk more.

Problem-Solving/Cognitive

Other:

Figure 4. Individualized Family Service Plan, Parent Statement of Needs Page

Page _____

Child's Name: ___Tyler Canoe_____

Date: ____9/30/94_____

OUTCOME NUMBER __1 A__:

   Mom wants Tyler to talk good.

BEGIN DATE	GOAL LTR	SERVICE/ACTION/INTERMEDIATE GOALS
10/4/94	1A	Tyler will use words at school at least 5x per day over the next 3 months.
		(name) (name) SLP will meet with teacher to develop program, consult with staff, co-teach child, monitor and review data; revise strategies during ½ hour block times -- 1 - 4 x per month.
		Tyler will use words throughout day during free play, gym, and music. Start with imitation, indirect cues. Stay with same words in beginning (Ex.: hi in hello song, bye in good-bye song)

Figure 5. Individualized Family Service Plan, Parent Concerns Page

Page_____

Child's Name __Tyler Canoe__

OUTCOME # & GOAL LETTER	CODE	90 DAY REVIEW DATE: 3/24/95
#1 A	3	Achieved! Much improvement in T. use of words in school.
		Used intense level of active sensory/motor play to bring
		Tyler out of shell. The more he was involved in music/
		movement and sensory activities, he began laughing and
		imitating adult comments. Now his speech is self-generated.
		Still needs work on responding to questions.

Signatures

_____ Teacher   Occupational therapist

_____ Speech-language pathologist   Music therapist

_____ Mother

Reviewed by Phone or Conversation

_____   _____

_____   _____

EVALUATION CODES: (Adapted from Dunst)
0 = no longer a perceived need, goal
1 = unchanged: still need, goal

2 = unresolved or partially attained: but improved
3 = resolved or attained to family satisfaction

Figure 6. Individualized Family Service Plan, 90–Day Review Page

As the toddler reaches preschool age, a transitional, interim IEP is written by the early childhood team and is forwarded to the new preschool setting. This temporary IEP gives the new school/preschool teacher vital information in determining future objectives for the permanent, yearly IEP.

Individual Education Plan

Objectives for children over age 3 are incorporated into the child's Individual Education Plan (IEP) (see Figure 7). The intent of the IEP is similar to that of the IFSP; however, it differs greatly from the IFSP in style, format, and dissemination of information.

Prior to determining an individual plan, the entire team assesses the child through direct observation, family survey or interview, and criterion-referenced assessment tools. The parents and school representatives then come together for a conference. Three issues are discussed at these meetings: (a) educational placement, (b) nature and degree of special education and related services, and (c) specific instructional objectives that will be addressed. Adhering to the Center's philosophy, the team develops goals which will stimulate the child to:

- Become actively engaged in the exploration and understanding of his/her environment.
- Communicate with adults and peers to request, question, and comment via various communicative models.
- Become as independent as possible in self-help areas.
- Interact with peers and adults in a variety of settings.
- Develop self-confidence and an eagerness to learn.
- Represent ideas and feelings through pretend play, dance and movement, music, art, and construction.
- Construct his/her own understanding of relationships among objects, people, and events.
- Increase competence in management of his/her body and acquire basic physical skills.

(CCBMR/DD, 1995)

The child's strengths, interest, and needs are assessed in various settings prior to determining goals. The team discusses possible target areas and strategies. A program is developed for the child which emphasizes the positive aspects of his or her repertoire. Specific goals are agreed upon by the family and the team in *cognitive/play, self-help, communication, social/emotional, and gross/fine motor* curricula areas.

The IEP lists date of initiation, anticipated duration and frequency, as well as types of related service. Children who attend CCBMR/DD classes have music therapy listed as a related service on their IEP (see Figure 7 [approval of a new state-mandated form pending at time of publication]). The child may have a separate music therapy goal (direct instruction format) or a goal that is being jointly implemented by several members of the team (collaborative consultation format). For instance, a child may have a specific classroom play objective that can be carried over to the music therapy setting. This objective could be written by the music therapist in direct instruction format (see Figure 8).

The same objective could be co-signed with the classroom teacher using the collaborative consultation format (see Figure 9). Using this format, the teacher would address the child's performance level in the classroom setting, briefly mentioning the child's behavior during music play.

Cuyahoga County Board of Mental Retardation and Developmental Disabilities
Individualized Education Program (IEP)

Student _____ Social Security # _____ DOB _____ School District _____

I. Conference Summary Data

Date of Conference _____
☐ Current IEP Reviewed   ☐ Areas of Student Need Determined   ☐ Goals/Objectives in Areas of Need
☐ Identification of Services & Supports Needed to Implement Plan   ☐ Determination of LRE   Next Conference Review Date _____

II. Services

The following checked (✓) services are to be provided in this plan. The amount of each service is indicated on the following pages.

☐ Special Education   ☐ Occupational Therapy   ☐ Physical Therapy   ☐ Speech & Language   ☐ Music Therapy   ☐ Nursing   ☐ Psychology
☐ Adapted Physical Education
☐ Other _____
☐ Transportation Needs _____

III. Participants

The undersigned have participated in the development of this plan.

Parent _____   Teacher / ITP _____

School District Representative _____

_____

_____

IV. Educational Program & Setting

The goals/objectives and services/supports identified in this plan will be implemented in an educational program for students with disabilities operated by the Cuyahoga County Board of MR/DD at _____. The extent of participation in regular education or contact with typically developing peers is _____.

Reasons for placement in a CCBMR/DD separate facility (if applicable): Having considered and reviewed the continuum of service delivery options, the IEP team has determined that placement in a separate facility is appropriate because (to be completed by school district representative): _____

V. Consent and Waiver of Notice

☐ I agree with the program content and educational placement specified in this plan
☐ I do not agree with some or all of the contents of this plan and withhold my consent until differences are resolved
☐ I waive my right to notification by certified mail

☐ Parent waived the right to participate in conference (documentation attached)

_____
Parent Signature & Date

Notes/Comments: _____

Figure 7. Cuyahoga County Board of Mental Retardation and
Developmental Disabilities, Individual Education Plan

IEP Instructional Objectives

Student _____
(child's name)

Page _____ of _____

Instructional Domains

- [ ] Functional Daily Living Skills
- [ ] Cognitive/Play
- [ ] Adaptive Behavior
- [x] Social/Emotional
- [ ] Vocational
- [ ] Communication
- [ ] Fine/Gross Motor
- [ ] Leisure/Recreation
- [ ] Self-Help

Related Services Areas

- [ ] Adapted Physical Education
- [ ] Speech & Language
- [x] Music
- [ ] Employment Training
- [ ] Occupational Therapy
- [ ] Psychology
- [ ] Other
- [ ] Physical Therapy

Date of Initiation: 9/5/95   Anticipated Duration: 1 school year   Frequency of Service: 30 minutes   2 - 4 x per month

Format

- [x] Direct Instruction
- [ ] Collaborative Consultation
- [ ] Monitoring

Present Level of Performance Statements

Child plays with a variety of rhythm instruments using two hands to hit together at midline. She can stabilize an instrument with one hand and strike it with a mallet held in her other hand. Child will play next to other children in a group but does not engage in spontaneous cooperative play or take part in a group song.

Annual Goal Statements

Child will increase her level of cooperative play in a music setting.

Student Learning Objectives

1) During group musical play, child will play instruments with a friend 3x per session for five sessions.

2) _____

Instructional Agent(s)/Title: _____ (signature), music therapist

Figure 8. Cuyahoga County Board of Mental Retardation and Developmental Disabilities, IEP Instructional Objectives (Direct Instruction Format)

IEP Instructional Objectives

Student _____
(child's name)

Page _____ of _____

Instructional Domains

- [ ] Functional Daily Living Skills
- [ ] Cognitive/Play
- [ ] Adaptive Behavior
- [X] Social/Emotional
- [ ] Vocational
- [ ] Communication
- [ ] Fine/Gross Motor
- [ ] Leisure/Recreation
- [ ] Self-Help

- [ ] Adapted Physical Education
- [ ] Speech & Language

Related Services Areas

- [X] Music
- [ ] Employment Training
- [ ] Occupational Therapy
- [ ] Psychology
- [ ] Other
- [ ] Physical Therapy

Date of Initiation: 9/5/95

Anticipated Duration: 1 school year

Frequency of Service: 30 min. per school day

Format

- [ ] Direct Instruction
- [X] Collaborative Consultation
- [ ] Monitoring

Present Level of Performance Statements

Child plays with a variety of toys and manipulatives.
She does not share toys but can be drawn into an activity
if she is offered an object that interests her (such as a
mallet to play upon a drum being held by an adult). Child will play
next to other children in a group but does not engage in spontaneous group games.

Annual Goal Statements

Child will increase her level of cooperative play.

Student Learning Objectives

1.) During play/music time, child will play with a friend 3x per day for five days

2.) _____

Instructional
Agent(s)/Title: _____ (signature), teacher; _____ (signature), music therapist

Figure 9. Cuyahoga County Board of Mental Retardation and
Developmental Disabilities, IEP Instruction Objectives
(Collaborative Consultation Format)

The language of the IEP in the early childhood setting is intended to be "reader friendly." The framework of the child's program assumes that:

- Intervention considers the whole child.
- Intervention is family-focused.
- Intervention supports the family's integration into the community.
- Intervention services are coordinated between agencies.
- Curriculum is guided by the belief that all children learn best by becoming actively involved in their play, environments and in interactions with other children and adults.

(CCBMR/DD, 1995)

Because of time constraints, it is usually impossible for the music therapist to attend IEP conferences. However, since the music therapist is part of the team that develops the IEP, he or she must sign the IEP and indicate how often the child will receive music therapy. When implementing the IEP, the music therapists take anecdotal notes after each session. Progress notes addressing each objective are sent home twice per school year. The IEP is valid for one school year but may be amended at any time.

Philosophical Considerations and Methodologies

The music therapist who works in an early childhood setting is presented with both an interesting yet challenging mission. One must keep abreast of current "best practice" philosophical approaches towards working with young children. For example, a recent trend in early childhood education is towards encouragement rather than praise (Hitz & Driscoll, 1988) when attempting to facilitate play or meet an objective. The child's efforts are therefore being affirmed rather than judged. What the child *can* do is encouraged and built upon in an educative rather than an eliminative strategy although these tactics seem foreign to those professionals who have been firmly entrenched in behavioral programming. Music therapists may actually have an edge in this type of methodology because of their musical training in improvisation and their therapeutic expertise regarding adaptation.

Educating children is a dynamic process. Best practices undergo constant scrutiny. Music therapy students need to become familiar with child development and current practices in the field. Behavioral and psychoanalytical approaches to music therapy appear to be the predominate strategies taught in college programs; perhaps more exposure to specific early childhood philosophical beliefs and methodology would be beneficial.

When working in a collaborative inclusion setting, music therapists may be called upon to coordinate the educational approaches of the different agencies. It is extremely important, therefore, to understand the similarities and differences of philosophy and methodology espoused by experts in early childhood education and how these affect the music therapy process. Remember, too, that although terminology may be different, intent may be similar. At the Center, the following theories predominate.

Developmentally Appropriate Practices

The National Association for the Education of Young Children (NAEYC) is a leader among organizations that follow, research, develop, and disseminate information on and for young children. Presently *Developmentally Appropriate Practice in Early Childhood Programs Serving Children from Birth Through Age 8* (Bredenkamp, 1987) represents the basis for teaching strategies with young children. These Developmentally Appropriate Practices (D.A.P.) guidelines inform educators, parents, administrators, policy makers, and others who are involved in the child's program that current research indicates that young children learn best in a concrete, play-based atmosphere. NAEYC (as cited in Brendenkamp, 1987), in its 1986 Policy Statement, includes these suggestions:

- Provide for all areas of a child's development through an integrated approach.
- Base planning on observations and recordings of each *child's* special interests and developmental progress.
- Plan the environment to facilitate learning through *interactive play* with adults, peers, and a variety of materials.
- Provide for a wide range of interests and abilities.

Music therapists may find the following strategies helpful when attempting to work within the D.A.P. guidelines:

- Use a multi-sensory approach (visual, auditory, tactile, vestibular, proprioceptive)
- Use a variety of modalities (e.g., props, puppets, pictures)
- Use repetition (repeat the song/activity, but also do it "another way")
- Use adapted or augmentative equipment if needed (e.g., switches, modifications to instruments)
- Use gestures or signs
- Help the child EXPERIENCE the music (via active involvement—moving, singing, playing, exploring).

Furthermore, the music therapy program must match the developmental level of the child. Within the framework of a play-based approach, the teaching strategies will change as the child grows and matures. There are many components in this process, and each plays an important role in the child's growth and development.

Music typically is an important part of every young child's day (Bayless & Ramsey, 1991; Music Educators National Conference, 1992). When implementing D.A.P. procedures, music becomes an essential part of the daily classroom environment. Therefore, the music therapist must understand the basic premise and philosophy of D.A.P. and develop new strategies using the music guidelines listed above to prepare service delivery models, assessments, and evaluations that fall within the play-based child-directed program. Although teachers are required by law to take data on the progress of the child, behavior management as a discipline does not really belong in D.A.P. programming. Music therapy practices in the early childhood setting may fit very nicely within D.A.P., if the therapist can "let go" of traditional styles and strategies often associated with service delivery.

Play-Based Approach

The *Transdisciplinary Play-Based Approach* (TPBA) by Toni Linder (1990) presents a succinct and understandable overview of this method. "Play" can be defined as an active engagement that is voluntary, spontaneous, and fun. The TPBA guidelines note six types of play, listed below. An application for music therapists is expressed within the parentheses.

1. *Exploratory*—discovering one's environment; includes repetitive motor movements (making noises with mouth or instruments; mouthing instruments; random exploration of instruments, using some or all of the senses).
2. *Relational*—using objects in play for the purpose for which they were intended (playing an instrument according to function; using music equipment such as a tape recorder correctly).
3. *Constructive*—manipulating objects for the purpose of constructing or creating something. The child has an end goal in mind and is thinking at a concrete level, but with a sense of order (sings song that tells a story with a beginning and an end; when playing a trap set knows to sequence sounds and put cymbal crash at a specific point).
4. *Dramatic play*—child pretends to do something or be someone (movement activities involving creative depiction of animal/object/person; using props such as a rhythm stick to depict a flute for representational play).
5. *Games with rules*—play involves child in activity with accepted rules or limits (songs with rules/expectations such as "Ring Around the Rosie").
6. *Rough and tumble play*—boisterous and physical, often group related (parachute play to music, creative movement, dancing). *Remember that an adult needs to monitor this type of play for safety reasons.

It is important to recognize that play skills do not just happen. There are definitive facilitation and procedural skills used in the play-based curriculum that lead to successful learning. This is a critical component of the play-based approach, yet it is one that is often overlooked. Be aware that free play within this framework may look the same as free play without facilitation, yet there is a crucial difference in the outcome.

Facilitating Play with Music

Linder (1990) suggests that the following six facilitation skills are necessary for play-based instruction (music examples have been added):

1. Follow the child's level and the child's choices. (Put out instruments and allow total freedom in playing. Imitate the actions of the child.)
2. Parallel play with the child; occasionally comment about the play action. (Play an instrument next to the child then intermittently sing or comment about what is taking place. This demonstrates how to play and gives the child the opportunity to play as he or she pleases. Indirectly the therapist is helping the child learn to label actions and objects. This is *adult* facilitated parallel play and far different from peer parallel play.)
3. Encourage any mode of communication the child may have (eye gaze, gestures, words, etc.) by imitating or responding in a turn-taking manner. (Play instruments and imitate both motor and vocal actions, echoing dynamic, pitch, and tempo levels. Offer the child a turn and encourage response via various modes.)
4. Let the activity govern the interaction and limit talking. (Hum along with the instrumental play or sing a nonsense syllable to attract attention to the play.)

5. Limit questioning and pause long enough to convey that the child's comments are valued. (Insert a comment or a musical phrase such as "You're playing the blue bells." This is simply an affirmation of the child's play.)

6. Once the child is comfortable interacting and playing, try to "bump up" the level of play. Model and expand upon his or her verbal or creative play ideas. (Whatever music skill the child has been performing, model the next step on the task analysis or show the child another way of doing the skill.)

This "bumping up" step is crucial and is often overlooked by those who do not fully understand the techniques used in D.A.P. If the child's level of play is not showing progress, this is a clue that "bumping up" may be needed.

The results of the interactions and progress in music should correlate to those seen by the interdisciplinary team in other environments. When the music therapy approach is play-based and child-directed in nature, there is a purpose, structure, and intent built into the planning and implementation of the session. It is not just play for the sake of play. The *children* are playing but the music therapist has enabled the play by adhering to the above guidelines and responding to the needs of the child.

High/Scope

The Head Start classes in the Center subscribe to the High/Scope curriculum which is guided by the belief that all children learn best by becoming actively involved in their play, environments, and interactions with other children and adults. Overall, the High/Scope philosophy calls for a thoughtfully chosen balance of individual, small, and large group activities that include child-initiated, child-directed as well as adult-facilitated and adult-structured activities that support children's development across all domains.

At the heart of this curriculum is a metacognitive strategy referred to as "Plan-Do-Review." This design supports the development of children's self-management, management of the environment, construction of knowledge, and communication about that knowledge. In the "Plan" stage, children think, rehearse, and make choices. In the "Do" phase, they act on choices, participate, and interact. In "Review," they recall, reflect, and evaluate (Hohmann & Weikart, 1990).

The High/Scope video "The Daily Routine" (Hohmann & Weikart, 1990) lists components of a typical classroom's day. How selected elements are addressed in inclusion, integrated, and reverse mainstreamed preschool music therapy classes has been added in parentheses:

- *Greeting circle*—lets children know session is beginning; offers a sense of security and consistency (each music session begins with a consistent "Hello" song).
- *Planning time*—a group experience that lets children orient to schedule and make choices ("Today in Music" chart shows a picture schedule of activities of the day. Children supplement the schedule by selecting pictures from the "Choices" poster that offers a variety of songs/instruments.).
- *Work time*—children carry out their choices at centers/stations and through play (music centers offer choices for exploratory play).
- *Clean up time*—a transition time that is part of the "doing" stage (songs help children close one activity and transition to the next while being a responsible part of the group).

- *Circle*—provides group and meeting time. May emphasize themes, music, or game. May be part of both the "Do" and the "Review" stage (before ending the music session, children refer back to the "Today in Music" poster and recall what took place).

Service Delivery Models

Service delivery of music therapy in the early childhood division of CCBMR/DD takes many forms. The music therapists see regularly scheduled classes which may be somewhat structured or may be quite improvisational and child-directed. Music therapists also serve as consultants for teachers, other specialists, parents, and the community and assist in the coordination of special events.

Regularly Scheduled Classes

There are many types of classroom models throughout the Center and its satellites. Several nonmusical variables affect how music therapy service is delivered. These include: the specific needs of the children in each class, the number of children in each class, the play levels of the children (and the potential for tolerating a group setting), and the availability of times for integration. Staffing and the spirit of cooperation among available team members present additional considerations. The classroom teacher or teacher assistant always attends each session. Regular music sessions are conducted either in the music room or in the classroom, depending upon the needs of the children and the schedules of the music therapists. The music room is large enough to be set up for either station play or group activity.

Types of Classes

Inclusion model. Two full inclusion kindergarten classes are housed at the Center. Eight young children with special needs and 16 typically developing children are in each class which is jointly taught by teachers from the Cleveland Public Schools and CCBMR/DD. These classes receive music therapy once a week. If time permits, the classes are divided into two sections to allow for necessary attention to adapting and enhancing activities. The sessions often follow theme ideas that are being explored concurrently in the classroom setting. Elements of music education (in the categorical areas of *singing, listening, playing, and moving*) are emphasized. At times, music and adapted physical education classes are combined into a longer time slot, affording greater opportunities for movement exploration.

Many preschool classes follow an inclusion model, with teachers being hired by both CCBMR/DD and Head Start. Ideally, these groups are split into two sections that receive music therapy ½ hour per week. Children are brought together for an opening circle and then experience music through a variety of avenues. The preschool classes are less structured than the kindergarten classes, yet both musical and nonmusical goals are implemented.

Integrated model. Other preschool classes follow an integrated model, with CCBMR/DD children and Head Start students being housed in separate classrooms that are connected by a sliding door. The door is opened for specific activities or play time throughout the day. These classes often come together for music therapy and adapted physical education classes. Many of the students in the CCBMR/DD classes have significant special needs and are perhaps better served primarily in a more restrictive classroom setting, yet music time offers a time for playing with typical children who serve as excellent role models and peer tutors. This type of service delivery model often is used in the satellite sites thereby giving CCBMR/DD classes the opportunity to share experiences with other agencies within the community. Music sessions often stress social goals and interaction.

Reverse mainstream model. CCBMR/DD offers some reverse mainstream classes for both preschool and toddler students. These are CCBMR/DD classes that have eight students with identified needs and up to four children without disabilities. These typical children often are siblings of other children in the building, children from the neighborhood, or those whose parents have expressed interest in this type of experience. The preschool music classes are conducted in a manner similar to those in the integrated or inclusion models. Toddler classes, however, are much more child-directed. For instance, the music therapist prepares the environment to encourage various levels of play. Often the activities present and expand upon a theme (e.g., *snow* or *ducks*), using manipulatives and props that call upon many different senses. Music therapists may also enter the child's play, using music to interact with the child or comment about the activity.

Self-contained model. A few classes (such as those for children with severe delays, autism or pervasive developmental disorder, or medical problems) are fully segregated. Music therapy for these classes may address goals in a more traditional behavioral approach or via a more individualized mode (such as one-on-one therapy with the assistance of the occupational or physical therapist). In some cases, such classes may follow a specialized program unique to the type of disability (e.g., autism). Nevertheless, activities are conducted with an emphasis on play and engagement.

Individual treatment model. Upon referral from a classroom teacher or team member, a child may qualify for individual music therapy. A limited number of time slots are available for this type of service delivery. This therapy is in addition to the child's regularly scheduled weekly music therapy class. It is reserved for the students who have difficulty with groups, who are highly motivated by music, or who show unusual musical talent.

Session Structure

Exploring the (musical) environment. The needs of some children who come to the music room are best met by exploring and discovering. These classes may come from any of the previously described classroom models. In the music room, stations are set up before the students enter the room. The children are free to choose which station they wish to enter and they have the freedom to move from one station to another.

Each station is designed by the music therapist to relate to the children's IFSP/IEP outcomes/ objectives. The stations may also incorporate the school's themes, seasons, or suggestions elicited from the staff. One station is always a quiet corner with a couch, bean bag chair, tape/record player, headphone set, and books to go along with available music. Another corner utilizes the "Instrument of the Month" (e.g., cube chairs set around a bass drum, with a wide variety of mallets). A round table houses many adapted instruments and switch-activated equipment. A drum table and Orff instruments are available for improvisation and constructive play. Yet another station may be an open area where the children play some type of cooperative musical game.

One picture board (titled "Today in Music") shows the general schedule of activities while another ("Choices") portrays songs, instruments, and props that can be selected. Pictures are laminated and backed with Velcro for quick and easy modifications.

Promoting interaction. Music therapists at the Center generally follow a child-directed mode of service delivery that emphasizes play facilitation. If interaction is the prime focus, music session components for integrated preschool and inclusive kindergarten classes additionally may adhere to the following guidelines.

First, each session should begin with a song which brings the children together and establishes the start of the class. The activities that follow should be planned to provide avenues for children to *experience* music across several cultures through singing, playing instruments, moving, listening, and creating. Though the music activities may foster classroom survival skills (such as taking turns and following directions), they should be mainly geared towards an integrated theory of play. In an effort to expand the children's responses, activities should vary by type and length and should include familiar and new songs. A portion of each session should be devoted to some aspect of social interaction. Finally, a good-bye song can help focus the children as a group and add closure to the session. Though the activities are planned by the therapist, they do represent some elements of choice for the children. Spontaneity is never discouraged and often presents a springboard for creative group endeavors and improvised play.

The development of social skills may be considered of highest priority by early childhood educators (Katz, 1988). Research indicates that young children with special needs gain more appropriate play skills and interact more readily in a socially integrated setting than in a separate setting (Guralnick & Groom, 1988; Jenkins, Speltz, & Odom, 1985). However, it appears that interaction is best obtained if teachers employ specific interaction strategies to promote play between children with special needs and their typical peers (Cavallaro, Haney, & Cabello, 1993; Jenkins, Odom & Speltz, 1989; Jenkins, Speltz & Odom, 1985; McLean & Odom, 1988; Odom et al., 1988).

Music therapy has been found to be an effective strategy for achieving such interaction (Gunsberg, 1988, 1991; Humpal, 1991; Hughes, Robbins, McKenzie, & Robb, 1990; Jellison, Brooks, & Huck, 1984). Music therapists at the Center encourage interaction by asking the staff to join in a circle formation, take part in the opening song, and mingle freely. Directions are given within a musical context to structure spontaneous and nonthreatening interaction. As social play progresses, the music therapist may facilitate interaction at the following levels:

- By issuing a directive (e.g., "Caryn, please dance with Lisa").
- By issuing an indirect request (e.g., "Greg, find a friend who has another cymbal").
- By providing a song that has a cue for choosing a partner (e.g., the lyric instructions for the musical game "Rig-a-Jig-Jig". . . "a friend of mine I happened to *meet*").
- By spontaneous selection or by a nondirective facilitation (e.g., "Everyone find a partner!"). (Dimmick & Humpal, 1990).

Staff and peer tutors assist those children who are less able to independently participate.

Consultation

Because music therapy functions as part of a team approach, teachers and other related service personnel may request ideas for the use of music beyond the scheduled music sessions. The music therapy staff offer assistance through several avenues.

Monthly music activity packets that include songs, artwork, and implementation ideas for holidays and general theme concepts (e.g., "transportation" or "animals") plus suggestions for their use in both structured and unstructured play have been developed for use in the classrooms. The music therapists record the songs contained in the packets and make the tapes available to the staff. Props made to enhance the songs may also be signed out from the music lending library.

One music therapist runs this lending library, called the "Music Express." The library contains resources, tapes, books, materials/equipment, and instruments. Each classroom has a music corner and is given a colorful empty "Music Express" box. On alternating Fridays, the music therapist and the "Music Express" visit toddler or preschool classrooms. Children and/or teachers may select a music activity and corresponding items to keep in their classroom music express box. On Mondays, the music therapist returns to each room and consults with the teacher and/or plays with the children using the items from their music box. Classrooms may keep the kit for 1 week.

Supplementary enrichment ideas are displayed on a "Staff Notes" bulletin board located in the music room. This bulletin board lists other tapes (both audio and video) and resources that are available for use. Upcoming cultural events, both at school and in the community, are posted. These may be a source of possible field trips for students and their families.

A major aspect of music consultation is helping teachers use music throughout their day in the classroom (such as facilitating relaxation in quiet time or enhancing station play). A music therapist may also demonstrate, build, or adapt equipment, although many such topics are addressed in group inservice training sessions. Consultation may be more beneficial when it pertains to the specific wants and needs of the individual teacher or the team.

The music therapists have block times in their schedules where they work with the teacher and children in the classroom setting. This allows for musical play and improvisation through a child-directed approach. By directly observing and interacting within the classroom, the music therapist is better able to offer specific suggestions to teachers for using music in various aspects of their particular classroom routine.

The Music Educators National Conference in its "Position Statement on Early Childhood Education" (1992), calls for a combined effort among parents, music specialists, and early childhood professionals to ensure that music becomes a natural and important part of every young child's growth and development. Music is a vital, necessary component in early childhood education. It is not an option, but is a part of the curricula "best practices" (Bayless & Ramsey, 1991). Therefore, it is extremely important for music therapists to provide the experiences that will ensure that music is used as part of the daily classroom routine. Music will enrich the lives of the children; hopefully, it will be a rewarding, effective part of the teacher's day, too.

To initiate this philosophy, the music therapy staff surveyed the entire staff of the Center to determine the "Top Ten for Little People." The music therapists taped their renditions of the survey's results and distributed the tapes to each teacher and related service personnel who requested them. Teachers were then able to sing along with a tape that was representative of the typical child's repertoire, thereby promoting normalization and using music in a nonthreatening way. It should be noted that not every staff member was at ease using music, and each individual had different abilities and interests in this area. The music therapy staff needed to accommodate the teacher's abilities and increase their comfort level in utilizing music.

Consultation may also become part of a team strategy for goal implementation. The development of transition songs is representative of this concept. For instance, the speech language pathologist may request a song to pair with an object as a cue for communicating an upcoming event:

Event: Going Home on the Bus
Object cue: Small plastic bus
Tune: "Happy Birthday"

It's time to go home,
It's time to go home.
Our school day is over,
To the bus we will go.

This next transition song prepares a child for handwashing. It was written to facilitate an occupational therapy goal for a child with tactile defensiveness:

Tune: "I'm Gonna Wash That Man Right Out of My Hair"

We're gonna wash that *dirt right off of our hands,
We're gonna wash that dirt right off of our hands,
We're gonna wash that dirt right off of our hands
And get real squeaky clean!

*paint, food, etc.

Family/Child Programs

Not all children served by CCBMR/DD are enrolled in classes at the Center or its satellite sites. Some come to these facilities with their families or are served mainly in the home. An early childhood specialist and supportive home services personnel work with the family to develop an IFSP for these children. There are actually two components to music therapy service delivery in this model. First, parents may be advised how to use music in play with their infants or children within their homes. The second component involves providing a group experience for young children and their parents or families at one of the early childhood sites.

Therapists may conduct an inservice to model activities that show parents how to utilize music at home. Simple suggestions for converting common household items into instruments or ways to inexpensively make instruments (from boxes, paper plates, cereal, etc.) are always welcomed. Parents may be asked to provide a blank tape prior to the session. The music therapist will sing the songs from the lesson and often offer written activity ideas, picture cues, and possible adaptations for use by the parents. If professionally recorded songs are incorporated in the guide, parents should be given a reference/resource list and addresses of where these items may be purchased. Remember to keep abreast of the copyright laws!

Often home-based students come to the Center or one of its satellite sites once a week for a group session. This enables parents to share concerns and experiences, exposes children to socialization with peers, and provides participants with the expertise of many specialists.

Parks (1986) believes that parent participation and interaction with the child during the early years can significantly effect the child's growth and development in later years. Parents can be helped to enhance the developmental skills and behaviors of their child by using key parent interaction strategies. Music activities furnish enjoyable means for such interaction. Likewise, families often ask for ways to use music to make play, or occupational, physical, or speech therapy exercises more interesting and motivating. This is truly collaboration in action.

Additional early childhood groups may be established to serve families from the community. Such groups provide enrichment opportunities and are open to any interested families. Children with a wide range of abilities have a time to play together as their families make new friends and learn strategies for parenting. Music, story time, crafts, creative movement, and snack time are coordinated around central themes. An early childhood specialist coordinates the group and utilizes support staff on a rotating schedule.

Finally, the music therapy and adapted physical education departments work together to provide a "Movement and Music" class for families and their young children. Conducted in the gym, this weekly program is geared towards educating parents how to purposefully play with their child using motor and music strategies.

Miscellaneous

Center special events. The music therapy department takes advantage of the tremendous wealth of cultural diversity in the Cleveland area. Performing groups and individual artists come to the Center and classes take field trips that introduce children to a wide array of enrichment opportunities. Care is taken to ensure that these events are appropriate for young children.

Believing that young children learn best by experiencing, the music and adapted physical education departments codirect "Music and Movement" days. All children in the Center attend these festive occasions during assigned 20–30-minute slots. As a group enters the gym, children come together for a few short songs. They are then introduced to the various stations within the area. Children explore the stations while all staff members assist. As selected background music plays, children may discover a pumpkin patch obstacle course or a cardboard box "sleigh"— complete with numerous and diverse bells. Much thought and preparation go into determining station ideas and coordinating efforts of the two departments. "Music and Movement" days are enthusiastically lauded by students, families, and staff personnel.

Public relations. CCBMR/DD's music therapy department is often called on to represent the mission of its employer. Each year the group devotes one week in March to promoting "Music in Our Schools Month." The music therapists become performers and present a musical revue that incorporates representative selections from MENC's World's Largest Concert program, vocal and instrumental solos, and large ensemble numbers. Audience participation is always solicited. This troupe takes its program to all CCBMR/DD sites and is often asked to perform for community events, such as headlining at the Very Special Arts Festival.

Music therapists are frequently asked to speak to professional or civic organizations, to share adaptation ideas with other agencies, to write for professional publications, or to present at conferences. CCBMR/DD encourages this professional involvement and recognizes the positive effects of such endeavors in the area of public relations.

Tips

1. Communicate expectations to other personnel involved in joint programming (see sample letter on following page).

2. Make a poster for each class that lists the children's names and IEP or IFSP objectives or outcomes. Hang this at the back of the room prior to each session for a quick visual reference.

3. Keep a folder or notebook for each class. Record anecdotal information immediately following each session.

4. Keep a notebook of lesson plans. Plans should list equipment, music, and brief procedure for each activity. Catalogue these plans by date and/or theme.

5. Use a multisensory approach and be aware of various learning modalities.

6. Repeat activities, but also do them "another way"—*expand* upon the child's experience bank.

7. Make classroom sets of props—enough for each child to have one (laminate these to preserve them for future use).

8. Check out books, records and tapes from the local library to preview before purchasing.

9. Encourage parent participation and support. Send home examples of songs, activities and resources that families can share with their child.

Sample Letter to Classroom Teachers

". . . music allows for all levels of responses on the part of all children. It is a universal language and is an effective tool in bringing children of various abilities together. It can be structured or unstructured, based upon the needs of the participants. Music is a fun experience and provides a stimulus for communication and verbalization."

(from CCBMR/DD's Policy Statement regarding the music mainstreaming program)

WHO: Head Start and CCBMR/DD preschool classes
WHAT: Integrated music classes
WHEN: See your individual schedule
WHERE: Usually in the music room (check with your music therapist).

A few "notes" to make our classes more harmonious:

* *Please be on time.*
* *Help the children put on their name tags.*
* *Keep the children in the same group each week* (even if some are absent).
* *Help the children mingle.*
* *Sit within the group and help any child who needs assistance.*
* *Participate in all activities* (this should be fun for **you**, too!).
* *Notify your music therapist* **in advance** *if your class will not be attending its music session.*

What you can expect from us:

* *We will provide nametag buttons for each child (these will remain in the music room).*
* *We will facilitate weekly music sessions and center special events.*
* *We will notify you in advance of any canceled sessions.*
* *We will make resources available for you to check out.*

   . . . and most important:

We will strive to assist you in any way we can to help you share the gift of music with your children. **PLEASE** feel free to come to us with any suggestions, comments or questions you many have. We look forward to working with you and your classes!

(Signed) Your Music Therapists

Coda

William Patrick Day Early Childhood Center in Cleveland, Ohio, has been operating as part of an early intervention interagency collaborative since September 1992. Innovative change has developed over time. The program is continually being fine-tuned; this process definitely has had its effects upon students, families, and staff of all agencies involved therein. As in all pilot projects, once the "water has been tested," some aspects of the process may be found to be working well and other aspects may need some "reality checks." Theoretically sound programs do not always work as intended once they are put into practice. The staff and administration of William Patrick Day Early Childhood Center are becoming familiar with current trends and have been deciphering which do and which do not transfer from theory into practice. Modifications and re-evaluation are ongoing. Moreover, as of this writing , there is a nationwide movement to re-examine the basic premises that guide D.A.P. in order to clarify best practices for *all* young children.

Unquestionably, child-initiated and play-based experiences appear to be beneficial to the education of the young child. Likewise, music is a very important part of the early childhood world of play. Therefore, it would seem that music therapists could benefit from learning more about early intervention and how music therapy may be utilized within this setting. The profession could indeed have a major role in the quickly expanding realm of early childhood education.

References

Andress, B. (1989). *Promising practices: Prekindergarten music education.* Reston, VA: MENC.

Andress, B., & Walker, L. M. (1992). *Readings in early childhood music education.* Reston, VA: MENC.

Bayless, K. M., & Ramsey, M. E. (1991). *Music: A way of life for the young child.* New York: Macmillan.

Boswell, J. (1984). The young child and music: Contemporary principles in child development and music education. *Proceedings of the Music in Early Childhood Conference*, Provo, UT. Reston, VA: MENC.

Bredenkamp, S. (1987). *Developmentally appropriate practices in early childhood programs serving children from birth through age eight.* Washington, DC: National Association for the Education of Young Children.

Cavallaro, C. C., Haney, M., & Cabello, B. (1993). Developmentally appropriate strategies for promoting full participation in early childhood settings. *Topics in Early Childhood Special Education, 13*(3), 293–307.

Cuyahoga County Board of Mental Retardation and Developmental Disabilities. (1995). *Early childhood program philosophy, curriculum guidelines, and operational standards.* Cleveland, OH: Author.

Dimmick, J. A., & Humpal, M. E. (1989). *A musical bridge: A guide to mainstreaming.* Cleveland, OH: Cuyahoga County Board of Mental Retardation and Developmental Disabilities.

Dimmick, J. A., & Humpal, M. E. (authors), Quill, M. (director). (1990). *Together as Friends.* [videotape]. Cleveland, OH: Cuyahoga County Board of Mental Retardation and Developmental Disabilities.

Dimmick, J. A., & Humpal, M. E. (1994). *Music therapy assessment and evaluations checklist: Early childhood.* Cleveland, OH: Cuyahoga County Board of Mental Retardation and Developmental Disabilities.

Gunsberg, A. S. (1988). Improvised musical play: A strategy for fostering social play between developmentally delayed and nondelayed preschool children. *Journal of Music Therapy, 25*(4), 178–191.

Gunsberg, A. S. (1991). A method for conducting improvised musical pay with children both with and without developmental delay in preschool classrooms. *Music Therapy Perspectives, 9,* 46–51.

Guralnick, M. J., & Groom, J. M. (1988). Peer interactions in mainstreamed and specialized classrooms: A comparative analysis. *Exceptional Children, 54*(5), 415–425.

Hanline, M. F., & Hanson, M. J. (1989). Integration considerations for infants and toddlers with multiple disabilities. *Journal of the Association for Persons with Severe Handicaps, 14*(3), 178–183.

Hitz, R., & Driscoll, A. (1988, July). Praise or encouragement? New insights into praise: Implications for early childhood teachers. *Young Children,* 6–13.

Hohmann, M., & Weikart, D. (producers). (1990). *The daily routine* [videotape]. Ypsilanti, MI: High/Scope Press.

Hughes, J., Robbins, B., McKenzie, B., & Robb, S. (1990). Integrating exceptional and nonexceptional young children through music play: A pilot program. *Music Therapy Perspectives, 8,* 52–56.

Humpal, M. E. (1990). Early intervention: The implications for music therapy. *Music Therapy Perspectives, 8,* 30–35.

Humpal, M. E. (1991). The effects of an integrated early childhood music program on social interaction among children with handicaps and their typical peers. *Journal of Music Therapy, 27*(3), 166–177.

Humpal, M. E., & Dimmick, J. A. (1993). Music at William Patrick Day Early Childhood Center. *Triad, 60*(6), 17–18.

Jellison, J., Brooks, B., & Huck, A. (1984). Structuring small groups and music reinforcement to facilitate positive interactions and acceptance of severely handicapped students in the regular music classroom. *Journal of Research in Music Education, 32*(4), 243–264.

Jenkins, J. R., Odom, S. L., & Speltz, M. L. (1989). Effects of social integration on preschool children with handicaps. *Exceptional Children, 55*(5), 420–428.

Jenkins, J. R., Speltz, M. L., & Odom, S. L. (1985). Integrating normal and handicapped preschoolers: Effects on child development and social interaction. *Exceptional Children, 52*(1), 7–17.

Katz, L. (1988). *Early childhood education: What research tells us.* Bloomington, IN: Phi Delta Kappa Educational Foundation.

Linder, T. (1990). *Transdisciplinary play-based assessment: A functional approach for working with young children*. Baltimore, MD: Paul H. Brankes Publishing Co.

Ludlow, B. L. (1987). *Preschool programs for handicapped children*. Bloomington, IN: Phi Delta Kappa Educational Foundation.

Mahoney, G. J., & Powell, A. (1984). *Transactional inclusive program: Teachers guide*. Farmington, CT: Pediatric Research and Training Center.

McDonald, D. T., & Simons, G. M. (1989). *Musical growth and development, birth through six*. New York, NY: Schirmer Books.

McGonigel, M. J., & Johnson, B. H. (1991). An overview. In B. H. Johnson, M. J. McGonigel, & R. K. Kaufmann (Eds.), *Guidelines and recommended practices for the individualized family service plan* (2nd ed.) (pp. 1–5). Bethesda, MD: Association for the Care of Children's Health.

McLean, M., & Odom, S. (1988). Least restrictive environment and social integration. *Division for Early Childhood White Paper*. Reston, VA: Division for Early Childhood of the Council for Exceptional Children.

Music Educators National Conference. (1992, Winter). Position statement on early childhood education. *Soundpost*, pp. 21–22.

Odom, S. L., Bender, M., Stein, M., Doran, L., Houden, P., McInnes, M., Gilbert, M., DeKlyen, M., Speltz, M., & Jenkins, J. (1988). *Integrated preschool curriculum*. Seattle, WA: University of Washington Press.

Overby, L. Y. (1991). *Early childhood creative arts: Proceedings of the International Early Childhood Creative Arts Conference*, Los Angeles, CA. Reston, VA: American Alliance for Health, Physical Education, Recreation, and Dance.

Palmer, M., & Sims, W. (1993). *Music in prekindergarten: Planning and teaching*. Reston, VA: Music Educators National Conference.

Parks, S. (1986). *Make every step count: Birth to 1 year: Developmental parenting guide*. Palo Alto, CA: VORT Corporation.

Robertson, L. H. (Ed.). (1992, Fall/Winter). One-stop service shopping is the hallmark at our new W.P. Day Early Childhood Center. *Insight*. Cleveland, OH: Cuyahoga County Board of Mental Retardation and Developmental Disabilities.

U.S. Congress. *Education for All Handicapped Children Act Amendments of 1986*, Public Law 99–457.

U.S. Congress. *Individual Disabilities Education Act of 1992*, Public Law 102–119.

Vander Ven, K. (1994). Professional development: A contextual model. In J. Johnson & J. B. McCracken (Eds.), *The early childhood career lattice: Perspectives on professional development* (pp. 79–88). Washington, DC: National Association for the Education of Young Children.

William Patrick Day Early Childhood Center. (1992). Pamphlet of the Cuyahoga County Board of Mental Retardation and Developmental Disabilities, Cleveland, OH.

Appendix

Name _____

MUSIC THERAPY ASSESSMENT and EVALUATIONS CHECKLIST

- Early Childhood -

Description

　　The following tool has been developed for use by music therapists who work in an early childhood setting. A description of the child can be noted under **CONSIDERATIONS,** *where specific information may be inserted. In the* **CATEGORY** *section, general music education categories (**Singing, Playing, Listening, and Moving**) and their component parts are arranged so that the therapist may check the child's highest level of mastery and the date of attainment. A* **CODE** *affords an abbreviated means of addressing other aspects and levels of the child's musical play.*

　　This <u>Assessment and Evaluation Checklist</u> *is meant to be used in conjunction with a general play-based assessment to determine global goals that address the needs of the whole child through developmentally appropriate practices. Thus, the child's* **PARTICIPATION AND ENGAGEMENT** *levels will reflect his/her stage of social play (i.e. Onlooker, Solitary, Parallel, Associative, or Cooperative). The levels sytem of the* **CATEGORIES** *helps verify the child's stage of cognitive play (i.e. Exploratory/ Sensorimotor, Manipulative, Constructive, Pretend, or Dramatic).* **TEAM NOTES** *can be incorporated into determining general programming and specific interdisciplinary strategies.*

　　The final page of this instrument lists the **IFSP / IEP OUTCOME / OBJECTIVE** *that has been selected by the music therapist. In addition, space is provided for describing the child's interests and repertoire (positive reinforcers / motivators and present level). This page serves a dual purpose. It can be duplicated and used as a* **PROGRESS NOTE** *that can be sent home, with a copy attached to the child's file.*

MUSIC THERAPY ASSESSMENT AND EVALUATION CHECKLIST
- EARLY CHILDHOOD -

CHILD'S NAME: _____ FACILITY: _____

Music Therapist: _____

CONSIDERATIONS
___ HEARING
___ VISION
___ COMMUNICATION
___ MOTOR
___ MEDICAL
___ SENSORY
___ PLAY
___ OTHER

CODE:

+ = child initiated

   facilitated by:

p = physical cue

g = gestural cue

v = verbal cue

a = adapted

CATEGORY Date:					
A. SINGING					
1. Vocalizes by:					
a. Babbling					
b. Speaking					
c. Whispering					
d. Shouting					
e. Humming					
2. Uses inflection in vocal play					
3. Imitates					
4. Sings on pitch					
5. Sings responses					
B. SOUND PLAY					
1. Uses body sounds in musical play by:					
a. Clapping					
b. Stamping					
c. Patting					
d. Other _____					
2. Reaches for sound source					
3. Plays instruments by:					
a. Swiping					
b. Scratching					
c. Shaking					
d. Striking with palm of hand					
e. Striking with mallet					

CATEGORY Date:			
B. SOUND PLAY (cont.)			
4. Uses sounds / inst. in play			
5. Chooses sounds / inst. to accompany song / story			
6. Labels sound / inst.			
7. Plays inst. in sequence			
8. Categorizes sounds / inst.			
9. Keeps steady beat			
10. Imitates simple rhythm			
11. Stops on cue			
12. Plays ensemble part			
C. LISTENING			
1. Alerts to sound			
2. Attends to sound (how?_____)			
3. Improvises to sound (how?_____)			
4. Listens quietly as music plays			
5. Responds to changes in: a. dynamics			
b. tempo			
c. rhythm			
d. timbre			
e. form			
f. texture			

CATEGORY Date:			
D. MOVING			
1. Enjoys moving to music			
2. Creates own actions			
3. Moves to personal beat			
4. Expresses feelings through movement			
5. Aware of body's position in space when moving			
6. Imitates actions			
7. Uses simple concepts during movement activities (e.g. "up")			
8. Uses dance steps, following directions of therapist / song			

PARTICIPATION & ENGAGEMENT			
1. Responds to music across different environments			
2. Watches others play			
3. Chooses music station / instrument independently a. Stays in chosen area _____ (e.g. "flits")			
b. Completes activity			
4. Engages with adult during musical play			
5. Plays next to another child			
6. Plays with another child			
7. Plays in group music activity			
8. Engages in independent functional music routine			
9. Uses music to transition			

TEAM NOTES

Music Therapy IFSP/IEP Outcome/Objective
PROGRESS NOTE
Early Childhood

Child's name _____

Music Therapist_____ Facility _____

Year:	Music Therapy IFSP/IEP Outcome/Objective

Progress Note 1:	Date:

Progress Note 2:	Date:

CHILD'S REPERTOIRE / CHOICES

IMPLICATIONS FOR CONTRACTUAL EMPLOYMENT AND PRIVATE PRACTICE

Ellen R. Griggs-Drane

Introduction

There is a misconception about employment options for music therapists. Initially, a recent music therapy graduate may only have sought a "40-hour-a-week with benefits" job. However, recent employment trends indicate that, as a result of downsizing and the loss of many full-time positions, employers are increasingly hiring contractual employees. By the year 2000, it is estimated that nearly 50% of the work force will be on a contractual or consulting basis (Reuer, 1996). This projection presents distinct possibilities for the music therapy profession. By marketing music therapy services to several facilities or schools, the equivalent of a full-time position can often be created for the contractual or private practice music therapy clinician.

As an example of how this process can happen, allow me to share the following personal journey. After completing the equivalency program and a master's degree in music therapy, I attempted to secure a full-time position at a local university-based community music school, Virginia Commonwealth University Community School for the Performing Arts (VCUCSPA). Although implementing a music therapy program at VCUCSPA was not possible due to state cut-backs, the administration expressed a strong interest in offering music therapy services since VCUCSPA had received many calls requesting such services. Based on these documented requests and my previous position on the VCUCSPA faculty as a music educator, the administration was able to "rehire" me without violating any of the state employment regulations.

Word-of-mouth is always the best advertising and a very effective marketing tool for any budding program. Before long, several students were being seen individually at the school and music therapy services were also being provided at various retirement centers, hospitals, and schools. The fact that I was on faculty at VCUCSPA and the school was already established in the community as well as the university helped a great deal in the music therapy program development. Any time a newly forming program or music therapy private practice can affiliate with a larger agency, it enhances the exposure and provides network opportunities.

In addition to my work at VCUCSPA, I established a private practice. My focus was to provide conveniently located music therapy and special music education services to community members and expand the music therapy services to a nearby suburb. Because I felt that I needed office space from which to conduct my business, I found myself frequently explaining music therapy to accountants and attorneys who would be my prospective neighbors. The common question I received from these professionals was, "Will you make noise?" After days of searching, a suitable office space was found, enabling the business to begin.

Initially, most of the referrals came from proactive parents looking for music education or music therapy services for their children. To familiarize parents with the benefits of music therapy, several inservices were provided for parent support groups or as part of the initial services at facilities. The community music school received a number of phone calls from individuals and agencies requesting any type of music experiences that would be available and appropriate for children with disabilities. Although clients and facilities can be very assertive in finding music therapy services, the music therapist should plan to market the profession either to all possible facilities or to a desired targeted population. Despite the fact that I was not able to market the music therapy program while at VCUCSPA due to the state cutbacks prohibiting new program development, the program steadily grew just through word-of-mouth and response to initial requests.

In addition to providing music therapy services that were paid directly by the clients and facilities, services were requested by the Children's Medical Center at Medical College of Virginia Hospital, which is a part of Virginia Commonwealth University. In order to provide music therapy services at the Center, funding was pursued through the funding office at the university. A music therapy program had previously been in place in the pediatric oncology division and had been funded through the Association for the Study of Childhood Cancer. In order to expand the music therapy services to include all pediatric patients, other external funding was required. Through the award of several grants from private agencies, a music therapy program was initiated that eventually grew into a full-time position.

Contractual Employment

Developing a music therapy contractually-based business and/or a private practice is an evolving process. Even though the terms *private practice* and *contractual based employment* are interchanged frequently, there are a number of differences associated with each. *Private practice* refers to providing services at a location other than the school/agency setting. It also refers to serving as a consultant and engaging in one-time assessment or program development projects. *Contractual employment* involves pursuing one or two facilities and serving in a part-time capacity. It is very possible and quite likely that a music therapist could provide both private practice and contractual services simultaneously.

Contractual opportunities for music therapists are available with a variety of populations. For a music therapist interested in working in the schools, the following settings would be options for contractual employment:

- Early Intervention Centers—school based and home based
- Preschool—wellness/developmental focus
- Traditional special education school settings
- Special Schools
- Consultant to regular, special, and music educators
- Adult Programs—sheltered workshops, group homes

When making initial contact with the school system or individual school, it is important to broaden the marketing focus. For example, describe how music therapy services will positively impact the existing programs in a variety of centers within the school system. Explain how music therapy services are unique, citing specific benefits. As a contractual employee, *do not* put all of your eggs in one basket. Make your services applicable to a variety of needs within the school. If agencies and schools are familiar with music therapy services available to them and the benefits, then a full-time job is more likely to develop. Exposure is the key.

Before the school system is contacted, consider what programmatic options are possible or what skills/expertise can be offered to the consumer. Develop a list of all the populations with whom you have worked. Include one-to-one and group experiences as well as nonmusic therapy experiences. Look at all experiences in dealing with this population and make this list an addendum to your resumé. This process will help focus on populations with whom you might begin providing services.

Once the decision has been made regarding the targeted population, a rationale needs to be developed as to why it is important that these individuals receive music therapy and what music therapy can offer that other disciplines do not. If the contractual music therapist does not have a clear idea of what the facility or school will need, an initial meeting should be planned to discuss exactly how music therapy will fit into the typical day. Determine when the students will be available for individual and group sessions and what locations will be receiving services. The successful execution of logistics will often make or break program development attempts.

The Initial Contact

Although it would be preferable if the initial contact could be a brief personal meeting with the contact person, the reality is that this contact will probably be in the form of a telephone call. Before this initial discussion, have a general idea of therapy services associated with each school/facility.

During the initial contact, the following questions should be considered: Have there been music therapy/music education services in the past? What specialists are on staff? What is a typical daily schedule? What are your expectations for this program? Is there a particular student/class/population that the contact person has in mind for receiving services?

Be prepared to answer certain questions: What is your fee structure? Do you provide your own instruments? Do you object to observers/other children in the classroom? Will you provide an inservice? Will you present to a parent group? Keep this conversation as brief as possible, yet obtain the necessary information so that you can put together a successful presentation.

The Presentation

As more details about the facility become known, consider scheduling a presentation for your contact person and any other individual or group of individuals associated with this venture. Typically, the contact person is one of the following individuals: the director of special education or music education of a school district, the child life therapist or special educator of a medical center or school, the case manager of a county, or a parent of a parent support organization. Your contact person may or may not be your funding source. Usually, the contact person is the music therapist's right-hand person to get the ball rolling. The presentation of the same material to another individual may take place at a later date, at which time specific budgets will need to be identified. It is advisable to include the following materials with the presentation:

1. *A handout that provides a brief overview of music therapy.* It is advantageous to have a handout that provides a brief overview of music therapy, including a historical perspective of the field, traditional and current populations, and the cost effectiveness of music therapy intervention. This also allows the participant to have supplemental literature to refer to at a later date.

2. *The Employer Alert Sheet.* The *Employer Alert Sheet* (Certification Board for Music Therapists, 1993) provides potential employers information regarding employing a board-certified music therapist.

3. *A brief subject review of related research articles.* Identify specific studies where music therapy has been effective with the target population.

4. *Population identification sheet.* Provide a brief definition of how music therapy is applied with this population. Include potential goals and examples of music therapy activities that relate to the identified goals.

5. *Music therapy video.* If one is planning to pursue both private practice and contractual employment, it is well worth the investment to purchase a music therapy video. The author recommends the *Music Therapy Makes a Difference* or *Music Therapy & Medicine: Partnerships in Care*, both available from AMTA, or the *Bodywatch Music and Health* video (MTI Film & Video, 1987). For many individuals, a video will be an effective way to present an image of music therapy.

6. *Resumé.* Develop an updated resumé to distribute to your contact person and your administrator only.

7. *AMTA brochure.* Consider purchasing copies of *Music Therapy Makes a Difference* (American Music Therapy Association, 1998). The use of professionally presented marketing materials is well worth the investment. Later, as the business develops, consideration of an individualized brochure specific to your program may be an option.

8. *Sample job descriptions.* Contact AMTA for a packet of sample job descriptions. Copy and distribute the sample job description for Music Therapist, School Setting. This is an excellent resource and may begin to provide a foundation for a permanent position.

9. *Business Card.* It is crucial to present yourself as a professional. Develop a business card and corresponding letterhead. Having business cards available can greatly assist in networking and the layout and printing costs are quite nominal.

Probably the most important thing to remember when developing both the initial and follow-up presentations is to be professional. By researching the setting and assembling a professional presentation packet, the music therapist is demonstrating a level of competence and professionalism. Also remember that it is much better to take your time and develop programs slowly, than to try to be all things to all people. See Figures 1 and 2 for examples of program proposals.

PROPOSAL FOR MUSIC THERAPY TRAINING AND MUSIC THERAPY CURRICULUM GUIDE AND PROGRAM DEVELOPMENT

Music Therapy Training

The definition, existing research, and application of music therapy, music education, and adaptive music education in the classroom will be addressed. Applicable activities will be demonstrated and a resource guide will be developed and presented to participants based on the activities reviewed in class.

The target population for the music therapy training will address the needs of the socioeconomic deprived student or at-risk student. As a result of this deprivation, several areas of delay are often noted: inadequate language development, perceptual and cognitive delay, poor self-concept and self-expression, lack of motivation, family disorganization and dysfunction, decreased attention span, and poor peer interaction and cooperation.

Music therapy is an effective medium in which to work with the at-risk student because it offers presentation of concepts in a multisensory approach. Due to the multiple areas of developmental delay that may occur, the use of all the senses prove to be an integrated and more effective approach. In addition, music therapy offers active participation of learning. Important cognitive gains are often seen through active exploration and manipulation of objects and/or instruments. Music also allows the educator to include prescriptive teaching: identifying weak areas of each student, planning music activities to strengthen these areas which allow all students to be included regardless of academic or musical ability.

Following the training, the learner will be able to:
- demonstrate an improvement of musical skills (vocal & instrumental)
- utilize instruments in order to include all students in activities
- include educational, emotional, social, and motor goals in a music activity
- monitor student progress in a music activities

Cost of Music Therapy Training
$400.00 per consultation × 8 = $3,200.00
Cost includes consultation visits (September, October, November, January, February, March, May, June), travel, preparation, presentation and materials.

Music Therapy Curriculum Guide and Program Development

The curriculum guide will specify the inclusion of music therapy services in the existing educational setting for Charlotte County Public Schools. Guidelines will be established for: regular education classrooms, self-contained and integrated special education classrooms, one-to-one and group settings, and the utilization of music therapy services on both the elementary and secondary levels.

The program development will establish pilot projects to test the reliability and user friendliness of the curriculum guide. It will include follow-up visits allowing for the identification of special needs and/or problem areas. In addition, the follow-up ensures the success and accurate implementation of the music therapy curriculum.

Cost of the Music Therapy Curriculum Guide and Program Development

Research time (20 hours × $35.00)	$ 700.00
Writing time (25 hours × $35.00)	$ 875.00
Implementation time	$ 680.00

Pilot Program = 2 site visits which includes 2 group sessions per visit ($100), 4 hours 1:1 time with the music therapist ($140), travel time ($140)

Follow-up time $ 1,050.00

This includes 3 site visits ($350 each). Inclusive in each site visit is 4 hours 1:1 time with the music therapist, editorial time ($70.00), travel time ($140.00)

Cost   = $ 3,305.00

Total Cost of Music Therapy Training Curriculum Guide & Program Development $ 6,505.00

Figure 1. Proposal for Music Therapy Training and Music Therapy
Curriculum Guide and Program Development

MUSIC THERAPY PROGRAM FOR ADULT ONCOLOGY

Music therapy is the use of music to provide an entertaining structured environment, prompt creativity, and provide multi-sensory experiences. Music therapy activities are designed to address specific therapeutic goals and objectives that aid in the achievement and maintenance of each individual's highest functioning level. Music therapy services are to be provided by a registered music therapist – board certified.

Music therapy goals and objectives may include:
- increasing self expression
- increasing self esteem
- assisting with physical goals for patients upon occupational/physical therapy referral
- providing patients with methods for relaxation and pain control
- providing opportunities for structured leisure activity
- providing patients with a participatory activity within the fine arts

Format for Music Therapy Sessions

Music therapy sessions will be provided for all adult oncology patients on both the general units and also in the Bone Marrow Transplant Unit. Sessions will either be one-to-one or small group and take place in each patient's room or, if available, a day room. Patients will be provided with a selection of activities: singing, instrument playing, music listening, movement, composition, conducting, lyrical discussions, and music theory/history.

Music Therapy Referrals

Music therapy referrals will be accepted from the following professionals: physicians, related therapeutic personnel, and nursing staff. Referrals will also be accepted from family members of the patient and will be discussed with appropriate staff members prior to intervention.

Home Referrals

Patients may receive music therapy during their time at home upon occupational therapy or related therapy/physician referral. The initiation or continuance of music therapy services for the patient while at home will assist in providing normalcy for the patient. In addition, if the patient has begun to make progress in the hospital, this will allow for continued success with professional assistance.

Music Therapy Protocol

Upon the receipt of a referral, the music therapist will have an initial session where an informal assessment will be conducted. Each therapist must chart on this initial session where the music therapy treatment plan will be identified. Goals and objectives will be established for each referred patient. It is the responsibility of the music therapist to follow each patient while hospitalized and determine if sessions should be conducted once or twice weekly. Prior to patient discharge, a discharge summary must be written and any follow-up plan identified, if necessary. When time permits, the music therapist may also see non-referred patients for informal sessions. It will be required for the music therapist to attend all applicable treatment team and patient care meetings.

Instrument Usage

All instruments are labeled and will be the responsibility of the music therapist. Each therapist may loan out any of the instruments to in-patients. It is the philosophy of the music therapy department that instrument/equipment loaners are necessary for the success of the music therapy services. Appropriate storage areas should be discussed with the nursing staff on each unit to ensure the safety of the instruments.

Figure 2. Music Therapy Program for Adult Oncology

Service Options

Anticipate the range of services that will be provided when working in a school setting. Services that may typically be provided include program development consults, individual and group assessments, group and one-to-one music therapy sessions, and music and special education consults. Documentation may be inclusive in these options or may be billed separately. It is appropriate and likely that service options provided for one school setting may be different from another setting. Focus on providing a music therapy program specific to the needs of the identified educational program.

Educational Presentations

As part of the total services provided to the school system, it is customary to give one complimentary inservice during each contract period, e.g., fall, winter, or summer semester. When writing the contract, indicate that any additional presentations will be billed accordingly. Although providing inservices can be tiresome at times, it is a necessity in order to educate others of the value of music therapy. The increased exposure could also mean an increased number of clients.

Assessments

Before providing services, a complete assessment should be conducted. In addition to the assessment, a comprehensive narrative needs to be completed, stating the assessment findings and allowing for the therapist's professional opinion and plan to be expressed. Whether you are to provide group, individual, or consulting services, develop an assessment that is appropriate to the situation. Obviously, for students seen individually, a more thorough assessment format is desirable. This type of service will need to be included with the negotiated rate or billed separately.

Group Session Provisions

When beginning the music therapy program in a new educational setting, communication is key to determining the expectations of the administrators. Again, be realistic about the services you can provide and the fees that should be billed. Which services (e.g., documentation, assessment, follow-ups, placements) will be provided as part of the group session? What is the preferred size of your group (e.g., small group = 2–4 students, large group = 5–10 students)? Is there a number that is not acceptable? Will the fees differ between the two group sizes? Is there an appropriate location? Will the services include transporting patients to sessions? If not, negotiate support staff for this task. Specify in the written contract any services that require the assistance of other professionals/aides. Although compromise is usually necessary, avoid compromising quality of services.

Individual Session Provisions

Usually one-to-one sessions within a school setting have been initiated by a parent or parent group. As the external clinician, the music therapist needs to become an active liaison between the treatment team and the parent. This type of referral will usually be privately funded by the parent. Sessions may take place inside the school during the school day or also at an off-campus site established by the music therapist.

Documentation

Be prepared to develop your own forms for assessments, treatment plans, treatment evaluations, and any other client-related documentation. Before using an original creation, study the existing documentation format used by the other treatment members. Keep goals/objectives relatively in the same location on the page and limit the length of the session narrative summaries. In addition, be very clear on your data collection techniques. Since parents and other professionals may be interested in your descriptive statistics, be prepared to defend the findings. If at all possible, include therapeutic goals from other disciplines to give accurate assessment of effectiveness of treatment.

Referral Process

Have a predetermined formula as to how the client load will be decided. Will services be provided to certain classes, all students, or on a referral basis? If solicitation of referrals from other professionals is the primary avenue for students to receive music therapy, then the development of a referral form is crucial. The referral form should provide the name of the student/patient being referred, date of birth, classroom/hospital unit or room, name of parents, classroom teacher/physician, diagnosis, reason for referral, and a signature block for the individual making the referral. Also be sure to include where the referral should be returned for efficient processing.

By providing services in a school setting, the music therapist makes him/herself very visible and stimulates a lot of interest. Anticipate additional referrals and a reasonable client load.

Access to Student's Records

It is vital that full access to all charts and records of clients and participation on the Individual Education Plan (IEP) be negotiated on the music therapy contract. In addition to receiving access to these records, the music therapist must also consider the time factor involved in reading files and bill accordingly.

IEP Team Process

Although the music educator is rarely involved with the IEP team, he or she still is expected to successfully integrate and educate the special needs students. Only after frustrating meetings with the guidance counselors do music educators typically learn of the specific needs of a student. Even after they have been enlightened as to the specifics of a student's special needs, there is often no support staff available to assist them.

The music therapist can be a valuable liaison between special and music educators, as well as parents and students for a successful music experience. IEP team participation should be negotiated during the initial stages of the contractual process. In order to serve the clients appropriately and to the best of one's ability, full participation in the IEP process is the desired expectation. Since it is unlikely that a contractual music therapist would participate in all of the client's team meetings, an informational exchange procedure needs to be developed. The contractual music therapist must be updated on all new educational and rehabilitative strategies. It is the responsibility of the contractual music therapist to facilitate this communication.

It must be stated in writing the amount of time/money agreed upon for assessments and IEP team participation when developing the contract. The music therapist may want to include these services within the total fee agreed upon for music therapy sessions. A word of caution: take the time to calculate the time involved so as not to short-change the determined billing fee. Be realistic when estimating the time involved with IEP participation and bill accordingly. Plan to attend all IEP meetings concerning the one-on-one clients. For the group session clients, plan to attend the two regularly scheduled meetings and then as you are available. This again will need to be factored into the fee structure.

Billing Procedures

If the contractual music therapist is hired on a part-time basis, payment will be the responsibility of the school and billing will not be necessary. If, however, the music therapist is on a contractual basis, billing procedures will need to be developed and initiated by the music therapist. Some options to consider include monthly billing following the provision of services or payment prior to services being rendered. Usually the latter is done when an outside funding source is involved, such as a grant or a private organization. In addition to direct pay options for service, the contractual music therapist may consider the grant or private funding options to initiate and sustain the music therapy program.

Independent and federal grants can be an option to get contractual programs started. For example, the author obtained independent grants to begin and maintain two pediatric medically-related programs. Once the programs were shown to be successful, the hospitals absorbed the expense and eventually developed a full-time position with benefits. Privately funded positions may be the result of the support of a community organization, professional or social fraternity, or a private donation to a facility with the focus to be targeted to the special needs child. Explore these options if a school or facility does not have a music therapy position in the budget.

The Contract

It would be nice if all business arrangements in life could be on the level of a gentlemen's agreement, but that is neither likely nor a good idea. It is a necessity that the contractually-based music therapist develop a legal and binding agreement *prior to* the initiation of services.

Development of a legal document requires careful attention. Henry, Knoll, and Reuer (1986) provide several examples of contracts as well as other tips for successful contract development. The following are some additional suggestions to consider when the music therapy contract is developed:

1. Include language in the contract regarding both parties' desire to enter into a professional affiliation. This allows the independent music therapist to become affiliated with a school, agency, or facility in the community. Should the music therapist wish to develop some promotional materials, an affiliation section could be included in order to enhance marketability and credibility.

2. All music therapy referrals should be directed to the contracted agency during the specified agreement and affiliation. This is especially important if the music therapist wishes to establish a business and hire additional music therapists.

3. Written approval of any and all photographing and video taping of any students and/or staff during music therapy sessions must be provided to the music therapist prior to the session. This protects both the music therapist and the students in the event inappropriate and personal use of photos is being attempted.

4. Clarify whether the contracted agency agrees to provide liability insurance. If the music therapist is providing his or her own liability insurance, market that feature to the potential employer. This eliminates a variety of concerns and therefore makes the hiring of the music therapist easier. To obtain information on liability insurance contact Maginnis and Associates, Inc., 1–800–345–6917 (Ohio Residents only), 1–800–621–3008 (all other states), or contact your local insurance company for rate comparisons. See Figures 3 and 4 for examples of contract forms.

Making the Transition to a Full-time Music Therapy Position

Many full-time positions have developed from initial contractually-based arrangements. Accountability and quality of services are of primary concern if a transition from contractual to full-time employment is to occur. There are a number of programmatic issues to consider as well when making this transition.

If the contractual music therapist provides the instruments, then the facility may need to consider purchasing instruments to start a program. If this is the case, will the full-time music therapist be expected to continue to provide services with personal instruments? How will the program alter once the full-time position begins? The employer may have different expectations regarding how and for whom services should be provided.

A final consideration is the time frame available to continue participating in treatment meetings and other professional activities, such as professional development and documentation. This is a very important aspect of time delegations and should be continued for programmatic consistency, if at all possible. The consideration of adding benefits should also be addressed. Discuss with your employer how much will be contributed to your benefits, compare it with your existing contractual arrangement, and double check the offered salary. Never sell yourself short. Negotiate to obtain the rate you deserve.

Private Practice

Once the foundation has been laid for the contractual business, development of a private practice will be less involved. Implementation of contractual arrangements is usually easier to begin than the private practice for the new entrepreneur. However, with organizational skills and some desirable personal attributes, a music therapist can develop a successful private practice. It is important to realize that establishing a private practice takes time; it should not be expected to "take off" immediately. Other outside employment may be necessary to supplement one's income until the client load increases. Persistence and patience are two desirable personal qualities to have before undertaking the private practice adventure.

Music Therapy Institute of Virginia
Richmond, Virginia

Contracting Agency: ABC University (ABC)
Address: ABC Lane
                         Anytown, USA
Contact Person: John Doe, Director
Contracted Agency: Music Therapy Institute of Virginia (MTI VA)
Address: P.O. Box 1000
                         Richmond, Virginia 23235
Contact Person: Ellen R. Griggs-Drane

The contracting agency, ABC, is in receipt of a gift from the Music Community Foundation. The contracting agency is engaging MTI VA to provide music therapy services at ABC for its pediatric patients. This will apply to both in-patient and out-patient status. The parties are desired to enter into an affiliation to accomplish this work.

In carrying out this agreement and affiliation, ABC staff agrees to do the following:
1.   Provide assistance with administrative needs during this contract period.
2.   Direct all music therapy referrals to MTI VA during the specified agreement and affiliation.

In carrying out this agreement and affiliation, MTI VA staff agrees to do the following:
1.   Evaluate clients referred to the music therapy program. Following the evaluation, target objectives and goals will be defined and individualized programs and procedures will be developed for each client.
2.   Provide direct service to clients according to the specified program.
3.   Document progress of each client, providing regular progress reports to staff.
4.   Consult with agency or hospital treatment team/Individual Education Plan team as requested during the weekly time commitment.
5.   Provide professional liability insurance for any staff member providing music therapy services.

Fees

The fee for professional services is $xx.00 per direct service hour for individual sessions and $xx.00 per direct service hour for group sessions. The following areas will receive music therapy services on a weekly basis:

Group Sessions		**Individual Sessions**	
Preschool/School Age	$38.25	Oncology Clinic Adolescent	$35.00
Oncology Clinic Preschool	$38.25		

Total Amount: $2,453.00 ($53.00 of complimentary services will be provided)

Inclusive in both individual and group sessions are session planning/preparation time and patient charting time. MTI VA does not charge for sick days, agency holidays or vacation time.

Total amount of contract fee: $ 2,400

Period of Performance

This agreement and affiliation will be in effect from February 10, 1996–July 7, 1996.

Payment Schedule

50% ($1,200) of the total contract fee is due and payable on or before March 1, 1996. The remaining 50% ($1,200) is due no later than June 1, 1996.

The undersigned agree to the terms stated herein.

_____   _____
John Doe, Director   Date   Ellen R. Griggs-Drane   Date
ABC   MTI VA

_____
Jane Doe, Chairman   Date
ABC Department of Music

Figure 3. Sample University Contract

Ellen R. Griggs-Drane, M.M., RMT-BC
1234 Whitworth Road
Richmond, Virginia 23235

Contracting Agency:	**Children's Hospital**
Address:	223 Music Therapy Drive
	Anytown, USA
Contact Person:	Jane Doe, Director
Contracted Agency:	**Ellen R. Griggs-Drane, M.M, RMT-BC (EGD)**
Address:	1234 Whitworth Road
	Richmond, Virginia 23235
Contact Person:	Ellen R. Griggs-Drane, Director

The contracting agency, Children's Hospital, is engaging EGD to provide music therapy services at the locations listed in this contract and any additional locations that are mutually agreed upon. Music therapy services are provided for individuals and groups with the responsibilities of EGD as listed below. The parties are desired to enter into an affiliation to accomplish this work.

In carrying out this agreement and affiliation, Children's Hospital agrees to do the following:
1. Provide locations for therapeutic intervention.
2. Assist the EGD therapists with patient referrals.
3. Assist the EGD in obtaining group members prior to the session time.
4. All music therapy referrals will be directed to EGD during the specified agreement and affiliation.
5. Provide EGD with written approval of any and all photographing and video taping of any patients and/or staff during music therapy sessions.

In carrying out this agreement and affiliation, EGD agrees to do the following:
1. Present in-service and/or information sessions for participating staff, parents, and other personnel as requested.
2. Evaluate clients referred to the program. Following the evaluation, target objectives and goals will be defined and individualized programs and procedures will be developed for each client.
3. Provide direct service to clients according to the specified program.
4. Document progress of each client providing regular progress reports to staff.
5. Consult with agency or hospital treatment team/Individual Education Plan team as requested.
6. Provide liability insurance for EGD.

Fees
    The fee for professional services is $xx.00 per direct service hour with a minimum of 4 hours weekly for individual sessions. EGD does not charge for sick days or agency holidays. This agreement and affiliation will be in effect from January 11, 1996 – April 19, 1996. At the conclusion of this time, the contract will expire unless another contract is agreed upon. Either party may terminate this contract with two weeks prior notice.

The undersigned agree to the terms stated herein.

_____   _____
Jane Doe, Director   Date   Ellen R. Griggs-Drane   Date
Child Life Department, Children's Hospital   MTI VA

_____
John Doe, Administrator   Date
Children's Hospital

Figure 4. Sample Hospital Contract

Taking Care of Business

Caution should be taken when developing a private practice, especially regarding required paperwork necessary for the bookkeeping needs of the business. Development of clinical documents will also need to be completed. Some forms that should be considered are: (a) permission to obtain and release information forms, (b) student history forms, (c) assessments, (d) referral forms, and (e) inquiry forms that should be kept accessible to account for the amount of interest being received and in what population area (see Figure 5). The history forms should request a thorough background of information including the results of any educational or medical testing.

Music Therapy Institute of Virginia
Inquiry Sheet

Date: _____

Time: _____

Name of caller: _____

Relation to interested party: _____

Name of potential client: _____

Agency (if applicable): _____

Address: _____

_____

Telephone: (_) ____ - _____ (work); (_) ____ - _____ (home)

Best time to call: _____; _____

Approximate age of individual: (circle)

Infant	Young Adult
Toddler	Adult
School Age	Geriatric
Adolescent	

Have they ever received music therapy services before?   Yes   No
Have they ever received music education services before?   Yes   No

Brief description of disability: Physical _____

Emotional _____

Psychiatric _____

Educational _____

Mentally Impaired _____

Head Trauma _____

Geriatric _____

Figure 5. Sample Inquiry Sheet

Serving as a private practice music therapist can be a natural segue in the school system. The music therapist can still provide support services to school systems while the primary focus of concern is the private client. Provision of one-on-one sessions in the private setting enables the music therapist to share clinical information with special educators and other therapists on a consultative basis. For example, if the client attends music therapy after school hours at the private music studio, the music educator may benefit from this programming, depending on the involvement of the music therapist with school personnel. Consultative services and additional time spent with teachers and administrators should be billed as services rendered outside of the typical music therapy session.

The private practice music therapist will often be contacted by a parent who is attempting to provide a musical experience for his or her child. This is especially true if music education is not provided the student, especially in a secondary education setting. As with any individual client, the music therapist should provide an assessment, develop a treatment plan, and implement therapeutic techniques. As part of the treatment plan, the music therapist should observe the student at school and discuss integration techniques with the special educator. In addition, options concerning placement in music education should also be addressed. Once professional school contacts have been made, the music therapist will be better able to articulate treatment possibilities.

Utilization of Classroom Goals in the Therapy Session

As the music therapist develops a professional rapport with the special educator and other related health professionals, a better understanding and implementation of interdisciplinary techniques may begin. For example, the author would always contact the classroom teacher and any other specialists who provided services to the music therapy client. Inclusion of other discipline goals accentuated the music therapy plan and also allowed for some cross-referencing of goal accomplishment. This provides crucial information supporting the validity and success of music therapy. It also provides the music therapist with a quality control measure of the music therapy services.

Communication With Parents and Educators

Proaction is the key in the development of the communication chain. Articulate all areas that need to be addressed on a weekly basis in the contract, highlighting responsibilities of the music therapist and responsibilities of the school. Keep in mind that the development of professional rapport is best facilitated by a genuine respect for the client and parents, combined with a desire to learn. When meeting with the parents, be prepared with pertinent questions and allow plenty of discussion time. Schedule meetings and phone calls to meet the individual needs of the parents and school personnel.

Serving as a Consultant to Other Educational Professionals

The role of the music therapy consultant may be quite diversified. The music therapist may serve as a parent and student advocate, supporting the need for music therapy techniques, music education mainstreaming, or inclusion options. The music therapist may also advocate that music therapy services be integrated within the academic setting, or may provide inservice training for music or special educators.

The special educator is usually the main link in the educational programming for the student. It is important for the music therapist to meet with this individual and discuss current intervention techniques, mainstreaming options, and how the use of music therapy may enhance current teaching strategies. Be prepared to discuss your assessment findings and treatment plan. If at all possible, make yourself available for interdisciplinary exchange. This will facilitate the development of a professional relationship and will ultimately enhance the program for your client.

As a private practice therapist, direct contact with the school will usually be the result of discussing the application of music therapy techniques that may be used with the student between the classroom and the music therapy session. It is especially important that the music educator understand why and how the use of music in the student's day is crucial to fully meet the needs of the student. If music education participation is written on the student's IEP, strongly encourage the music educator to become involved with this process. Also emphasize that whatever is stated on the IEP is legally binding for the music educator to provide. Support services may be necessary in order for the music educator to comply with the IEP.

There are many strategies the music therapist may offer the music educator concerning rehearsal techniques, teaching basic music concepts, successful integration of the special needs student into the music education classroom, adaptation of instruments and notation, and musical expectations the music educator should have of the special needs student. Music may be, and often is, the arena where the special needs student shines. It is very important to communicate to the music educator the structure of success without limiting the student's musical progress.

The attitudes of the music educator will vary based on levels of experiences and current job responsibilities. The private practice music therapist may also see a difference between general, choral, and instrumental instructors. In order to be effective, the music therapist must tread lightly until the attitudes of the music educator are determined. The information-sharing process must be done in a respectful manner if techniques are to be successfully implemented.

Another important contact is the inclusion specialist. This individual may be a part of the school faculty or may be employed through a state or federal grant. The role of the inclusion specialist is to make the student's transition from the special education environment into the regular education setting as smooth as possible. As part of the job responsibilities, the inclusion specialist may present an overview of the needs of the mainstreamed student to the music class in order to inform both the students and the teacher of specific diagnosis and characteristics. This individual is also a valuable resource for the music therapist to enhance the success level of the music mainstreamed student.

The music therapist may also request a meeting with all teachers and specialists from whom the client receives direct services. This usually includes the special educator and other specialists (e.g., occupational therapist, physical therapist, speech therapist, and a vision specialist). It is important to make a professional contact with all of these individuals in order to identify goals that are being addressed in their specific disciplines and to share how goals are effectively being addressed in the music therapy session with the student. Put each of these professionals on your mailing list for assessments, treatment plans, and summary reports.

Independent Consultant Opportunities

Establishing oneself as an independent music therapy consultant takes some strategic planning. First, identify colleges, universities, and the program directors in your state and surrounding counties. When contacting an institute of higher education, arrange to meet with several key people (e.g., director of music therapy, director of music education, chairperson of the music department, and the director of special education). Also contact any other departments that may need the services of a music therapy consultant and schedule meetings. These meetings are merely to discuss the role of music therapy, explaining the services to be offered, and to identify the individuals who may benefit from the music therapy services. Following each brief phone call, follow up with a letter thanking the individual for his or her time and include a business card and an AMTA brochure for future reference.

Networking with these individuals is important since they usually get the calls from members of the community requesting services, often in the form of, "My daughter responds to music; however, she is not eligible for services in our school district. Can you help me?" The music therapy consultant has now identified himself or herself to the community as having the ability and the desire to provide services.

For example, as a result of a contact made to the assistant chairman of the music department at a local university, the author received calls from that university's preschool assistance center. The center was designed to provide support services to preschool students within the state free of charge. The center contacted the necessary professionals to assist with the issues and then reimbursed the professional consultant fee rate. The author was hired to provide support services to both a music educator and a special educator in the areas of effective programming and implementation in a rural school district. An in-depth follow-up report was required by the assistance center, who then forwarded it to the teachers.

In addition to schools, contact other local agencies that provide support to children. For example, Head Start Centers and programs through Social Services make excellent contacts and provide opportunities for networking due to the large numbers of children serviced. Another way to make your services known is to participate in a community health fair. The music therapist should contact elementary and secondary schools to determine if health fairs and special needs fairs are conducted at a school. This is done in some areas and basically targets special services that are provided for school-age children in the community. This is a great marketing opportunity with minimal expense, usually only the cost of your booth rental and handouts.

Another option to develop consulting opportunities is to contact local parent support groups and local agencies. The author was very successful in marketing music therapy services and identifying needs and implications of music therapy to specific populations during presentations to support groups for parents and their children with Down syndrome, autism, cancer, and mental impairments. In addition, contact the local American Lung Association, American Cancer Society, the United Way and any other related organizations that are active in your area.

Business Development

Before starting a private practice, the author enrolled in many "starting your own business" and "writing the business plan" entrepreneurial seminars. In addition, it is recommended that the potential private practice clinician purchase some books on the subject area of starting a small business and independent consulting. Holtz (1988) offers the following suggestions for those becoming independent consultants:

1. Set aside a cash flow to live on for the first 9 to 12 months.
2. Develop your public speaking skills.
3. Locate a good accountant and an attorney.
4. Write a business plan and expand slowly.
5. Write a marketing plan. Update this at least twice a year.
6. Be sure your targeted population needs your services.
7. Charge clients what you are worth.
8. Be an expert and represent yourself as such.
9. Develop a good business card.
10. Keep focused. Don't try to be all things to all people.
11. Use a good brochure.

Another option to consider when developing a private practice is whether the business will be for-profit or not-for-profit. If it is for-profit, there are a number of models that will need to be considered, such as sole proprietorship, partnership, or corporation.

A sole proprietorship means that all assets are in your name and the owner is solely responsible for all assets and liabilities. The IRS defines a sole proprietorship as a "business that has no existence apart from you, the owner" (Behnke, 1996 p. 63). With a sole proprietorship, one is able to hire part-time employees. A second option would be a partnership. This means that the business would be divided between partners or divided as stated in the initial agreement. Be very sure that the two partners share the same long-term goals, philosophy, and focus for the business. The third option is development of a corporation. There appears to be some debate on the pros and cons of this decision. The corporation has its own identity and is responsible and liable, not the individual. Most independent consultants who incorporate form small corporations and sell stock privately, not to the general public (Holtz, 1988).

A business license is usually required if you earn over a certain amount of money during a 1-year period. The music therapy private practice clinician or consultant would be responsible to pay a percentage of the gross earnings to purchase the license. In addition, the clinician/consultant is also responsible for state and federal taxes. Given the complexity of business contracts and tax laws, it is strongly recommended that an attorney be hired to review any business arrangements and contracts. In addition, an accountant is crucial in establishing your business books and assisting the newly self-employed person at the dreaded tax time.

Private practice clinicians may decide to develop a name for their business or simply use their personal name. If the location of your business has never heard of music therapy, it may be advantageous to develop a business name with the words "music therapy" within the title to help in marketing your business (e.g., "Music Therapy Institute of Virginia"). Consider using your personal name if it is better known in your community and will be a better identification source for potential clients. If you chose a business name, check with your county or city to determine if professional businesses need to be registered. Registration of your business name puts the name on the state register so no one in your state can use that name. This is essentially a protection for the small business owner.

Marketing

Once the business has been named and registered, a business license has been obtained, and a business plan developed, you are now ready to market your services. The simplest way is to be listed within the music instruction listing in the Yellow Pages. This can provide your business with excellent exposure, especially for individuals seeking music instruction for children with special needs. In most cases, the community members seeking instruction have never considered music therapy as an option. When you are listed as a business in the Yellow Pages, you will be charged for a business telephone line. Although this is more expensive than your personal telephone line, it is deductible.

Another method for effective marketing is advertising in a local newspaper. The music therapist may want to consider having an open house if he or she has an office or a studio. Another angle for newspaper publicity is to contact the newspaper and ask for a vignette focusing on an individual and/or some other aspect of your services that would be particularly interesting to the consumer. This has the potential to generate additional community interest.

The author did contact a marketing firm to conduct a direct mailing targeting the parents of children with special needs but found these mailing lists were not available for any type of direct mail services. The most effective type of advertising, however, is probably the good old word-of-mouth. This is especially true if the music therapist has developed a small contractual business and become "affiliated" with a school or a major medical facility.

Fee Structure

The most painstaking part of this entire process is determining the fee structure for music therapy services. While this may vary depending on locations, there are factors that should be taken into consideration: overhead of a studio/office, utilities, liability insurance costs, costs of instruments, travel expenses (gas, upkeep of car), legal and professional services, repairs, supplies, bank service charges, and advertising or marketing. Major medical costs will also need to be factored in if the business owner is not covered under a spouse's policy. In the event the business owner is interested in purchasing major medical benefits through the business, pursue a group of small business owners. There is usually an insurance company which targets small business owners, allowing individuals to buy-in as a group plan. This is a much more economical route.

There is a relatively simple formula that is used to calculate a realistic hourly rate. Information necessary to complete this formula includes the desired monthly salary, the average monthly expenses, and the number of monthly billable hours. At this point, the number of billable hours may not be determined; however, calculate the number of desired hours. Plug this information into the formula below and it will determine the hourly rate.

$$\frac{\text{desired monthly salary}}{\text{\# of monthly billable hours}} + \frac{\text{average monthly expenses}}{\text{\# of monthly billable hours}} = \text{hourly rate}$$

The private practice clinician needs to develop a fee structure based on the above formula and also based on the market rate. Discuss fee schedules with other professionals in your immediate area in order to learn some realistic expectations of the market worth.

Is All of This Really for Me?

The music therapist considering private practice should conduct a personal assessment to determine if this is truly a desired approach. The road of the private clinician is certainly exciting, never boring, and allows for personal and professional growth. However, one needs to consider both the pros and cons before beginning such an adventure. For the music therapist who enjoys working with a variety of populations, is highly motivated, and is a self-starter, this is a good choice. Remember, the small business owner is the boss, sets deadlines, takes the initiative to make new contacts, and is also the one to fix the broken equipment. The flipside to that is the small business owner is the one who enables the community to participate in the benefits of music therapy and initiates program development within new settings. It is an exciting adventure guaranteed to be full of surprises, headaches, and rewards.

References

American Music Therapy Association. (1998). *Music therapy makes a difference* [Brochure]. Silver Spring, MD: Author.

Behnke, C. (1996). A music therapist and sole proprietorship. *Music Therapy Perspectives (14)*1, 63–65.

Certification Board for Music Therapists. (1993). *The employer alert sheet* [Brochure]. Midlothian, VA: Author.

Henry, D., Knoll, C., & Reuer, B. (1986). *Music works A handbook of job skills for music therapists*. Stephenville, TX: Music Works.

Holtz, H. (1988). *How to succeed as an independent consultant*. New York: John Wiley & Sons.

Music and health [Video]. (1987). (Available from MTI Film & Video, 420 Academy Drive, Northbrook, IL 60062.)

National Association for Music Therapy (Producer). (1994). *Music therapy makes a difference* [Video]. Silver Spring, MD.

National Association for Music Therapy (Producer). (1996). *Music therapy and medicine: Partnerships in care* [Video]. Silver Spring, MD.

Reuer, B. (1996). Posturing for the changing world consulting as a career option. *Music Therapy Perspectives 14*(1), 16–20.

GLOSSARY

adaptation. Any procedure intended to meet an educational situation with respect to individual differences in ability and purpose.

adaptive behavior. Addresses self-help, independent functioning, and personal and social responsibility as is appropriate for a same-age peer and according to one's culture group.

age appropriate. Experiences and/or a learning environment that support predictable growth and development in the physical, social, emotional, and cognitive domains that are typical for children at specific chronological ages.

aphasia. Impaired ability to use language or articulate ideas due to brain injury or stroke.

appropriate education. A standard, required by IDEA, which guarantees that students with disabilities receive an educational program individually tailored to their abilities and needs.

appropriate environment. Surroundings that are suited to both the age and the individuality of all children present.

appropriate practice. Techniques or a style used with children that is age and individually appropriate.

assessment. The process of determining the presence of a disability and students' current functioning levels through observation and testing procedures.

assistive listening devices (ALDs). Equipment, like hearing aids, that help individuals with hearing impairments use their residual hearing.

associative play. A type of play in which a child plays with others in a group and subordinates individual interests to those of the group.

at-risk. Students that have a greater chance of experiencing difficulties developmentally or at school due to social, economic, environment, or biological factors.

attention deficit (hyperactivity) disorder (ADD). A condition characterized by a persistent pattern of inattention and/or hyperactivity-impulsivity that is more frequent and severe than is typically observed in persons at a comparable level of development.

best practices. Refers to the kinds of content, formats and delivery models that best meet the needs of participants.

center-based services. Educational services that are provided at a central location, typically through a classroom type format.

cognition. Application of intellect as opposed to feelings/affect in mental process.

communicative competence. How well an individual can communicate with others, typically gauged in terms of oral language.

communicative disorders. An impaired ability to function well in the communication process because of a speech or language disorder.

continuum of services. A wide selection of services that are available so an appropriate education can be provided to each student with special needs.

cross-categorical. Classes available to students with a variety of disabilities usually according to level of severity.

curriculum. A systematic grouping of content, activities, and instructional materials.

device. Any specific aid, tool, or piece of equipment used to assist a student with a disability.

dyslexia. A reading disorder due to impaired processing skills.

early childhood programs. Preschool, day care, and early infant school programs that involve students with disabilities and their families, designed to improve the speech, language, social, and cognitive skills of the students attending.

Education for All Handicapped Children Act (EHA). See Individuals with Disabilities Education Act.

eligibility. Determination of whether a child meets the criteria to receive special education services.

evaluation. A comprehensive term which includes screening, assessment, and monitoring activities.

free appropriate public education (FAPE). A major standard set forth in PL 94–142, now called the Individuals with Disabilities Education Act (IDEA), which states that students with disabilities are entitled to a free appropriate public education which often includes supportive services and highly individualized educational programs.

functional skill. A skill or task that will be used in the individual's normal environment.

Individual Education Plan (IEP). A written plan of instruction required by IDEA for every school-age youngster receiving special education; the plan must include a statement of the individual's strengths and weaknesses, long-term and short-term goals and objectives, and all special services required.

Individual Education Plan Committee (IEPC). A meeting of appropriate persons in order to: (a) review the multifactored evaluation team report; (b) determine the nature and degree of special education and related services needed by the child, if any; (c) develop an IEP for a child determined to be in need of special education in accordance with all the Administrative requirement code; and (d) determine the least restrictive environment in which to deliver educational services in accordance with IEP.

Individual Transition Plan (ITP). A written plan that identifies the skills and supportive services that an individual needs to function in the community after schooling is completed.

Individualized Family Service Plan (IFSP). A written plan required by IDEA for children under the age of three who receive special preschool programs; identifies and organizes services and resources to help families reach their goals for their children.

Individuals with Disabilities Education Act (IDEA). Formerly referred to as the Education for All Handicapped Children Act (EHA); originally passed as PL 94–142 in 1975, amended in 1986 by PL 99–457 to also provide instruction and services to infants and toddlers, amended and reauthorized again in 1990 under PL 101–476, which strengthened transitional programs for adolescents and young adults with handicaps; ensures a free appropriate public education in the least restrictive environment for all children and youth with disabilities.

inservice. A developmental activity that a teacher undertakes singly, or with other teachers, after receiving his or her initial teaching certificate, and after beginning professional practice. It is a process designed to foster personal and professional growth for individuals within a respectful, supportive, positive climate having as its aim both learning for students and continuous, responsible self-renewal for educators and schools.

integration. Participation of children with disabilities in regular classroom settings with typically developing children.

Intermediate Care Facilities for the Mentally Retarded (ICF/MR). Federally funded community-based living centers or group homes where individuals with mental retardation reside.

LEA (Local Education Agency). The public school district which is responsible for a student's education.

learning disability. A disorder where the individual possesses average or above intelligence but is substantially delayed in academic achievement. It may result in an imperfect ability to listen, think, speak, read, write, spell, or to do mathematical calculations. The term includes such conditions as perceptual disabilities, brain injury, minimal brain dysfunction, dyslexia, and developmental aphasia.

least restrictive environment (LRE). To the maximum extent appropriate, children with disabilities, including children in public or private institutions or other care facilities, are educated with children who are not disabled, and that special classes, separate schooling, or other removal of children with disabilities from the regular educational environment occurs only when the nature or severity of the disability is such that education in regular classes with the use of supplementary aids and services cannot be achieved satisfactorily.

mainstreaming, integration, inclusion. While mainstreaming does not necessarily always mean full day, complete instructional and social placement in a regular classroom, for the purposes of this text, mainstreaming, integration, and inclusion will refer to the placement of children with disabilities into general music education settings.

multiple disabilities. Concomitant impairments (such as mental retardation-blindness, mental retardation-orthopedic impairment, etc.) the combination of which causes such severe educational problems that they cannot be served in special education programs solely for one of the impairments. The term does not include deaf-blindness.

parallel play. A situation in which a child plays independently with materials similar to those used by children playing in close proximity. Social contact is minimal.

physical play. Action that is frequently social, may be competitive, and includes rough-tumble activities.

preservice. College courses and training taken prior to obtaining a baccalaureate degree.

preservice teachers. College and university students who have not received a baccalaureate degree.

Public Law 94–142. A law passed in 1975 requiring that public schools provide a "free, appropriate public education" to school aged children regardless of handicapping conditions (also called the Education of the Handicapped Act).

Public Law 101–476. A recent update of PL 94–142, the "Individuals with Disabilities Act (IDEA)" mandates among other things, a free, appropriate public education for all children with disabilities, and provides guidelines for individual educational plans (IEP) and a continuum of placement options (LRE).

Regular Education Initiative (REI). A position held by some special educators that students with disabilities should be served in regular education classrooms and not be "pulled out" to attend special classes; an attempt to reform regular and special education so they are a combined system that maximizes mainstreaming.

self-contained classroom. This is one type of placement on the continuum of least restrictive environments. Special needs students spend the majority of their school day in a self-contained special education class, but may be integrated into one or two other classes with nondisabled peers.

serious emotional disturbance.
1. A condition exhibiting one or more of the following characteristics over a long period of time and to a marked degree that adversely affects a child's educational performance:
   a. An inability to learn that cannot be explained by intellectual, sensory, or health factors;
   b. An inability to build or maintain satisfactory interpersonal relationships with peers and teachers;
   c. Inappropriate types of behavior or feelings under normal circumstances.
   d. A general pervasive mood of unhappiness or depression;
   e. tendency to develop physical symptoms or fears associated with personal or school problems.
2. The term includes schizophrenia. The term does not apply to children who are socially maladjusted, unless it is determined that they have a serious emotional disturbance.

speech or language impairment. A communication disorder such as stuttering, impaired articulation, a language impairment, that adversely affects a child's educational performance.

transdisciplinary. An effective team approach to IEP development and problem-solving which involves "role release" on the part of the team members resulting in problem-solving through a mutual sharing of all disciplinary perspectives. One professional is assigned the role of "primary" service provider.

typically developing child. A child who is not identified as having a disability.

unidisciplinary. Professionals from various disciplines (education, speech, motor, etc.) provide intervention services to the same child with little or no contact or consultation among themselves.

RESOURCES

ASSOCIATIONS/ORGANIZATIONS

Music Therapy/Music Education

American Music Therapy Association (AMTA)
8455 Colesville Road, Suite 1000
Silver Spring, MD 20910
Phone: (301) 589–3300
Fax: (301) 589–5175

Music Educators National Conference (MENC)
1806 Robert Fulton Drive
Reston, VA 22091
Phone: (800) 336–3768
Fax: (703) 860–1531

Disabilities – General

Council for Exceptional Children (CEC)
1920 Association Drive
Reston, VA 22091
Phone   (703) 620–3660
Fax: (703) 264–9497

National Council on Disability (NCD)
1331 F Street, NW, Suite 1050
Washington, DC 20004
Phone: (202) 272–2004
Fax: (202) 272–2022

National Easter Seal Society
230 West Monroe Street, Suite 1800
Chicago, IL 60606
Phone: (312) 726–6200
Fax: (312) 726–1494

National Organization for Rare Disorders (NORD)
P.O. Box 8923
New Fairfield, CT 06812–8923
Phone: (800) 999–6673

Autism

Autism Research Institute
4182 Adams Avenue
San Diego, CA 92116
Phone: (619) 281–7165
Fax: (619) 563–6840

Autism Society of America
7910 Woodmont Avenue, Suite 650
Bethesda, MD 20814
Phone: (800) 328–8476

More Advanced Autistic People (MAAP)
P.O. Box 524
Crown Point, IN 46307
Phone: (219) 662–1311

The Autism Network for Hearing and Visually Impaired Persons
c/o Dolores and Alan Bartel
7510 Oceanfront Avenue
Virginia Beach, VA 23451
Phone: (804) 428–9036

Deaf/Hard of Hearing

Alexander Graham Bell Association for the Deaf
3417 Volta Place NW
Washington, DC 20007–2778
Phone: (202)337-5220
            (800) HEAR–KID

American Society for Deaf Children
2848 Arden Way, Suite 210
Sacramento, CA 95825–1373
Phone: (800) 942–2732

National Association of the Deaf (NAD)
814 Thayer Avenue
Silver Spring, MD 20910–4500
Phone: (301) 587–1789

Early Childhood

National Association for the Education of the Young Child (NAEYC)
1834 Connecticut Avenue, NW
Washington, DC 20009

Early Childhood Music Newsletter
c/o School of Music, University of Oregon
1225 University of Oregon
Eugene, OR 97403–1225

Early Childhood Music Association
2110 27th Avenue
Greeley, CO 80631

Early Childhood Connections
(a publication of Early Childhood Music Association)
Foundation for Music-Based Learning
P.O. Box 4274
Greensboro, NC 27404–4274

AMTA Early Childhood Information Network
Co-Chairpersons:

    Ronna Davis   Marcia Humpal
    22450 Douglas Road   26798 Mangrove Lane
    Shaker Heights, OH 44122   Olmsted Falls, OH 44138

Juvenile Justice

Juvenile Justice Resource Center/Clearinghouse
1600 Research Blvd.
Rockville, MD 20850
Phone: (800) 638–8736

National Council on Crime and Delinquency (NCDC)
685 Market Street
Suite 620
San Francisco, CA 94105
Phone: (415) 896–6223

National Institute on Juvenile Justice and Delinquency Prevention (NIJJDP)
(U.S. Department of Justice)
633 Indiana Ave. NW
Suite 800
Washington, DC 20531
Phone: (202) 307–2942

Office of Juvenile Justice and Delinquency Prevention (OJJDP)
(U.S. Department of Justice)
633 Indiana Ave. NW
Suite 742
Washington, DC 20531
Phone: (202) 307–0751

Learning Disabilities

Children and Adults with Attention Deficit Disorders (CHADD)
499 Northwest 70th Avenue, Suite 109
Plantation, FL 33317
Phone: (305) 587–3700

Council for Learning Disabilities (CLD)
P.O. Box 40303
Overland Park, KS 66204
Phone: (913) 492–8755

Learning Disabilities Association of America (LDA)
4156 Library Road
Pittsburgh, PA 15234
Phone: (412) 341–1515 *or* (412) 341–8077

National Center for Learning Disabilities
99 Park Avenue
New York, NY 10016
Phone: (212) 687–7211

Orton Dyslexia Society
Chester Building, Suite 382
8600 LaSalle Road
Baltimore, MD 21286–2044
Phone: (410) 296–0232 *or* (800) 222–3123

Mental Retardation

The Association for Persons With Severe Handicaps (TASH)
29 W. Susquehanna Avenue, Suite 210
Baltimore, MD 21204
Phone: (800) 828–8274
E-mail: tashbalt@aol.com

National Down Syndrome Society
666 Broadway, 8th floor
New York, NY 10012–2317
Phone: (800) 221–4602

National Down Syndrome Congress
1605 Chantilly Drive, Suite 250
Atlanta, GA 30324
Phone: (800) 232–6372

National Fragile X Foundation
1441 York Suite, Suite 303
Denver, CO 80206
Phone: (800) 688–8765

The ARC
500 E. Border Street, Suite 300
P.O. Box 1047
Arlington, TX 76010
Phone: (800) 433–5255

International Rett Syndrome Association
9121 Piscataway Road, Suite 2B
Clinton, MD 20735
Phone: (800) 818–7388
E-mail: irsa@paltech.com

Physical Disabilities

United Cerebral Palsy Associations
1660 L Street NW, Suite 700
Washington, DC 20036–5602
Phone: (800) 872–5827

Muscular Dystrophy Association
3300 E. Sunrise Drive
Tucson, AZ 85718–3208
Phone: (800) 572–1717

Spina Bifida Association of America
4590 MacArthur Blvd. NW, #250
Washington, DC 20007–4226
Phone: (800) 621–3141

Visual Impairments

American Foundation for the Blind
11 Penn Plaza
New York, NY 10001
Phone: (800) 232–5463

Blind Children's Center
4120 Marathon Street
Los Angeles, CA 90029
Phone: (800) 222–3566

National Association for Parents of the Visually Impaired
P.O. Box 317
Watertown, MA 02272–0317
Phone: (800) 562–6265

National Organization of Parents of Blind Children
1800 Johnson Street
Baltimore, MD 21230
Phone: (410) 659–9314

MATERIALS FOR PLANNING INCLUSIVE
MUSIC EDUCATION/MUSIC THERAPY SESSIONS

Adair, A. J. (1984). *Ready-to-Use Music Activities Kit.* West Nyack, NY: Parker Publishing Company.

Adair, A. J. (1992). *Start With Song: 201 Ready-to-Use Interdisciplinary Activities for Young Learners.* West Nyack, NY: Parker Publishing Company.

Ardley, N. (1989). *Eyewitness Books—Music.* New York: Alfred Knopf, Inc.

Bayless, K. M., & Ramsey, M. E. (1991). *Music: A Way of Life for the Young Child.* New York, NY: Merrill-Macmillan Publishing Company.

Benderly, B. L. (1980). *Dancing Without Music: Deafness in America.* Garden City, NY: Anchor Press/Doubleday.

Birkenshaw-Fleming, L. (1989). *Come On Everybody Let's Sing!* Toronto, Canada: Gordon V. Thompson Music.

Chastain, L. D. (1983). *A Handbook on the Use of Songs to Teach Autistic and Other Severely Handicapped Children.* White Oak Press, P.O. Box 123, Route 3, Goodhue, MN 55017.

Clark, C., & Chadwick, D. (1980). *Clinically Adapted Instruments for the Multiply Handicapped.* St. Louis, MO: MMB Music, Inc.

Clarkson, G. (1985). *Stop, Look and Listen.* San Diego, CA: Kjos West.

Coleman, K., McNairn, P., & Shioleno, C. (1996). *Quick Tech Magic: Music-Based Literacy Activities.* Solana Beach, CA: Mayer Johnson Company.

Elliott, B. (1982). *Guide to the Selection of Musical Instruments with Respect to Physical Ability and Disability.* St. Louis, MO: MMB, Inc.

Estabrooks, W., & Birkenshaw-Fleming, L. (1994). *Hear & Listen! Talk & Sing!* Toronto, Canada: Arisa Publishing.

Farnan, L., & Johnson, F. (1988). *Everyone Can Move.* Hal Leonard Publications.

Farnan, L., & Johnson, F. (1988). *Music Is for Everyone.* Hal Leonard Publications.

Fiarotta, N., & Fiarotta, P. (1993). *Music Crafts for Kids: The How-To Book of Music Discovery.* New York, NY: Sterling Publishing Company.

Freeman, A. (1960). *Ring Along Old Favorites.* Long Beach, CA: Cantabile Press.

Freeman, A. (1989). *Ring Along Christmas Favorites.* Long Beach, CA: Cantabile Press.

Gibson, D., & Scruggs, J. (1984). *Songs to Brighten Your Day.* Austin, TX: Educational Graphics Press.

Ginglend, D. R., & Stiles, W. E. (1965). *Music Activities for Retarded Children.* Nashville, TN: Parthenon Press.

Grant, R. (1977). *A Developmental Music Therapy Curriculum for the Mildly Mentally Retarded.* University of Georgia. Order from: University Microfilms, #77–29, 760.

Gray, C. (1993). *The Sound Story Book* [Series]. Arlington, TX: Future Education.

Hoermann, D., & Bridges, D. (1988). *Catch A Song.* Nashville, TN: Incentive Publications, Inc.

Hunt, B. (1984). *Count Me In.* London, England: A & C Black.

Janiak, W. C. (1978). *Songs for Music Therapy.* St. Louis, MO: MMB Music, Inc.

Jeunesse, G., & Delafosse, C. (1994). *Musical Instruments: A First Discovery Book.* New York: Scholastic, Inc.

Jones, J. (1987). *I Feel Good All Over.* 1845 Bromilow, Las Cruces, NM 88001. Phone: (505) 521–3416.

Jones, J. (1987). *Spread A Little Sunshine.* 1845 Bromilow, Las Cruces, NM 88001. Phone: (505) 521–3416. Theodore Presser Company.

Lehman, P. (Ed.). (1994). *Teaching Examples: Ideas for Music Educators.* Reston, VA: Music Educators National Conference.

Levin, G., & Levin, H. (1977). *A Garden of Bell Flowers.* Bryn Mawr, PA: Theodore Presser Company.

Levin, G., & Levin, H. (1981). *Learning Songs.* Bryn Mawr, PA: Theodore Presser Company.

Lindeman, D. A. (Ed.) (1995). *Strategies for Teaching.* Reston, VA: Music Educators National Conference.

Michel, D. E., & Jones, J. L. (199). *Music for Developing Speech and Language Skills in Children.* St. Louis, MO: MMB Music, Inc.

Mitchell, L. (1991). *One, Two, Three . . . Echo Me!* West Nyack, NY: Parker Publishing Company.

Moss, J., & Raposo, J. (1992). *The Sesame Street Songbook.* New York, NY: Macmillan Publishing Company.

Musselwhite, C. R. (1985). *Signs and Symbols for Children.* Asheville, NC.

Nash, G. C., Jones, G. W., Potter, B. A., & Smith, P. F. (1977). *The Child's Way of Learning.* Sherman Oaks, CA: Alfred Publishing.

Nelson, E. (1989). *Everybody Sing and Dance.* Cleveland, OH: Instructor Books.

Nocera, S. (1979). *Reaching the Special Learner Through Music.* Morristown, NJ: Silver Burdett Company. (Currently out of print)

Nordoff, P. (1972). *Spirituals for Children to Sing and Play.* Bryn Mawr, PA: Theodore Presser Company.

Nordoff, P. (1977). *Folk Songs for Children to Sing and Play.* Bryn Mawr, PA: Theodore Presser Company.

Nordoff, P. (1979). *Fanfares and Dances.* Bryn Mawr, PA: Theodore Presser Company.

Nordoff, P., & Robbins, C. (1962). *The First Book of Children's Play Songs.* Bryn Mawr, PA: Theodore Presser Company.

Nordoff, P., & Robbins, C. (1968). *Fun for Four Drums.* Bryn Mawr, PA: Theodore Presser Company.

Nordoff, P., & Robbins, C. (1968). *The Second Book of Children's Play Songs.* Bryn Mawr, PA: Theodore Presser Company.

Nordoff, P., & Robbins, C. (1969). *Pif-Paf-Poltrie.* Bryn Mawr, PA: Theodore Presser Company.

Nordoff, P., & Robbins, C. (1973). *Songs for Children.* Bryn Mawr, PA: Theodore Presser Company.

Nordoff, P. & Robbins, C. (1980). *The Fifth Book of Children's Play Songs.* Bryn Mawr, PA: Theodore Presser Company.

Nordoff, P., & Robbins, C. (1980). *The Fourth Book of Children's Play Songs.* Bryn Mawr, PA: Theodore Presser Company.

Nordoff, P., & Robbins, C. (1980). *The Third Book of Children's Play Songs.* Bryn Mawr, PA: Theodore Presser Company.

Palmer, H. (1981). *Hap Palmer Favorites*. Sherman Oaks, CA: Alfred Publishing Company.

Pinson, J. (1983). *Handbells for Special Populations*. Sellersville, PA: Schulmerich Carillons, Inc.

Pliska, G., & Madelaine, G. (1993). *Praise for the Singing: Songs for Children*. Boston, MA: Little, Brown & Company.

Powell, H. (1983). *Game Songs with Professor Dogg's Troupe*. London, England: A & C Black.

Raffi. (1984). *The Raffi Singable Songbook*. Ontario, Canada: Chappell.

Raffi. (1986). *The 2nd Raffi Songbook*. New York, NY: Crown Publishers, Inc.

Robbins, C., & Robbins, C. (1980). *Music for the Hearing Impaired and Other Special Groups*. St. Louis, MO: MMB Music, Inc.

Rosene, P. E. (1984). *Making Music with Choirchime Instruments*. Carol Stream, IL: Agape.

Sacks, O. (1989). *Seeing Voices*. Berkeley, CA: University of California   Press.

Schmitt, C. (1987). *Music and Dance*. Little Falls, MN: St. Francis Music Center.

Sebba, J. (1986). *Playalong Songs*. London, England: Hamish Hamilton.

Sharon, Lois & Bram. (1980). *Elephant Jam*. San Francisco, CA: McGraw-Hill Ryerson Limited.

Smith, R. B. (1984). *Music Dramas for Children with Special Needs*. St. Louis, MO: MMB Music, Inc.

Walden, D. E., & Birkenshaw, L. (1980). *The Goat with Bright Red Socks*. Toronto, Canada: Berandol Music Limited.

Walters, C., & Totten, D. (1991). *Sing A Song All Year Long*. MN: T. S. Denison & Company, Inc.

Warren, J. (1983). *Piggyback Songs*. Everett, WA: Warren Publishing House.

Warren, J. (1984). *More Piggyback Songs*. Everett, WA: Warren Publishing House.

Warren, J. (1988). *Holiday Piggyback Songs*. Everett, WA: Warren Publishing House.

Warren, J. (1990). *Animal Piggyback Songs*. Everett, WA: Warren Publishing House.

Warren, J. (1990). *Piggyback Songs for Infants and Toddlers*. Everett, WA: Warren Publishing House.

Williams, S. (1985). *Round and Round the Garden*. Oxford, England: Oxford University Press.

Wirth, M., Stassevitch, V., Shotwell, R., & Stemmler, P. (1983). *Musical Games, Fingerplays and Rhythmic Activities for Early Childhood*. West Nyack, NY: Parker Publishing Company.

Witt, B. (1984). *TOTAL Tunes*. Communication Skill Builders, 3130 N. Dodge Blvd., P.O. Box 42050, Tucson, AZ 85733.

Suppliers of Music Therapy/
Music Education Equipment

West Music Company
P.O. Box 5521
1212 5th Street
Coralville, IA 52241
Phone: 1–800–397–9378
Representative: Kirsten Nelson, RMT–BC

This company carries high quality rhythm instruments, as well as inexpensive guitars. They also carry autoharps, a selection of electronic keyboards, activity/resource books, records and tapes. When the 800 number is called, a music therapy consultant is available for questions and information.

Rhythm Band, Inc.
P.O. Box 126
Fort Worth, TX 76101
Phone: 817–335–2561

This company is a convenient source for purchasing the high quality "Malmark" choir chimes.

National Music Supply
P.O. Box 14421
St. Petersburg, FL 33733
Phone: 1–800–383–6006

This company is one of the most inexpensive sources for purchasing a Suzuki "Omnichord," which is a very practical, adaptable piece of equipment to use with students who have special needs.

The Musical Rainbow Company
P.O. Box 626
908 W. Fayette Avenue
Effingham, IL 62401
Phone: 1–800–200–7213

This company provides innovative, quality and safe musical products for use with the young child—musical tools that can be used to inspire creativity, music and movement, and music therapy.

Peripole
2041 State Street
Salem, OR 97301
Phone: 1–800–443–3592

This company sells basic rhythm and percussion instruments useful for working with early childhood and elementary aged students.

Rhythmic Independence
Musical Alternatives for the Physically Challenged
P.O. Box 24181
Tempe, AZ 85285–4181
Phone: 609–921–0231

This small company manufactures and sells a series of mounting devices for rhythm instruments specifically for use with individuals with physical limitations that prevent them from playing instruments in a typical manner.

Ablenet
1081 Tenth Avenue S.E.
Minneapolis, MN 55414
Phone: 612–379–0956

This company makes various types of pressure switches which can be used to operate devices such as small tape recorders and the Suzuki "Omnichord." Pressure switches are especially helpful if there are students in the classroom who have severe physical limitations. Consult with an occupational or physical therapist for more detailed information about these types of products.

Enabling Devices
Division of Toys for Special Children
385 Warburton Avenue
Hastings-on-Hudson, NY 10706
Phone: 914–478–0960

This company, which is a division of Toys for Special Children, sells a communication device called the "Cheap Talker," which is easy to use in music therapy sessions.

Mayer-Johnson Company
P.O. Box 1579
Solana Beach, CA 92075
Phone: 619–481–2489

This company is the source for books containing the Picture Communication Symbols. Also, the company carries IBM and Macintosh software which allows the user to print out specific combinations and arrangements of symbols needed by a student. Consult with a speech therapist for additional information about products from this company.

Crestwood Company
6625 N. Sidney Place
Milwaukee, WI 53209–3259
Phone: 414–352–5678

This company is a source for a small adapted tape recorder and other augmentative communication devices.

Fred Sammons, Inc.
Bissell Health Care Co.
P.O. Box 32
Brookfield, IL 60513–0032
Phone: 1–800–323–1700

This company carries all types of Velcro including: Velcro in two parts (hook and latch) as well as one wrap Velcro. The company is also the source for foam to make built-up mallet handles.

Nellie Edge Resources, Inc.
P.O. Box 12399
Salem, OR 97309–0399
Phone: 503–399–0372

This company carries large black and white "Big Books" which illustrate different familiar children's songs. Each large book comes with a master that can be used to make small "mini" books for the students. The music therapist will have to color and laminate all purchased "Big Books."

Educational Network
Materials for the Whole Language Classroom
P.O. Box 426
Hilmar, CA 95324
Phone: 209–668–4142

This company is a source for Big Books based on different songs. Some of the many titles available include: Wheels on the Bus, All I Really Need, Everything Grows and Mr. Sun. The Big Books are printed on black and white cards, and the music therapist must do the coloring and laminating.

The Learning Workshop
3000 8th Street SE
East Wenatchee, WA 98802
Phone: 1–800–752–0663

This company is an additional source for Big Books based on different songs. Each Big Book also includes an activity kit or extension packet to expand the types of strategies that can potentially be used in a session. The company provides workshops around the United States that allow participants to make materials to take back to the their classrooms.

The Book Lady, Inc.
8144 Brentwood Industrial Drive
St. Louis, MO 63144
Phone: 1–800–766–READ

This company has an extensive catalog containing a large selection of music books including: songs and rhyming stories, music related stories, folk literature and biographies. Free catalogs are available on request.

Folkmanis Puppets
1219 Park Avenue
Emeryville, CA 94608
Phone: 415–654–7756

This company will sell their high quality puppets wholesale to educational or therapeutic organizations. The wholesale prices are about one third of the retail prices seen in local stores. Write for a catalog using the school letterhead, since this company does not sell to individuals.

Dancing Colors
Emily Day
P.O. Box 61
Langley, WA 98260 (on Whidbey Island)
Phone: 360–221–5989

This company sells colorful scarves for dancing, costuming and environments. In addition, the company sells face paints, dance clothes, books, training videos and music tapes.

BuddyBanz
117 19th Avenue East
Seattle, WA 98112
Phone: 206–324–0671

This company sells a product called the Buddy Banz. This is a high tensile circular band sheathed in a bright accordion of plush fabric. It expands to a generous 15 feet in diameter and can be used in movement activities with all ages in groups of up to 12. A booklet of suggested exercises accompanies each order of a Buddy Banz. There are two sizes available: large—holds up to 12 students, and small—holds up to 6 students.

Chime Time
2440–C Pleasantdale Road
Atlanta, GA 30340–1562
Phone: 1–800–477–5075

This company sells a variety of products related to movement activities, including records and tapes, as well as items such as hoops, balls, ribbons, and put-together dolls.

Lakeshore Learning Materials
2695 E. Dominguez St.
P.O. Box 6261
Carson, CA 90749
Phone: 1–800–421–5354

This company carries a wide variety of durable and high quality educational toys and learning materials for pre-school through elementary developmental levels.

Music for Little People
P.O. Box 1720
Lawndale, CA 90260
Phone: 1–800–727–2233

This company has a wide assortment of children's cassette tapes and CD's, as well as videotapes and books. They are an excellent source of multi-cultural music.

World Class Tapes
670 Airport Blvd., Suite 1
P.O. Box 7611
Ann Arbor, MI 48107
Phone: 1–800–365–0669

This company sells short blank tapes at wholesale prices. They sell only quality tapes, such as BASF. Tape length ranges from 5 minutes, 10 minutes all the way to 2-hour tapes. The 5- or 10-minute tapes are handy for recording short specific music excerpts for clients.

The Little Warehouse, Inc.
5505 Valley Belt Rd.
Cleveland, OH 44131
Phone: 216–398–0022

This company sells cassette tapes of various lengths, beginning with the 5-minute length.

Music in Motion
P.O. Box 833814
Richardson, TX 75083–3814
Phone: 1–800–445–0649

This company carries music education items and musical gifts for all ages. They have an excellent supply of books that illustrate lyrics of familiar songs.

Prelude: Springboards to Creativity
3360 Spruce Lane
Grapevine, TX 76051
Phone: 817-481-2323

This company provides inexpensive materials for adapted musical activities such as songbooks and musical aid kits. They also offer workshops on the use of music to facilitate learning for children and adolescents with disabilities.

Future Education, Inc.
422 Lamar Blvd. East, Suite 106
Arlington, TX 76011
Phone: 1–800–489–0727

The company carries the "Sound Story" books, a series discribing sound situations in a concrete fashion that is helpful for individuals with autism.

Suggested Readings/Additional References

Deaf Culture

Benderly, B. L. (1980). *Dancing without music: Deafness in America.* Garden City, NY: Anchor Press/Doubleday.

Gannon, J. R. (1981). *Deaf heritage: A narrative history of deaf America.* Silver Spring, MD: National Association of the Deaf.

Garretson, M. (1990). *Communication issues among deaf people.* Silver Spring, MD: National Association of the Deaf.

Garretson, M. (1991). *Perspectives on deafness.* Silver Spring, MD: National Association of the Deaf.

Kannapel, B. (1980). Personal awareness and advocacy in the deaf community. In W. C. Stokoe, *Sign language and the deaf community.* Silver Spring MD: National Association of the Deaf.

Lane, H. (1984). *When the mind hears: A history of the deaf.* New York: Random House.

Neisser, A. (1983). *The other side of silence.* Washington, DC: Gallaudet University.

Padden, C. (1980). The deaf community and the culture of the deaf people. In W. C. Stokoe, *Sign language and the deaf community.* Silver Spring, MD: National Association of the Deaf.

Padden, C., & Humphries, T. (1988). *Deaf in America: Voices from a culture.* Cambridge, MA: Harvard University Press.

Sacks, O. (1989). *Seeing voices.* Berkeley, CA: University of California Press.

Stokoe, W. C. (1980). *Sign and culture.* Washington, DC: Linstock Press.

Music and the Deaf

Amir, D., & Schuchman, G. (1985). Auditory training through music with hearing impaired preschool children. *Volta Review, 87,* 333–343.

Baird, S. (1979). A technique to assess the preference for intensity of musical stimuli in young hard-of-hearing children. *Journal of Music Therapy, 6,* 6–11.

Bang, C. (1986). A world of sound and music. In E. Ruud (Ed.), *Music and health* (pp. 19–36). Oslo, Norway: Norsk Musikforlag.

Bang, C. (1977). *A music event.* Hicksville, NY: M. Hohner, Inc.

Birkenshaw-Fleming, L. (1990). Music can make a difference. In A. A. Darrow (Ed.), *Proceedings from the Second National Conference on Music and the Hearing Impaired at Gallaudet University* (pp. 14–20). Lawrence, KS: The University of Kansas.

Buechler, J. (1982). *Music for handicapped children: Hearing impaired.* Washington, DC: National Association for Music Therapy.

Coffman, D., Gfeller, K., Coffman, S., & Darrow, A. A. (1992). A computer-assisted comparison of melodic and rhythmic discrimination skills in hearing impaired and normally hearing children. *The Arts in Psychotherapy, 18,* 449–454.

Dalgarno, G. (1990). A computer-based music system for the hearing impaired. In A. A. Darrow (Ed.), *Proceedings from the Second National Conference on Music and the Hearing Impaired at Gallaudet University* (pp. 31–42). Lawrence, KS: The University of Kansas.

Dalgarno, G. (1990). Technology to obtain the best musical sound for hearing impaired listeners. In A. A. Darrow (Ed.), *Proceedings from the Second National Conference on Music and the Hearing Impaired at Gallaudet University* (pp. 43–59). Lawrence, KS: The University of Kansas.

Darrow, A. A. (1979). The beat reproduction response of subjects with normal and impaired hearing: An empirical comparison. *Journal of Music Therapy, 16*, 6–11.

Darrow, A. A. (1984). A comparison of the rhythmic responsiveness in normal hearing and hearing impaired children and an investigation of the relationship of the rhythmic responsiveness to the suprasegmental aspects of speech perception. *Journal of Music Therapy, 21*, 48–66.

Darrow, A. A. (1985). Music for the deaf. *Music Educators Journal, 71*(6), 33–35.

Darrow, A. A. (1987). *A comparison of vocal ranges of hearing impaired and normal hearing children.* Unpublished manuscript, The University of Kansas, Lawrence.

Darrow, A. A. (1987). Exploring the art of sign and song. *Music Educators Journal, 74*(1), 32–35.

Darrow, A. A. (1987). An investigative study: The effect of hearing impairment on the music aptitude of young children. *Journal of Music Therapy, 24*, 88–96.

Darrow, A. A. (1988). Music and the hearing impaired: A review of the research with implication for music educators. *Update: Applications of Research in Music Education, 7*(2), 10–12.

Darrow, A. A. (1989). Music therapy in the treatment of the hearing impaired. *Music Therapy Perspectives, 6*, 61–70.

Darrow, A. A. (1990). The effect of frequency adjustment on the vocal reproduction accuracy of hearing impaired singers. *Journal of Music Therapy, 27*, 24–33.

Darrow, A. A. (Ed.). (1990). *Proceedings from the Second National Conference on Music and the Hearing Impaired at Gallaudet University.* Lawrence, KS: The University of Kansas.

Darrow, A. A. (1990). The role of hearing in understanding music. *Music Educators Journal, 77*(4), 24–27.

Darrow, A. A. (1991). An assessment and comparison of hearing impaired children's preference for timbre and musical instruments. *Journal of Music Therapy, 28*, 48–59.

Darrow, A. A. (1992). The effect of vibrotactile stimuli on the identification of pitch change by hearing impaired children. *Journal of Music Therapy, 29*, 103–112.

Darrow, A. A. (1993). The role of music in deaf culture: Implications for music educators. *Journal of Research in Music Education, 41*, 93–110.

Darrow, A. A. (1995). Music therapy and the hearing impaired. In T. Wigram, R. West, & B. Saperston (Eds.), *A handbook of music therapy.* Chichester, West Sussex: Carden Publications Limited.

Darrow, A. A., & Bolton, B. (1988, April). *A comparison of rhythmic performances by hearing and mainstreamed hearing impaired children.* Paper presented at the Music Educators National Conference, Indianapolis, Indiana.

Darrow, A. A., & Cohen, N. (1991). The effect of programmed pitch practice and private instruction on the vocal reproduction accuracy of hearing impaired children: Two case studies. *Music Therapy Perspectives, 9,* 61–65.

Darrow, A. A., & Gfeller, K. (1987, November). *Verbal identification of music concepts by hearing impaired children.* Paper presented at the National Association for Music Therapy Annual Conference, San Francisco, California.

Darrow, A. A., & Gfeller, K. (1988). Music therapy with hearing impaired children. In C. A. Furman (Ed.), *Effectiveness of music therapy procedures: Documentation of research and clinical practice* (pp. 137–174). Silver Spring, MD: National Association for Music Therapy.

Darrow, A. A., & Gfeller, K. (1991). A study of public school music programs mainstreaming hearing impaired students. *Journal of Music Therapy, 28,* 23–39.

Darrow, A. A., & Goll, H. (1989). The effect of vibrotactile stimuli via the SOMATRON™ on the recognition of rhythmic concepts by hearing impaired children. *Journal of Music Therapy, 26,* 115–124.

Darrow, A. A., & Heller, G. N. (1985). William Wolcott Turner and David Ely Bartlett: Early advocates of music education for the hearing impaired. *Journal of Research in Music Education, 33,* 269–279.

Darrow, A. A., & Starmer, G. J. (1986). The effect of vocal training on the intonation and rate of hearing impaired children's speech: A pilot study. *Journal of Music Therapy, 23,* 194–201.

Edwards, E. (1974). *Music education for the deaf.* South Waterford, ME: The Merriam Eddy Co.

Fahey, J., & Birkenshaw, L. (1972). Bypassing the ear: The perception of music by feeling and touch. *Music Educators Journal, 58*(8), 44–49.

Fisher, J. (1991). *The effect of three selected sensory presentation conditions on the pitch matching accuracy of normal hearing and hearing impaired children.* Unpublished master's thesis, The University of Kansas, Lawrence, KS.

Fisher, J., Baker, B., & Darrow, A. A. (1989, November). *The effect of two selected variables on the tonal perception of hearing impaired children.* Paper presented at the National Association for Music Therapy Annual Conference, Kansas City, Missouri.

Ford, T. A. (1985). *The effect of musical experiences and age on the ability of deaf children to discriminate pitch of complex tones.* Unpublished doctoral dissertation, University of North Carolina, Greensboro.

Ford, T. A. (1990). Development of rhythmic concepts and skills. In A. A. Darrow (Ed.), *Proceedings from the Second National Conference on Music and the Hearing Impaired at Gallaudet University* (pp. 21–30). Lawrence, KS: The University of Kansas.

Ford, T. A., & Shroyer, E. H. (1987). Survey of music teachers in residential and day programs for hearing impaired students. *Journal of the International Association of Music for the Handicapped, 3,* 16–25.

Galloway, H. F., & Bean, M. F. (1974). The effects of action songs on the development of body-image and body-part identification in hearing impaired preschool children. *Journal of Music Therapy, 11,* 125–134.

Gengel, R. W. (1969). Practice effects in frequency discrimination by hearing impaired children. *Journal of Speech and Hearing Research, 12,* 847–855.

Gfeller, K. (1986). Music as a remedial tool for improving speech rhythm in the hearing impaired: Clinical and research considerations. *Music Education for the Handicapped Bulletin, 2,* 3–19.

Gfeller, K. (1987). Songwriting as a tool for reading and language remediation. *Music Therapy, 6*(2), 28–38.

Gfeller, K. (1988, April). *A comparison of hearing aids and tactile aids in facilitating accuracy of profoundly deaf children on rhythm subtest of the PMMA.* Paper presented at the Music Educators National Conference, Indianapolis, Indiana.

Gfeller, K. (1990). A cognitive-linguistic approach to language development for preschool children with hearing impairments. *Music Therapy Perspectives, 8,* 47–51.

Gfeller, K. E. (1992). Music therapy in the treatment of sensory disorders. In W. B. Davis, K. E. Gfeller, & M. H. Thaut (Eds.), *An introduction to music therapy theory and practice* (pp. 209–233). Dubuque, IA: Wm. C. Brown Publishers.

Gfeller, K., & Baumann, A. (1988). Assessment procedures for music therapy with hearing impaired children: Language development. *Journal of Music Therapy, 25,* 192–205.

Gfeller, K., & Darrow, A. A. (1987). Music as a remedial tool in the language education of hearing impaired children. *The Arts in Psychotherapy, 14,* 229–235.

Gfeller, K., Lansing, C., Fryauf-Bertschy, H., & Hurtig, R. (1990, November). *Rhythmic perception by hearing impaired children using assistive devices.* Paper presented at American Speech and Hearing Association National Conference, Seattle, Washington.

Gray-Thompson, H. (1985). *The use of picture song books on the vocabulary development of hearing impaired children.* Unpublished masters thesis, The University of Kansas, Lawrence.

Klajman, S., Koldej, E., & Kowalska, A. (1982). Investigation of musical abilities in hearing-impaired and normal-hearing children. *Folia Phoniatrica, 34,* 229–233.

Korduba, O. M. (1975). Duplicated rhythmic patterns between deaf and normal hearing children. *Journal of Music Therapy, 12,* 136–146.

Leach, K. (1982). *Discrimination of musical elements made by hearing impaired residential school children.* Unpublished masters thesis, University of Kansas, Lawrence.

Madsen, C. K., & Mears, W. G. (1965). The effect of sound upon the tactile threshold of deaf subjects. *Journal of Music Therapy, 2,* 64–68.

Rickard, P., Robbins, C., & Robbins, C. (1990). Experiences in developing a creative language arts program. In A. A. Darrow (Ed.), *Proceedings from the Second National Conference on Music and the Hearing Impaired at Gallaudet University* (pp. 11–13). Lawrence, KS. The University of Kansas.

Rileigh, K. K., & Odom, P. B. (1972). Perception of rhythm by subjects with normal and deficient hearing. *Developmental Psychology, 7,* 54–61.

Robbins, C., & Robbins, C. (1980). *Music for the hearing impaired: A resource manual and curriculum guide.* St. Louis, MO: Magnamusic-Baton.

Robbins, C., & Robbins, C. (1990). Musical activities with young deaf children. In A. A. Darrow (Ed.), *Proceedings from the Second National Conference on Music and the Hearing Impaired at Gallaudet University* (pp. 8–10). Lawrence, KS: The University of Kansas.

Schatz, V. (1990). Using percussion to teach music concepts and enhance music and movement experiences. In A. A. Darrow (Ed.), *Proceedings from the Second National Conference on Music and the Hearing Impaired at Gallaudet University* (pp. 85–92). Lawrence, KS: The University of Kansas.

Sheldon, D. C. (in press). The Illinois School for the Deaf band: An historical perspective. *Journal of Research in Music Education.*

Shroyer, E. H., & Ford, T. A. (1986). Survey of music instruction and activities in residential and day schools for hearing impaired students. *Music Education for the Handicapped Bulletin, 2,* 28–45.

Solomon, A. L. (1980). Music in special education before 1930: Hearing and speech development. *Journal of Research in Music Education, 28,* 236–242.

Spitzer, M. (1984). A survey of the use of music in schools for the hearing impaired. *The Volta Review, 86,* 362–363.

Squires, V. L. (1982). *The beat maintenance and beat reproduction response of hearing-impaired and normal hearing children on sustained and percussive temporal intervals.* Unpublished master's thesis, University of Kansas, Lawrence.

Staum, M. J. (1987). Music notation to improve the speech prosody of hearing impaired children. *Journal of Music Therapy, 24,* 146–159.

Sterritt, G. M., Camp, B. W., & Lipman, B. S. (1966). Effects of early auditory deprivation upon auditory and visual information processing. *Perceptual and Motor Skills, 23,* 123–130.

Weibe, J. (1989). *The effect of adjusted frequency on the tonal perception of older hearing-impaired adults.* Unpublished masters thesis, The University of Kansas, Lawrence.

Woike, D. O. (1987). *Preferred audio response equalization in the hearing impaired.* Unpublished manuscript, Ohio State University, Columbus.

Juvenile Justice

Howell, J., Krisberg, B., Hawkins, J., & Wilson, J. (Eds.) (1995). *A sourcebook on serious, violent, and chronic juvenile offenders.* London: Sage Publications, Inc.

Watts, E. (Ed.). (1992). *Juvenile caseworker: Resource guide.* Laurel, MD: The American Correctional Association.

Learning Disabilities

Ingersoll, B. D., & Goldstein, S. (1993). *Attention deficit disorders and learning disabilities.* New York: Doubleday.

Pierangleo, R., & Jacoby, R. (1996). Parents' complete special education guide. West Nyack, NY: Simon & Schuster.

Trace. R. (1994). Aphasia: New directions in research, treatment and service. *Advance for Speech-Language Pathologists & Audiologists, 4*(5), 12.

Music Research: Individuals With Disabilities

Cognitive Disabilities

Atterbury, B. W. (1983). A comparison of rhythm pattern perception and performance in normal and learning-disabled readers, age seven and eight. *Journal of Research in Music Education, 31*(4), 259–270.

Bixler, J. (1968). Musical aptitude in the educable mentally retarded child. *Journal of Music Therapy, 5*(2), 41–43.

Bruscia, K. E. (1981). Auditory short-term memory and attentional control of mentally retarded persons. *American Journal of Mental Deficiency, 85*(4), 435–437.

Buker, G. (1966). *A study of the ability of the educable mentally retarded to learn basic music rhythm reading through the use of a specified structured classroom procedure.* Unpublished doctoral dissertation, University of Oregon, Eugene.

Cohen, N. S. (1992). The effect of singing instruction on the speech production of neurologically impaired persons. *Journal of Music Therapy, 29*(2), 87–102.

Davis, W. B., Wieseler, N. A., & Hanzel, T. E. (1983). Reduction of rumination and out-of-seat behavior and generalization of treatment effects using a non-intrusive method. *Journal of Music Therapy, 20*, 115–131.

Decuir, A. A., & Braswell, C. E. (1978). A musical profile for a sample of learning-disabled children and adolescents: A pilot study. *Perceptual and Motor Skills, 46*, 1080–1082.

DiGiammarino, M. (1990). Functional music skills of persons with mental retardation. *Journal of Music Therapy, 27*(4), 209–220.

DiGiammarino, M. (1994). Functional music leisure skills for individuals with mental retardation. *Music Therapy Perspectives, 12*(1), 15–19.

Dorow, L. G. (1976). Televised music lessons as educational reinforcement for correct mathematical responses with the educable mentally retarded. *Journal of Music Therapy, 13*, 77–86.

Edenfield, T. N., & Hughes, J. E. (1991). The relationship of a choral music curriculum to the development of singing ability in secondary students with Down syndrome. *Music Therapy Perspectives, 9*, 52–55.

Eisenstein, S. R. A. (1974). Effects of contingent guitar lessons on reading behavior. *Journal of Music Therapy, 11*, 138–146.

Eisenstein, S. R. A. (1976). A successive approximation procedure for learning music symbol names. *Journal of Music Therapy, 13*, 173–179.

Ellis, D. (1982). *Differences in music achievement among gifted and talented, average, and educable mentally handicapped fifth- and sixth-grade students.* Unpublished doctoral dissertation, University of North Carolina, Greensboro.

Freeman, I. A. (1986). *Rhythmic beat perception in a Down's syndrome population: A computerized measure of beat accuracy and beat interval response.* Unpublished doctoral dissertation, The University of North Carolina, Greensboro.

Garwood, E. C. (1988). The effect of contingent music in combination with a bell pad on enuresis of a mentally retarded adult. *Journal of Music Therapy, 25,* 103–109.

Gfeller, K. E. (1982). *The use of melodic-rhythmic mnemonics with learning disabled and normal students as an aid to retention.* Unpublished doctoral dissertation, Michigan State University, East Lansing.

Gfeller, K. E. (1983). Musical mnemonics as an aid to retention with normal and learning-disabled students. *Journal of Music Therapy, 20,* 179–189.

Gfeller, K. E. (1984). Prominent theories in learning disabilities and implications for music therapy methodology. *Music Therapy Perspectives, 2,* 9–13.

Gilbert, J. P. (1983). A comparison of the motor music skills of non-handicapped and learning disabled children. *Journal of Research in Music Education, 31*(2), 147–155.

Grant, R., & LeCroy, S. (1986). Effects of sensory mode input on performance of rhythmic perception tasks by mentally retarded subjects. *Journal of Music Therapy, 23*(1), 2–9.

Hauck, L. P., & Martin, P. L. (1970). Music as a reinforcer in patient-controlled duration of time-out. *Journal of Music Therapy, 7,* 43–53.

Holloway, M. S. (1980). A comparison of passive and active music reinforcement to increase preacademic and motor skills in severely retarded children and adolescents. *Journal of Music Therapy, 17,* 58–69.

Hughes, J. E., Robbins, B. J., Smith, D. S., & Kinkade, C. F. (1987). The effects of participation in a public school choral music curriculum on singing ability in trainable mentally handicapped adolescents. *Music Education for the Handicapped Bulletin, 2*(4), 19–35.

James, M. R., Weaver, A. L., Clemens, P. D., & Plaster, G. A. (1985). Influence of paired auditory and vestibular stimulation on levels of motor skill development in a mentally retarded population. *Journal of Music Therapy, 22,* 22–34.

Jellison, J. A., & Duke, R. A. (1994). The mental retardation label: Music teachers' and prospective teachers' expectations for children's social and music behaviors. *Journal of Music Therapy, 31*(3), 166–185.

Jorgenson, H. (1971). Effects of contingent preferred music in reducing two stereotyped behaviors of a profoundly retarded child. *Journal of Music Therapy, 8,* 139–145.

Kaplan, P. R. (1977). *A criterion-referenced comparison of rhythmic responsiveness in normal and educable mentally retarded children.* Unpublished doctoral dissertation,

Kleckley, D. M. (1989). *The effects of stress and music on test performance for the learning-disabled and students in remedial classes.* Unpublished doctoral dissertation, University of South Carolina.

Lehr, J. K. (1977). *An investigation of music in the education of mentally and physically handicapped children in the United Kingdom, with particular reference to the course, Music for Slow Learners, at Dartington College of Arts.* Unpublished doctoral dissertation, Ohio State University, Columbus.

Madsen, C. K. (1979). The effect of music subject matter as reinforcement for correct mathematics. *Bulletin of the Council for Research in Music Education, 59,* 54–58.

Madsen, C. K., Dorow, L. G., Moore, R. S., & Wemble, J. U. (1976). Effect of music via television as reinforcement for correct mathematics. *Journal of Research in Music Education, 24,* 51–59.

McCarty, B. C., McElfresh, C. T., Rice, S. V., & Wilson, S. J. (1978). The effect of contingent background music on inappropriate bus behavior. *Journal of Music Therapy, · 15,* 150–156.

McLeish, J., & Higgs, G. (1982). Musical ability and mental subnormality: An experimental investigation. *British Journal of Educational Psychology, 52,* 370–373.

Miller, D. M., Dorow, L., & Greer, R. D. (1974). The contingent use of music and art for improving arithmetic scores. *Journal of Music Therapy, 11,* 57–64.

Miller, L. K., & Orsmond, G. (1994). Assessing structure in the musical explorations of children with disabilities. *Journal of Music Therapy, 31*(4), 248–265.

Moore, R., & Mathenius, L. (1987). The effects of modeling, reinforcement, and tempo on imitative rhythmic responses of moderately retarded adolescents. *Journal of Music Therapy, 24,* 160–169.

Nocera, S. D. (1981). *A descriptive analysis of the attainment of selective musical learnings by normal children and by educable mentally retarded children mainstreamed in music classes at the second and fifth grade level.* Unpublished doctoral dissertation, University of Wisconsin, Madison.

Orsmond, G. I., & Miller, L. K. (1995). Correlates of musical improvisation in children with disabilities. *Journal of Music Therapy, 32*(3), 152–166.

Pujol, K. K. (1994). The effect of vibrotactile stimulation, instrumentation, and precomposed melodies on physiological and behavioral responses of profoundly retarded children and adults. *Journal of Music Therapy, 31*(3), 186–205.

Reynolds, B. J. (1989). The effect of training on vocal tone and hiss production for mentally retarded adolescents (abstract). *Missouri Journal of Research in Music Education, 26,* 112–113.

Rosene, P. E. (1976). *A field study of wind instrument training for educable mentally handicapped children.* Unpublished doctoral dissertation, University of Illinois, Urbana.

Saperston, B. M. (1986). *The relationship of cognitive, language, and melodic development of normal children and retarded children and adults.* Unpublished doctoral dissertation, University of Texas, Austin.

Shehan, P. K. (1981). A comparison of medication strategies in paired-associate learning for children with learning disabilities. *Journal of Music Therapy, 18,* 120–127.

Steele, A. L. (1968). Programmed use of music to alter uncooperative problem behavior. *Journal of Music Therapy, 5,* 103–107.

Stratford, B., & Ching, E. Y. (1983). Rhythm and time in the perception of Down's syndrome children. *Journal of Mental Deficiency Research, 27,* 23–38.

Strong, A. D. (1991). The relationship between hemispheric laterality and perception of musical and verbal stimuli in normal and learning disabled subjects. *Dissertation Abstracts, 51,* 3663 A–4A.

Talkington, L. W., & Hall, S. M. (1970). A musical application of Premack's hypothesis to low verbal retardates. *Journal of Music Therapy, 7,* 95–99.

Van Camp, D. J. (1990). An investigation of the effects of a researcher-designed string music curriculum on the playing skills of mildly mentally handicapped middle school students grouped in homogeneous and heterogeneous classes. *Dissertation Abstracts, 50,* 3884A.

Walker, J. B. (1972). The use of music as an aid in developing functional speech in the institutionalized mentally retarded. *Journal of Music Therapy, 9,* 1–12.

Zenatti, A. (1975). Melodic memory tests: A comparison of normal children and mental defectives. *Journal of Research in Music Education, 23*(1), 41–52.

Communication Disabilities

Bergendal, B., & Talo, S. (1969). The response of children with reduced phoneme systems to the Seashore Measures of Musical Talents. *Folio Pboniatrica, 21,* 20–38.

Cassidy, J. W. (1992). Communication disorders: Effect on children's ability to label music characteristics. *Journal of Music Therapy, 29*(2), 113–124.

Cohen, N. S. (1995). The effect of vocal instruction and Visi-Pitch™ feedback on the speech of persons with neurogenic communication disorders: Two case studies. *Music Therapy Perspectives, 13*(2), 70–75.

Cohen, N. S., & Ford, J. (1995). The effect of musical cues on the nonpurposive speech of persons with aphasia. *Journal of Music Therapy, 32*(1), 46–57.

Cohen, N. S., & Masse, R. (1993). The application of singing and rhythmic instruction as a therapeutic intervention for persons with neurogenic communication disorders. *Journal of Music Therapy, 30*(2), 81–99.

Kracke, I. (1975). Perception of rhythmic sequences by receptive aphasic and deaf children. *British Journal of Disorders of Communication, 10,* 43–51.

Michel, D. E., & May, N. H. (1974). The development of music therapy procedures with speech and language disorders. *Journal of Music Therapy, 11,* 74–80.

Reid, D. H., Hill, B. K., Rawers, R. J., & Montegar, C. A. (1975). The use of contingent music in teaching social skills to a nonverbal, hyperactive boy. *Journal of Music Therapy, 12,* 2–18.

Seybold, C. K. (1971). The value and use of music activities in the treatment of speech-delayed children. *Journal of Music Therapy, 8,* 102–110.

Sparks, R., Helm, N., & Marin, A. (1974). Aphasia rehabilitation resulting from melodic intonation therapy. *Cortex, 10,* 303–316.

Physical Disabilities

Howell, R. D., Flowers, P. J., & Wheaton, J. E. (1995). The effects of keyboard experiences on rhythmic responses of elementary school children with physical disabilities. *Journal of Music Therapy, 32*(2), 91–112.

Johnson, S. (1989). *Therapeutic use of music in gross motor upper extremity rehabilitation.* Master's thesis, Colorado State University, Fort Collins.

Lehr, J. K. (1977). *An investigation of music in the education of mentally and physically handicapped children in the United Kingdom, with particular reference to the course, Music for Slow Learners, at Dartington College of Arts.* Unpublished doctoral dissertation, Ohio State University, Columbus.

Sato, C. (1960). Survey on vocal pitch range of cerebral palsied children. *Cerebral Palsy Review, 21*(5), 4–5, 8–9.

Thaut, M. H. (1985). The use of auditory rhythm and rhythmic speech to aid temporal muscular control in children with gross motor dysfunction. *Journal of Music Therapy, 22*, 108–128.

Thaut, M. H. (1988). Rhythmic intervention techniques in music therapy with gross motor dysfunction. *Arts in Psychotherapy, 15*, 127–137.

Thaut, M. H., Schleiffers, S., & Davis, W. B. (1990). Analysis of EMG activity in biceps and triceps muscle in upper extremity gross motor task under the influence of auditory rhythm. *Journal of Music Therapy, 26*, 64–88.

Wolfe, D. E. (1980). The effect of automated interrupted music on head posturing of cerebral palsied individuals. *Journal of Music Therapy, 17*, 184–206.

Sensory Disabilities

Amir, D., & Schuchman, G. (1985). Auditory training through music with hearing impaired preschool children. *Volta Review, 87*, 333–343.

Brown, K. R. (1991). Effects of a music-based memory training program on the auditory memory skills of visually-impaired individuals. *Dissertation Abstracts, 52*, 877A.

Bruscia, K. E., & Levinson, S. (1982). Predictive factors in optacon music-reading. *Journal of Visual Impairment and Blindness, 76*(3), 309–312.

Darrow, A. A. (1979). The beat reproduction of subjects with normal and impaired hearing: An empirical comparison. *Journal of Music Therapy, 16*(2), 91–98.

Darrow, A. A. (1984). A comparison of rhythmic responsiveness in normal and hearing-impaired children and an investigation of the relationship of rhythmic responsiveness to the suprasegmental aspects of speech perception. *Journal of Music Therapy, 21*(2), 48–66.

Darrow, A. A. (1987). An investigative study: The effect of hearing impairment on musical aptitude. *Journal of Music Therapy, 24*(2), 88–96.

Darrow, A. A. (1990). The effect of frequency adjustment on the vocal reproduction accuracy of hearing impaired children. *Journal of Music Therapy, 27*(1), 24–33.

Darrow, A. A. (1991). An assessment and comparison of hearing impaired children's preference for timbre and musical instruments. *Journal of Music Therapy, 28*(1), 48–59.

Darrow, A. A. (1992). The effect of vibrotactile stimuli via the SOMATRON™ on the identification of pitch change by hearing impaired children. *Journal of Music Therapy, 29*(2), 103–112.

Darrow, A. A. (1993). The role of music in Deaf culture: Implications for music educators. *Journal of Research in Music Education, 41*(2), 93–110.

Darrow, A. A., & Cohen, N. (1991). The effect of programmed pitch practice and private instruction on the vocal reproduction accuracy of children with hearing impairments: Two case studies. *Music Therapy Perspectives, 9*, 61–65.

Darrow, A. A., & Gfeller, K. (1991). A study of public school music programs mainstreaming hearing impaired students. *Journal of Music Therapy, 28*(1), 23–39.

Darrow, A. A., & Goll, H. (1989). The effect of vibrotactile stimuli via the SOMATRON on the identification of rhythmic concepts by hearing-impaired children. *Journal of Music Therapy, 26*(3), 115–124.

Darrow, A. A., & Starmer, G. J. (1986). The effect of vocal training on the intonation and rate of hearing-impaired children's speech: A pilot study. *Journal of Music Therapy, 23*, 194–201.

Edwards, J. V. (1991). *The relationship of contrasting selections of music and human field motion (hearing impaired).* Unpublished doctoral dissertation, New York University.

Eisenson, J., Kastein, S., & Schneiderman, N. (1948). An investigation into the ability of voice defectives to discriminate among differences in pitch and loudness. *Journal of Speech and Hearing Disorders, 23*(5), 577–582.

Ford, T. A. (1987). Survey of music teachers in residential and day programs for hearing-impaired students. *Journal of the International Association of Music for the Handicapped, 3*(1), 16–25.

Ford, T. A. (1988). The effect of musical experience and age on the ability of deaf children to discriminate pitch. *Journal of Music Therapy, 25*(1), 2–16.

Galloway, H. F., & Bean, M. F. (1974). The effects of action songs on the development of body-image and body-part identification in hearing-impaired preschool children. *Journal of Music Therapy, 11*, 125–134.

Gfeller, K. E. (1986). Music as a remedial tool for improving speech rhythm in the hearing-impaired: Clinical and research considerations. *MEH Bulletin, 2*, 3–19.

Gfeller, K. E. (1987). Songwriting as a tool for reading and language remediation. *Music Therapy, 6*, 28–38.

Gfeller, K. E., & Baumann, A. A. (1988). Assessment procedures for music therapy with hearing-impaired children. *Journal of Music Therapy, 25*, 192–205.

Gfeller, K. E., & Darrow, A. A. (1987). Music as a remedial tool in the language education of hearing-impaired children. *The Arts in Psychotherapy, 14*, 229–235.

Gfeller, K., & Lansing, C. (1992). Musical perception of cochlear implant users as measured by the Primary Measures of Music Audiation: An item analysis. *Journal of Music Therapy, 29*(1), 18–39.

Heim, K. E. (1963). *Musical aptitude of seven high school students in residential schools for the blind as measured by the Wing Standardized Test of Musical Intelligence.* Unpublished master's thesis, University of Kansas, Lawrence.

Jackson, A. L. (1975). *An exploratory study using a group piano approach in an original comprehensive course for the older blind beginner.* Unpublished doctoral dissertation, Northwestern University, Evanston.

Korduba, O. M. (1975). Duplicated rhythm patterns between deaf and normal hearing children. *Journal of Music Therapy, 12*(3), 136–146.

Kracke, I. (1975). Perception of rhythmic sequences by receptive aphasic and deaf children. *British Journal of Disorders of Communication, 10*, 43–51.

Madsen, C. K., & Darrow, A. A. (1989). The relationship between music aptitude and sound conceptualization of visually impaired. *Journal of Music Therapy, 26*(2), 71–78.

Pitman, D. J. (1976). The musical ability of blind children. *American Foundation for Blind Research Bulletin, 11*, 63–79.

Rileigh, K. K., & Odom, P. B. (1972). Perception of rhythms by subjects with normal and deficient hearing. *Developmental Psychology 7*, 54–61.

Sakurabayshi, H. Y., Satyo, Y., & Uehara, E. (1956). Auditory discrimination of the blind. *Japanese Journal of Psychology of the Blind, 1*, 3–10.

Shroyer, E. H., & Ford, T. A. (1986). Survey of music instruction and activities in residential and day schools for hearing-impaired students. *MEH Bulletin, 2*(1), 28–45.

Sposato, M. (1982). *Implications of maximal exploitation of residual hearing on curriculum planning in music education for hearing impaired children.* Unpublished doctoral dissertation, State University of New York, Buffalo.

Stankov, L., & Spilsbury, G. (1978). The measurement of auditory abilities of sighted, partially sighted, and blind children. *Applied Psychological Measurement, 2*, 491–503.

Staum, M. (1987). Music notation to improve the speech prosody of hearing-impaired children. *Journal of Music Therapy, 24*, 146–159.

Sterritt, G. M., Camp, B. W., & Lippman, B. S. (1966). Effects of early auditory deprivation upon auditory and visual information processing. *Perceptual and Motor Skills, 23*, 123–130.

Social Disabilities

Applebaum, E., Engel, A. L., Koegel, R. L., & Imhoff, B. (1979). Measuring musical abilities of autistic children. *Journal of Autism and Developmental Disorders, 9*(3), 279–285.

Buday, E. M. (1995). The effects of signed and spoken words taught with music on sign and speech imitation by children with autism. *Journal of Music Therapy, 32*(3), 189–202.

Edgerton, C. L. (1994). The effect of improvisational music therapy on the communicative behaviors of autistic children. *Journal of Music Therapy, 31*(1), 31–62.

Eidsen, Jr., C. E. (1990). The effect of behavioral music therapy on the generalization of interpersonal skills from session to the classroom by emotionally handicapped middle school students. *Journal of Music Therapy, 26*(4), 206–221.

Frith, U. (1972). Cognitive mechanisms in autism: Experiments with color and tone sequence production. *Journal of Autism and Childhood Schizophrenia, 2*, 160–173.

Giacobbe, G. A., & Graham, R. M. (1978). The responses of aggressive emotionally disturbed and normal boys to selected musical stimuli. *Journal of Music Therapy, 15*(3), 118–135.

Goldstein, C. (1964). Music and creative arts therapy for an autistic child. *Journal of Music Therapy, 1*, 135–138.

Hollander, F. M., & Juhrs, P. D. (1974). Orff-Schulwerk, an effective treatment tool with autistic children. *Journal of Music Therapy, 11*, 1–12.

Kostka, M. J. (1993). A comparison of selected behaviors of a student with autism in special education and regular music classes. *Music Therapy Perspectives, 11(2)*, 57–60.

Litchman, M. D. (1976). The use of music in establishing a learning environment for language instruction with autistic children. *Dissertation Abstracts International, 37*, 4992A. (University Microfilms No. AAD93-15947)

Mahlberg, M. (1973). Music therapy in the treatment of an autistic child. *Journal of Music Therapy, 10*, 189–193.

Nelson, D., Anderson, V., & Gonzales, A. (1984). Music activities as therapy for children with autism and other pervasive developmental disorders. *Journal of Music Therapy, 21,* 100–116.

Obrecht, V. L. (1991). The effect of baroque background instrumental music on academic productivity and on-task performance of emotionally behaviorally disordered students. *Dissertation Abstracts, 52,* 1676A.

O'Connell, T. (1974). The musical life of an autistic boy. *Journal of Autism and Childhood Schizophrenia, 4,* 223–229.

Ornitz, E. M. (1974). The modulation of sensory input and motor output in autistic children. *Journal of Autism and Childhood Schizophrenia, 4,* 197–216.

Saperston, B. (1973). The use of music in establishing communication with an autistic mentally retarded child. *Journal of Music Therapy, 10,* 184–188.

Schmidt, D., & Edwards, J. (1976). Reinforcement of autistic children's responses to music. *Psychological Reports, 39,* 571–577.

Sherwin, A. (1953). Reactions to music of autistic children. *American Journal of Psychiatry, 109,* 823–831.

Stevens, E., & Clark, F. (1969). Music therapy in the treatment of autistic children. *Journal of Music Therapy, 6,* 98–104.

Thaut, M. H. (1980). *Music therapy as a treatment tool for autistic children.* Unpublished master's thesis, Michigan State University, East Lansing.

Thaut, M. H. (1983). A music therapy treatment model for autistic children. *Music Therapy Perspectives, 1,* 7–13.

Thaut, M. H. (1987). Visual vs. auditory (musical) stimulus preferences in autistic children: A pilot study. *Journal of Autism and Developmental Disorders, 17,* 425–432.

Thaut, M. H. (1988). Measuring musical responsiveness in autistic children: A comparative analysis of improvised musical tone sequences of autistic, normal and mentally retarded individuals. *Journal of Autism and Developmental Disorders, 18,* 561–571.